Y0-CCN-824

To Quiet the Fears of Others

The Story of a World War II Army Nurse

By Linda Dudik, Ph.D.

American Private First Class Adolph R. Hassenrik landed in northern France on July 8, 1944 as part of the 137th Infantry Regiment. His unit joined in the Battle for Normandy as Allied troops moved inland from the beaches against entrenched Germany forces. Private Hassenrik was killed in action on August 4, 1944. He left behind a wife, a toddler son, and a daughter yet to be born.

That daughter, Alice Waskowitz, and her husband Richard have made generous donations to the World War II Experience. They have thus helped to make Army nurse Lillian Krell Swerdlow's story available to others. If Private Hassenrik had only been wounded and not killed, he might have become one of Lillian's patients.

Most details of Private Hassenrik's WW II story have been lost to history, but its outline remains a part of Alice's family lore. She will hand it down to her children and grandchildren. They will remember a man who served when called to duty during the greatest war of the twentieth century. We should do the same for him and for all who paid the ultimate price in a global war against fascism.

Copyright © 2014 by the World War II Experience
All rights reserved, including the right of reproduction in whole or in part in any form. ISBN 978-0-9856108-1-4

Printed in the United States of America

You know them, the men and women of the World War II Generation. Depending on your age, they are your husband, your wife, your parents, your grandparents, or perhaps your great-grandparents. Together, members of that generation lived through two momentous events--the Depression and then the greatest war of the 20th century. They drew upon an inner strength to sustain them throughout both of those ordeals.

We dedicate this book to them, especially to Lillian Krell Swerdlow who served in the Army Nurse Corps during World War II. Stationed at an American military hospital located in the English countryside, Lillian received the wounded from the famous D-Day landings at Normandy as well as from the Battle of the Bulge six months later.

When sharing the story of those fifteen months overseas, Lillian admits, "I held up very well when I was on duty." But, she confessed, she cried when her shift ended. Despite how she felt emotionally, Lillian remained "strong," as she put it, as she cared for patients. In accordance with the oath Lillian took as a member of the Army Nurse Corps, she worked to "quiet the fears of others."

In so doing, Lillian displayed the strength of character that the World War II Generation drew upon through four long years of a costly two-front war.

Contents

The Army Nurse Corps Pledge

"As an Army nurse I accept the responsibilities of an officer in the Army Nurse Corps.

I shall give faithful care to the men who fight for the freedom of this Country and to the women who stand behind them.

I shall bring to the American soldier, wherever he may be, the best of my knowledge and professional skill.

I shall approach him cheerfully at all times, under any conditions I may find.

I shall endeavor to maintain the highest nursing standards possible in the performance of my duties.

I shall appear fearless in the presence of danger and *quiet the fears of others* to the best of my ability.

My only criticism shall be constructive. The reputation and good name of the Army Nurse Corps and of the nursing profession shall be uppermost in my thoughts, second only to the care of my patients.

I shall endeavor to be a credit to my country and to the uniform I wear."

DeWitt MacKenzie and Major Clarence Worden, *Men Without Guns* (Philadelphia, 1945), p. 10

A sketch of Lillian by one of her patients

Chapter 1

Lillian's Sense of History:
Argentinean and Brooklyn Beginnings

A conversation with Lillian Krell Swerdlow immediately impresses upon the listener the strong sense of history she possesses. During World War II, Lillian served as an Army nurse in England where she took care of American casualties from such famous battles as the landings on the beaches of Normandy in June 1944 and the Battle of the Bulge in December 1944. But in a conversation with Lillian, one would have to draw that out of her. Left to herself, what she would share is the story of her family--her parents, grandparents, and great-grandparents. That personal history is what she wants later generations to recall. Alongside of it, however, should also stand the history of her World War II service. But first is the story of her family, which to Lillian is what must be preserved above all else. In an acknowledgement to the chronological nature of History, it is also the beginning point for any story on Lillian.

In 1999 she wrote down for her family the story of her father's childhood in Argentina. Entitled *The Little Jewish Gaucho*, her name as author appears on the cover page as "Lillian R. Krell Swerdlow." The first three parts of that name reflect her paternal heritage, with "Lillian Ruth Krell" being her given name at birth. Adolfo Krell was her father. He was the first generation in the Krell family born in the Argentinean geographical region known as the pampas. Located in the central-eastern area of the country, it covers about one-quarter of

Argentina. Lillian likens the pampas to the vast prairie lands of the central United States. In the nineteenth century, the rich soil in both areas could produce crops such as wheat and corn but only if immigrants could be tempted to settle there. Lillian characterizes Adolfo as "a great storyteller." As such, he detailed to his only daughter when she was growing up the story of how the Krells immigrated to Argentina and how he came to the United States. It is a story that reflects themes found in Jewish history of emigration and discrimination, especially, as Lillian points out, the pogroms.

Adolfo, age 18

The tale begins with one Baron Maurice von Hirsch, born in Germany in 1831. Hirsch came from a family of great wealth. His marriage to a woman of similar background augmented the financial resources he could draw upon. Moved by events such as what the Russian Jews endured in the pogroms, Hirsch formed the Jewish Colonization Association in the late nineteenth century. Its goal was to assist the emigration of European Jews from countries that targeted them for, as Lillian explains, their "destruction as a people." Hirsch wanted to return Jews to an agrarian livelihood. He wanted to prove "that the Jews have not lost the agricultural qualities their forefathers possessed. I shall try to make for them a new home in different lands, where, as free farmers, on their own soil, they can make themselves useful to the country." Hirsch personally provided the funds to relocate Jews to North and South America. He saw Argentina as an especially attractive destination for his people. The Jewish Colonization Association purchased large tracts of land in the pampas. Hirsch himself oversaw many of the details of his philanthropic work to relocate Jews who were persecuted and thus interested in becoming pioneers in a new land.[1] Members of the Krell family in Lithuania were such individuals, ones who Lillian calls "survival people."

Isaac Krell

Lillian's paternal great-grandparents immigrated to the pampas as part of the Jewish exodus sponsored by Baron von Hirsch's colonization society. She knows the story of the Krell family in Argentina because of the oral history passed down to her from her father. Along with hundreds of other families, Isaac and Libe Ruchel Krell, with their four sons and a daughter, settled in an area of the pampas the Jewish immigrants named Colonia de Mauricio Hirsch. Lillian identifies the colony as located in the township of Carlos Casares in the Argentinean province of Santa Fe. Isaac became the rabbi ("ruv" in Jewish) for the settlement. One of the Krell sons, Gershon, married a young fellow immigrant, a woman named Eva Berkevitch-Hellman. Eva came from Bessarabia, a region in Eastern Europe that, depending upon the time period, was controlled by various powers such as the Ottoman Empire, Russia, or Romania.

Eva Krell

Unlike Gershon, Eva did not immigrate with her parents. Her mother died in childbirth when Eva was only five or six years old. Her father gave Eva to the Hellmans, a family that was going to Argentina. Gershon and Eva Krell came to have two children, one of whom was Adolfo Krell, Lillian's father, born on December 5, 1898. Gershon died of appendicitis when his son was only three years old. When this happened, Eva had just given birth fifteen days earlier to their second child, Leon. Eva turned to her husband's parents for help. She intended to move to Buenos Aires where she hoped to find employment in a small kosher hotel in the only occupation she knew, that of a cook. Because she was nursing, Eva planned to take her infant son with her. But she left Adolfo on the pampas with Gershon's parents, Ruv Isaac and Libe Ruchel Krell. As testimony to the love Adolfo came to have for his paternal grandmother ("bubbie" in Jewish), when he became a father many years later, Adolfo named his firstborn child "Lillian" after Libe Ruchel, her great-grandmother. Adolfo lived on the pampas with his grandparents for seven years. When he was about ten, Eva came to reclaim her son. She had met and married a kind widower, Jose Jasid. Along with his children, Eva and her two sons would begin a new family life together in Buenos Aires. Because Adolfo loved his grandparents and his life on the pampas, the move greatly saddened Lillian's father. Nevertheless, he went to live with Eva and Jose, who made the young boy feel loved upon their first meeting.[2]

When he became a father years later, Adolfo told the above story to Lillian many times. He also included in those hours of storytelling details on how he came to live in the United States and how he met the American-born Jewish woman he married. According to Lillian, because of Argentina's conscription law, Adolfo served in the Navy where he intended to pursue an education in engineering. The ship the young sailor served on docked in Philadelphia on January 1, 1918. Adolfo sought out an uncle, his father's brother, Bernardo Krell. Bernardo was the oldest son of Isaac and Libe Ruchel Krell. Farming on the pampas held no interest for him. He was more mechanically-minded. Bernardo thus left Argentina and came to the United States. Adolfo knew his uncle worked in New York City. Adolfo remembered that Bernardo owned a business that made labor-saving devices in the needle trade. His company bore his name, the Krell Art Attachment Company. Adolfo also knew the business was located off of Broadway, probably the most famous street in the city. As Adolfo told the story to Lillian, he walked and walked, almost all night, the length of Broadway. Imagine the smile he must have had when he located the building where his uncle had his business. Bernardo urged his nephew to, in essence, "jump ship" and remain in the United States. Adolfo did so. He wanted, however, to return to his ship in order to gather his personal belongings. But Bernardo advised against that, so Adolfo had, literally, only the clothes on his back. As another mark of her sense of history, Lillian still has today the very sailor's suit Adolfo wore that cold New Year's Day in January 1918. A lanyard accompanies the outfit with the words "Chaco" and "Escuela de Mechanicos" on it, the first word being the name of the ship and the other phrase designating the area Adolfo was studying.

As he had promised his nephew, Bernardo taught Adolfo a trade, that of a sewing machine mechanic. Adolfo stayed in that occupation for his entire, working life. When he arrived in the United States, Adolfo spoke Yiddish, Spanish, and Italian fluently, all of which he had learned in his native Argentina. Those languages served him well in his job where he repaired the sewing machines in the garment factories. He could easily converse with the young Yiddish and Italian immigrant women who worked there. But none of them captured his attention. No, he fell in love, at first sight as he told the story to Lillian, with a young woman he saw in a dance hall.

According to Lillian, her mother, Esther Ernst, was born on June 11, 1900 in Brooklyn, New York.[3] What Lillian knows of this side of the family comes from stories handed down by her maternal grandmother and mother. Entries for the Ernst family in the 1900, 1910, and 1920 Federal Censuses, however, document some additional information that can be added to the oral history. Lillian's maternal grandparents are usually listed as Israel and Betsy/Bessie Ernst, although those are Americanized versions of their given names of Isidor and Basha respectively. (Israel is a derivation of Isidor's Yiddish name. Lillian recalls hearing people call her grandmother "Bessie," so that name is not merely a creation of the census taker.) Depending upon which census is used, Isidor was born around 1872 or 1874 and Basha around 1875 or 1876. Lillian clearly remembers family stories that identify Romania as Isidor's country of birth.[4] Basha even told Lillian about Romanian country dishes she learned to make for her husband. Census entries for Basha all identify her native land as Austria. Depending upon which census is used, Esther's mother immigrated to the United States in 1885, 1889, or 1890.[5] (Oral history within the family places Basha in Brooklyn in 1888 because of a fall she took in a historic blizzard that year; Lillian thus believes the 1885 entry for her grandmother's immigration is more correct than the last two entries.) The year Isidor arrived in America also varies as either 1872 or 1874.[6] Oral history handed down through Lillian identifies Castle Garden as the processing station for both Basha and

Isidor. When they entered the United States, it was the nation's number one immigration station until its closure in 1890. From its beginning as a processing center in 1855, until it ceased such operations in 1890, over 7,000,000 immigrants came through Castle Garden.[7] Basha and Isidor were just two of them.

According to stories handed down to Lillian, her grandfather emigrated from Romania because he could not get along with his father. Isidor believed his father gave preferential treatment to his siblings. When he became a father, Isidor would not do that with his children. In the 1910 Census, the Ernst children were listed as Lizzie (age twelve), Esther (age nine), Pauline (age eight), and William (one year old).[8] A fifth child, Abraham (nicknamed "Bromie"), was born around 1914.[9] Regardless of which census is consulted, the Ernsts always lived in Brooklyn. The family was poor even though, according to Lillian, Isidor came from a well-to-do Romanian family, and he could read and write in more than one language. As Lillian explains it, in America he had no trade. Isidor identified his occupation in the 1900 Census as a candy peddler and in the 1910 Census as a laborer. The Ernsts had no money for hospital births. Esther told her children that a midwife delivered her, but the woman did not record Esther's birth with the proper authorities. This oversight caused problems years later for Esther when she tried to prove she was indeed born in the United States.

Even though her father Adolfo introduced Lillian to his Argentinean family through hours of storytelling, it is the Ernst family that she came to know so well and to love so much. One aspect of Basha's physical appearance that Lillian vividly remembers was a pronounced limp. When she was thirteen or fourteen years old, Basha worked in a factory. One day in March of 1888, a powerful snow storm hit New York City. It became known as the Blizzard of 1888. It paralyzed the city. For decades, New Yorkers remembered it as the worst

Basha 1930s

storm in their lifetime.[10] The blizzard certainly was one Basha could never forget because it marked her forever. She fell on the icy street and fractured her foot. The Ernsts took her to Bellevue Hospital, but Basha became frightened, fearful that her foot would be amputated. She begged her father to take her home, which he did. The fracture was never properly set. For the rest of her life, what Lillian characterizes as "a forty-five degree limp" became part of her grandmother's walk. Unlike her mother, Esther did not work in the factories at such a young age.

Esther attended a public school, but years later it burned down, destroying all of the records. She appears to have remained in school until around the eighth grade based on stories Esther told her daughter. Yet Lillian also recalls her mother telling her she was "left back" more than once, meaning a teacher or administrator decided that Esther had not absorbed the skills assigned to a certain grade level. She was thus kept back a grade when classmates progressed on to the next, higher level. Lillian believes Esther might have been around fifteen or perhaps even sixteen when she finally graduated from the eighth grade. (Lillian describes her mother as "ashamed" because she never finished her education. Years later, when Lillian was married, Esther attended night school and received a high school diploma.) Lillian attributes Esther's academic problems to the difficulty her mother had in getting help at home with her studies since Basha was illiterate. When Esther was in her mid-teens, she lied about her age, pretending she was eighteen in order to get a job at a Loft Candy store. With her tall figure and long hair that she piled atop her head in an adult fashion, no one questioned her age. At first, Esther worked as a saleslady. But in time, she secured a position as a window dresser for the company. The salary she brought in helped the Ernst family, even more so after the death of her father Isidor in the 1918 flu epidemic.

On a broader scale, however, the epidemic that took Isidor's life was really a pandemic, a global outbreak of an influenza virus that claimed the lives of at least fifty million people and perhaps as many as one hundred million throughout the world. Globally, accurate record keeping simply broke down due to the inability of countries to do or to keep up with the paperwork documenting these deaths. What we do know is that over a two year period that began in 1918, the very year that Lillian's grandfather died, the flu strain killed more human beings than any other epidemic in all of human history.[11] And these numbers are only for those who did not survive the pandemic. It is impossible to know how many became ill but did not die. One study estimates that the flu killed two to four percent of those who came down with it.[12] Doctors identified pneumonia as the immediate cause of death. Within the United States, the epidemic struck an estimated 2.5 million out of a population of 100 million.[13] Of the number of Americans who became ill, at least 675,000 died.[14] Isidor Ernst was one of them. In New York City where he and his family lived, hundreds of thousands came down with the flu; at least thirty-three thousand did not survive.[15]

The financial situation of the Ernsts became even more precarious after Esther's father died. In the 1920 Census, Basha identified herself as a widow with no occupation. She told the census taker that she could not read or write.[16] With a walk marked by her distinct limp, Basha had three daughters and two sons to provide for after Isidor died. According to Lillian, her grandmother took in piece-work, making buttonholes on shirts and blouses. She was paid based upon how many items she made. The 1920 Census lists the family of six as living in Brooklyn Assembly District 6, or Williamsburg as Lillian identifies it. According to Lillian, after her grandfather died the landlord in the building where the Ernsts lived allowed them to continue to stay there rent-free if Basha became the building's janitress. With her short height and pronounced limp, the job must have been a difficult one for Basha. She moved from floor to floor in the multi-storied building, carrying a bucket and mop up and down the staircase. Lillian remembers accounts from Basha of how she lifted heavy bags of trash in the course of her work.

Esther's life dramatically changed, in a positive way, about a year after her father's death. One night, she went to a local dance hall in Brooklyn, the Roseland Ballroom. Adolfo Krell was also there. Lillian characterizes her father as a "wonderful, wonderful" dancer, especially of the tango. While that dance originated in nineteenth century Europe, its popularity grew in Argentina from immigrants who brought the dance into their newly adopted country. For its time, people identified the tango as risqué because the man held the woman close to him with his right arm around her. In its early history, aside from the waltz and the Polka, the tango was unique in demanding close physical contact between the dance partners. The way the man held the woman shocked most observers. In fact, Adolfo told Lillian that he had once been arrested in Buenos Aires for dancing the tango. A student of the dance's history sees its growth in Buenos Aires as understandable given the sex ratio of men to women. As in other frontier societies, male immigrants outnumbered women who came to Argentina. As a result, the tango became a method by which a young man could please a woman on the dance floor, holding her closely. Some thought too closely.[17] Adolfo's skill at performing the tango unquestionably brought him to the attention of other visitors to the Roseland Ballroom in Brooklyn. Perhaps it was even what first attracted Esther Ernst, who also dropped in one night after a day at the Loft Candy store. In any event, the attraction appears to have been mutual. Family history recounts a prediction Adolfo supposedly told a friend as he watched Esther walk across the floor, "I'm going to marry her." He must have spoken that phrase in Yiddish, Spanish, or Italian, the only languages he spoke fluently upon his arrival in New York. Esther told Lillian that she could not understand Adolfo when he spoke English in that first meeting at the Roseland Ballroom, but Yiddish would have given them a common language. Stories told to Lillian indicate a two-year courtship before Adolfo and Esther married, probably in 1921.

Adolfo 1920

Chapter 2

Childhood and Adolescent Years:
A Nursing Career Takes Root

Before the wedding could take place, however, a Jewish custom had to be circumvented. A younger sister was not to wed until her older sister married. Esther had one sister, Elizabeth, who was about two years older than Esther. Having lost her father, Esther looked to her mother for a way out of this dilemma. As the story was recounted to Lillian, Basha sought the advice of their landlord. Since Elizabeth (Lilly) and Esther were close in age, the landlord suggested the family simply pretend that Lilly was the younger sister, which they did. But recall that Esther's birth had not been recorded with the proper authorities, her school records had been lost in a fire, and now, liberties were taken with birth years for the two oldest Ernst daughters. There is one negative consequence to Esther's marriage that impacted her and not Adolfo. She temporary lost her United States citizenship. In 1907 Congress passed an Expatriation Act. It was a decade when xenophobia was strong, largely as the result of a tidal wave of recent immigration from Southeastern Europe. The law stripped citizenship rights from American-born women who married aliens, even if the wife continued to live in the United States.[18] Years later, Esther told Lillian she only learned about her loss of citizenship when she tried to vote. Her mother accepted the consequences of the law, using the phrase "that is the way it was." One imagines Esther uttering that phrase with a shrug of her shoulders and her hands palms up, indicating there was nothing she could do about it.

At first, the newlywed couple did not stay in Brooklyn. When he married, Adolfo had a job in Johnstown, New York, a town about two hundred miles north of New York City. Esther's move there with her husband was the first time she had ever left Brooklyn. Although glove manufacturing was then Johnstown's major industry, the family's oral history has Adolfo employed in a shirt factory.[19] In keeping with the culture of the era, Adolfo would not let his wife work outside of the home. Esther must have been lonely for her mother and siblings, especially when she became pregnant with their first child. Urging her husband to move back to Brooklyn, Adolfo asked Esther to speak with his Uncle Bernardo, who helped his nephew get a job back in New York City. The young Krells returned to Brooklyn before Lillian's birth in 1922. Esther wanted to be near Basha at such a critical time. Like her mother before her, Lillian was born in Brooklyn, but Esther did not give birth at home as Basha had. Instead, Esther delivered their first child in a hospital, Beth Moses Hospital in Brooklyn, on April 1, 1922. Lillian thus became the first Ernst-Krell born in a hospital. As noted earlier, Adolfo wanted to name their daughter after his 'Bubbie" who had raised him on the Argentinean pampas. According to Lillian, however, it was Esther who changed "Libe Ruchel" to "Lillian Ruth" in an acknowledgment of the English-speaking country her father now lived in.

The Krells remained in Brooklyn for about the next seven years. The borough covers eighty square miles, an area as large as Chicago. It is divided into five distinct geographical sections--Downtown Brooklyn, North Brooklyn, West Brooklyn, Middle Brooklyn, and East Brooklyn. Well over two million people lived in the borough. In the 1930s, the decade after Lillian was born, one-third of Brooklyn's population was foreign-born and more than twenty Jewish communities existed in the borough.[20] Lillian's small family lived in more than one area of Brooklyn. In the late 1920s they resided in an apartment above some stores in East Flatbush, a new area in East Brooklyn. The population of East Flatbush grew in the 1920s, when the Krells lived there, as a result of the "overflow" from adjacent neighborhoods.[21] Other areas of Brooklyn whose names sound very familiar to Lillian because she lived near them are Williamsburg and Bushwick (both in North Brooklyn) and the Bedford section (in Middle Brooklyn).[22] Regardless of what specific neighborhood Lillian lived in, she remembers growing up in Brooklyn's distinct Jewish neighborhoods. The butcher shop sold only kosher meat and residents spoke Yiddish on the streets.

Lillian's earliest childhood memory dates from when she was in kindergarten, so the year would have been around 1927. She came down with whooping cough, or pertussis, its medical name. She had difficulty breathing, so her parents took her on ferry boat rides to Staten Island where the moist air helped her. A first memory usually comes from a powerful moment in one's early life, and Lillian's recollection is no different. One of those events, the whooping cough or the ride she took, would have been enough to impress her young mind. Together, those trips certainly became a strong memory. The uncontrollable, violent coughing, characteristic of whooping cough, obviously became the root of this childhood memory for Lillian. The coughing can end with a "whoop" sound, hence the common name for the infection. It becomes difficult to breathe. Whooping cough originates as a bacterial infection in the upper respiratory tract. It can lead to several life-threatening complications, such as pneumonia, brain damage, and even death. When the infection first appeared, Esther probably thought her young daughter had just a cold. Lillian would have had a runny nose and slight fever, perhaps even diarrhea. These symptoms appear about a week after a person is exposed to the bacteria. The severe coughing begins ten to twelve days later, so Esther and Adofo endured several sleepless nights attending to and worried about their child. Once Lillian began coughing, the spells must have frightened her parents. The coughing can become so severe that a child can vomit and even become unconscious. Today a vaccination can prevent the disease and antibiotics can check the infection, but neither was available in the 1920s.[23] Perhaps older women in the neighborhood, maybe even Basha, recommended the ferry rides. The high humidity from the Upper Bay in New York's harbor would help Lillian to breathe.

Even a young child who was not so seriously ill would remember the myriad of activities she saw that day. The Upper Bay is the center of New York's port. Five miles long and four miles wide, the bay stretches from Staten Island to Brooklyn, where Lillian and her parents boarded the ferry. After paying a five-cent fare, the Krells walked onto a double-ended boat. The barn-red superstructure probably caught their eye. Even though old, the boat made the five-mile trip to Staten Island in twenty minutes, time enough for Lillian to feel the effects of the moist air and breathe more easily. While riders could sit on benches inside of the boat, her parents probably stayed out on the decks, holding Lillian close to them. If the boat itself was not such a sight to be recalled, certainly what the Krells saw as they made the five-mile trip would have caught the attention of even a small, sick girl--the web-like appearance of the Brooklyn Bridge; the huge Castle Williams on Governors Island; the imposing brick buildings on Ellis Island where government officials processed immigrants when they entered the United States; the one-hundred and fifty-one foot tall Statue of Liberty, standing on a one hundred and forty-two foot pedestal, appeared to salute Brooklyn from its home on Bedloe Island; and Manhattan's tall buildings that seemed to rise out of the water. All of these offered sights that would have struck Lillian. In addition to the visual images, just the sounds a child heard would stay with her, sounds that came from the "scurrying traffic whose strident voice mingles whistle blasts with the hollow clang of bell buoys and the screams of softly wheeling gulls."[24]

In February 1926, the year before Lillian suffered the bout of whooping cough, Adolfo filed a "Declaration of Intention" to become a United States citizen. Almost three years passed before he formally received his "order of admission," late in December 1928.[25] By that time, Adolfo and Esther had a second child, George, born in 1927. Perhaps the now father-of-two finalized his citizenship application with an eye toward a business venture he attempted in 1928-1929. Plans for it may have been on his mind for several years. With his Uncle Bernardo, Adolfo wanted to open an export business between New York City and Buenos Aires, exporting American sewing machines to Argentina during its mercantile development. He intended for Esther and the children to go with him to Argentina to set up the company, but his wife refused to do so. She told him he first had to "do well" before she would leave her home. While he was gone, Esther and her two children moved in with her mother and three siblings who still lived at home.[26] Seven people now lived together in Basha's small, cold water flat where only the kitchen's coal stove supplied heat in the cold winter months. Adolfo was gone for about a year. Lillian dates his departure months before the Stock Market Crash in October 1929. That dramatic decline in stock prices eliminated capital that banks could draw upon to make loans. Her father could no longer hope to secure the financial backing he needed to start his own business. For the Ernst family, the Crash became a watershed event for them, a marker between a life that might have been and the one it became.

Lillian age 5

Lillian remembers her father being gone for a year or so. Adolfo must have left early in 1929 since he was in New York City in December 1928 when he signed his "order of admission" to become a citizen. Financially stranded in Argentina after the Stock Market Crash destroyed his dream of founding a machinery export company,

Adolfo needed money to come home. Esther negotiated a loan from one of Basha's cousins, a Mrs. Green. He booked passage on the ship the *American Legion*, which docked in New York City on January 14, 1930.[27] Adolfo joined his wife and children only temporarily in Basha's apartment. Once reunited, the Krells moved to their own place, a ground floor apartment in a five-story building on 1 Vernon Avenue, off of Nostrand Avenue, in the Bushwick area of Brooklyn. It was about a thirty minute walk to Basha's apartment from the Krell's new home, so Lillian saw her grandmother ("Bubbie") often. Basha, perhaps because of her illiteracy, encouraged her granddaughter to learn all that she could when she began school. Lillian remembers her grandmother putting nuts and raisins on Lillian's books, saying "learning should be sweet." And even though Basha could hardly speak English, she and Lillian sang together in that language the 1892 song, "Daisy Bell," about "a bicycle built for two." Its refrain, "Daisy, Daisy, give me your answer, do" still brings a smile, and tears, to Lillian's face as the song evokes memories of time spent with Bubbie Basha. Lillian believes the Krells stayed on Vernon Avenue for a few years. Because of the Great Depression that began in 1930, Adolfo lost the job he had gotten upon his return from Argentina. But a New York City shirt factory that was moving to Fall River, Massachusetts offered him a position as a machinist if he would relocate there.

Esther and Adolfo

Lillian was about ten years old when they left Brooklyn, making 1932 the year of their arrival in Fall River. Located in the most southern part of Massachusetts, over two hundred industrial plants operated in Fall River. The water power furnished by a river that ran through the town, the moist climate that favored the weaving of cotton fibers, and the seaport that allowed the entrance and departure of ships made Fall River a natural location for textile mills. It was a major move emotionally for Esther. Aside from her and Adolfo's short time in Johnstown after they married, she had never lived outside of Brooklyn's Jewish neighborhoods. Yet in Fall River, French Canadian Catholics dominated. French translations were chiseled alongside English inscriptions on city monuments. French songs could be heard on radios that played in restaurants.[28] Catholic churches outnumbered the one or two Jewish temples that Lillian remembers. Lillian also recalls Canadian and Portuguese residents throughout their new community. The Krells were the only Jewish family in their neighborhood. In spite of this major cultural difference, Esther adjusted well to the move. Lillian recalls her mother's explanation for this. The Jewish community in Fall River lived on a wealthier side of town. Esther simply felt more comfortable with her French, Canadian, and Portuguese neighbors in the Flint area of Fall River. The neighborhood was also not far from the factories, which Adolfo could easily reach by car or bus.

Lillian, George, and their parents rented the second floor of a two-story house with a big backyard, something Lillian had never had before, having been born and raised in New York City. A French Canadian couple, the Laravies, occupied the ground floor. The owners of the house, another Catholic family, lived in the attic. Lillian remembers their name as "Caldwell," with their daughter "Charlotte." The 1930 Federal Census lists William and Charlotte Caldwell, along with their daughter, named after the mother, as living in Fall River.[29] Living among so many Catholics, Lillian quotes her mother as saying, "We must respect our neighbors." As such, the Krells were sensitive to two Sabbaths, the Jewish one on Saturdays that they observed and the Catholic one on Sundays that they respected. Esther was careful never to hang out her laundry on Sundays. She even offered to watch their neighbors' children while they attended Mass. According to Lillian, she and her

Esther 1930s

family were "very accepted and well-liked in the community." Lillian's public school understood her religious background only too well when her mother kept her home on Jewish holidays such as Rosh Hashanah and Yom Kippur. In spite of this, Lillian states, "We blended in very well." So much so that one day a priest mistook Lillian for a Catholic child. Esther had suggested that Lillian help Charlotte study her Catechism since Charlotte seemed to have a reading problem. When Lillian began public school in Fall River, however, she became the one who needed help.

Placing Lillian at the correct grade level proved to be a problem. In Brooklyn, she attended a large school where the system promoted children twice a year. Students were enrolled in, for example, 3A or 3 B, indicating two different levels of the third grade. But in Fall River, the system had no such distinction. It promoted only once a year. Lillian thinks she moved when she was in 3 B in the Brooklyn school system. Fall River put her back six months to just grade 3. If this was not embarrassing enough for her, Lillian found her grades slipping. Arithmetic quickly became her most difficult subject, largely due to Fall River's emphasis on Roman Numerals. Lillian did not know what they even were. She remembers how her frustration drove her to tears. As Lillian admits, "I never forgot the agony I felt in not understanding." In spite of the Depression, Esther hired a neighbor's daughter, who was studying to be a teacher, to tutor Lillian.

By the time she entered Durfee High School in Fall River, Lillian knew where she wanted her education to take her. She had decided to become a nurse. Lillian credits a Portuguese friend, Maria Urcelay, as the major influence on her choice of a career. As Lillian explains, Maria was "the first professional woman I ever met." Maria had been born in the Azores about 1892. As a child, she immigrated to America in 1901. In 1922 a man from Spain, Leandro Urcelay, also came to the United States. Maria and Leandro married, and in 1930 the couple had two young children. But unlike the vast majority of married women, Maria continued to work as a registered nurse at Union Hospital. In the 1930 Census, Leandro lists his occupation as a "chauffeur" for a hospital, which Lillian identifies as Union Hospital. She remembers him as an ambulance driver. Maria's widowed sister, who lived with the Urcelays, cared for the children when Maria and

Leandro worked at the hospital.[30] Maria and Esther became friends after Adolfo checked into Union Hospital for some minor surgery. He screamed in Spanish after the surgery, which led Maria to ask Leandro to act as a translator for her with Adolfo. Lillian thus first met Maria in her capacity as a nurse. About thirty years separated them, making Maria someone Lillian could easily look up to as a role model. She asked Maria many questions about nursing, including her decision to pursue that vocation. Maria shared with the young girl how her own strict father had refused to accept her career choice, forcing Maria to leave home. Although Lillian points to Maria as the primary factor in her decision to pursue nursing, without realizing it, Bubbie Basha may have influenced Lillian in two ways. First, Lillian knew the story behind her grandmother's limp. If she would have had proper medical attention after her fall, Basha might have avoided, or at least mitigated, the severe limp that marked her during most of her life. Second, when Lillian was about fifteen years old, Basha was diagnosed with breast cancer. She underwent radiation treatment, which burned her skin, at Post Graduate Hospital in New York City. What looked like boils appeared on her chest. When Basha visited the Krells, she slept in her granddaughter's room. Lillian put ointment on the burns and gave her grandmother medication for the discomfort she felt. Nevertheless, she remembers Basha crying out at night in pain. Lillian was very close to her grandmother and it could be that Basha's two medical conditions moved Lillian toward medicine as did the example set by Maria.

At Durfee High School, a student could choose one of three educational tracks--one prepared him/her for a technical career, another for commercial school, and the last for admittance to college. Lillian's father wanted her to choose the second course of study. Adolfo thought his only daughter should work in an office that specialized in international trade. With his own Latin America background, Adolfo urged Lillian to take classes that would prepare her for a commercial school. And, she should also take courses in Spanish, her father's native language. That would make her even more attractive for a job in an office that specialized in international business. But once she entered high school, Lillian wanted to enroll in college track classes. She knew she needed Latin, algebra, and math courses if she was to apply to a nursing school. Before she graduated from high school, Lillian took two years of Spanish to please her father. But in the Ernst household, Lillian identifies her mother as "the decision maker." And Esther supported Lillian's choice to follow in the footsteps of Esther's friend Maria. With her mother's backing, Lillian took classes to prepare her for a career in nursing. While at Fall River, the Krell family in 1936 welcomed the birth of a third child, Jerry.

Durfee High School

As it turned out, however, Lillian's time at Durfee High School was abruptly interrupted when she was in her sophomore year. After taking a salary cut, Adolfo heard about the possibility of a new job from a thread salesman, Joe Stein. The position, however, was in Holyoke, a town on the eastern side of Massachusetts. It was at a well known dress manufacturing company. The job paid about twice the salary Adolfo received in Fall River. With that in the offering, the Krells moved to Holyoke. Lillian describes herself as "heartbroken" on having to leave Fall River. She responded to her father's announcement of the move "in a flood of tears." Her life was so full in Fall River, with friends she cared about and a high school she felt a part of. But there was nothing Lillian could do. Her mother tried to console her, ensuring Lillian that, "When we get the kitchen curtains up, it will be home again." Promising to deliver on that pledge, the Krells moved about one hundred miles east. Culturally, they found a kindred spirit in their new home in Holyoke. They rented an apartment where the landlady, Mrs. Beltsky, turned out to be Jewish. The woman saw how unhappy Lillian was. She offered to introduce her new tenant to some Jewish girls her own age. Mrs. Beltsky also had a son she wanted Lillian to meet. As in Fall River, the population in Holyoke was overwhelmingly Irish and French, so the Krells were again surrounded by Catholics.[31] Lillian remembers many Polish residents, as well. As promised, Mrs. Beltsky brought three Jewish girls and her son over to meet Lillian. They became her best friends. More young people Lillian's age awaited her at the local high school.

While Holyoke High School was smaller than Durfee High in Fall River, it offered a college-track curriculum similar to the one Lillian had been following. The only significant difference was the absence of any Spanish classes at Holyoke High. Because of that, Dr. Connant, the principal, could not give his new student credit for the language classes she had taken in Fall River. With her father still hoping that Lillian would become fluent in Spanish, Adolfo hired a student from Mexico who was attending nearby Smith College to tutor her. By this action, Adolfo showed how important it was to him that his daughter became fluent in his native language. If the school could not supply a Spanish teacher, the family would do so in spite of the monetary cost. In all probability, Adolfo wanted Lillian to learn Spanish to further his own plans for her future, plans that promised a post-graduation visit to his family in Buenos Aires. A job in international business would follow upon Lillian's return to the United States. Needless to say, it was difficult for Adolfo to give up these plans for his only daughter. If such considerations moved him to hire the Spanish tutor, Adolfo was in for a disappointment. Lillian still wanted to become a nurse. And her will, with Esther's support, proved stronger than her father's dream for her.

Chapter 3

Life as a Probie
1940-1941

Over the course of her nurse's training at New York City's Mount Sinai Hospital, Lillian encountered both expected and unexpected situations. She anticipated the demanding, daily academic regimen--four hours inside of the classroom followed by an eight hour shift on the hospital wards. Lillian characterizes herself as "dedicated to her studies." With a smile undoubtedly brought on by the recollection, she explains how she stuffed clothing in a glass opening on top of the door to her room to block out the lamplight. Nursing school rules dictated lights out at 9:30 P.M., but Lillian had studying to do. In the classrooms where nurses and physicians lectured the students, she "always sat in front of the class." Depending on what shift Lillian had, hours caring for patients on hospital wards followed or preceded time in the classroom. She expected the hard work required of a nursing student. What she did not anticipate was how little time off she had--just one day a month with only a three-week break in the summer. Jewish students such as Lillian did not even receive consideration on Friday evenings so they could attend Temple. She also could not have foreseen an incident with one of the doctors only a few months before graduation. It almost resulted in her expulsion from nursing school. In the end, none of this stood in her way of becoming a nurse. Regardless of the situation before her, Lillian was determined to complete her studies. Even though she does not characterize herself as such, Lillian possessed a strong will that was exceptional for a woman of her era.[32]

Lillian began her training just after some significant changes occurred in the field of nursing. The profession itself was a fairly young one. The idea of formally trained nurses grew out of the high casualties armies suffered in nineteenth century wars. In England, Florence Nightingale advocated such training after her experiences in the Crimean War. The Civil War in the United States led to a similar conclusion. In that conflict, approximately twenty thousand American women, from all economic classes and ethnicities, volunteered to assist in the care of the wounded. Their service reflected what had been the norm up to that time--untrained women as caregivers. Such a tradition was rooted in a cultural view of women. Throughout early American history, the sick were attended to in the home. The nineteenth-century defined that as the "Woman's Sphere" of responsibility, giving a new phrase to an old idea. As one historian of the mid-nineteenth century explains, "Home... still represented the best, safest, and most comforting site for treatment and care as well as for birthing and dying."[33] But modern wars proved that tens of thousands of young men died far from home and family. The conflicts also provided evidence that formally trained nurses could save some of them. By 1940, when Lillian began her studies at Mount Sinai, nursing schools had only been in existence for about sixty years. Hospitals ran such schools.

While public hospitals existed in the nineteenth-century, the majority of Americans still preferred home to hospital when they became ill. The Jews' Hospital in New York City opened its doors in 1855. (Its name changed to Mount Sinai Hospital eleven years later.) Originally, untrained nurses worked with patients, who were primarily the poor. The hospital characterized its own staff in those years as "frequently careless and inefficient women."[34] As the nineteenth century progressed, the need to professionally train nurses grew as urban populations increased. With them came even more unsanitary conditions in the cities. The spread of infectious diseases could sweep through communities. In 1873 Bellevue Hospital in New York City began the first formal nursing program in the United States, copying the English nursing schools that Nightingale founded in the 1860s. Hospitals in other cities followed suit. In 1881 Mount Sinai Hospital accepted its first class of young women who would be professionally trained in the field of nursing.[35]

When Lillian began her education at Mount Sinai Hospital almost sixty years later, some aspects of the nursing school experience remained unchanged from what those first nurses went through. Most prominently, young women like Lillian agreed to "trade work for knowledge," meaning, they paid no tuition. Instead, the student nurses became the primary care giving labor force. Hospital-based training schools offered a diploma to their students at the end of the program. Graduation indicated an education in what was known as "scientific nursing." Its curriculum included the study of anatomy, physiology, chemistry, and bacteriology.[36] Yet in the very same decades when Lillian was growing up, some fundamental changes occurred in the world of nursing. In the late nineteenth and early twentieth centuries, the typical patient came from the working class. In the 1920s, however, more and more middle and upper class patients entered the hospitals when they became ill. Another change concerned the status of nurses. Within the medical community, nursing came to be seen more as a profession instead of a "service occupation." Perhaps in response to this new perception, schools raised their standards. In 1927 Mount Sinai Hospital lengthened its training from a two-year to a three-year program; this became the typical time required by most states when it came to the medical licensing of graduate students.[37]

In the 1930s, the Great Depression accounted for even more changes. The economic collapse resulted in "devastating effects" to the nursing profession. Over eight hundred hospital-based nursing schools closed in the 1930s.[38] But one impact could be seen as positive from the vantage point of the newly graduated nurse. Since the beginnings of the hospital-based nursing school in the 1880s, those who graduated from them sought employment as private duty nurses in American homes. Such positions, however, could be difficult to secure. It was not until the mid-1930s that "the old system of staffing hospitals primarily with nursing students began to crack." What followed was what one scholar calls "the great transformation" as nursing school graduates came to find employment as staff members in hospitals.[39] Leaders in the nursing profession had been recommending this change to "relieve students of their complete responsibility" of hospital patients. Hospitals came to see the economic benefit they could reap since any graduate nurses they hired could be "let go…and rehired" as the patient population fluctuated.[40] In the midst of the Depression, hospital administrators valued such flexibility.

By the end of the 1930s, nurses' training underwent one other fundamental change that, luckily, posed no problem for Lillian given her academic background. A 1928 statistical study of American nurses documented an oversupply and a rising unemployment rate. This was before the Great Depression began two years later. If entrance requirements were raised, the number of women who qualified for admittance to nursing schools would decline; this would be one way to address the oversupply problem. But the 1928 report documented another unsettling statistic. Almost half of the nursing school graduates that year had not completed high school. The report continued by noting that prestigious business offices placed more rigorous demands upon stenographers, typists, and file clerks than hospitals required of women who applied to nursing school.[41] Added to this embarrassing fact was the recognition that health care in the hospitals had become more "complex" by the 1930s. Depression-era nurses now had to calculate the correct medical doses, interpret surgical orders, and record the changing status of patients on their individual charts.[42] It is not surprising that by 1940, hospital-based nursing schools insisted that all applicants have at least a high school degree. This significantly decreased the number of women who could apply since only twenty-eight percent of white women in 1940 had graduated from high school.[43]

As noted earlier, Lillian began her nurse's training in the fall of 1940 at Mount Sinai Hospital. She had applied to four schools--Massachusetts General Hospital in Boston; Brown University's nursing program in Providence, Rhode Island; and two New York City institutions, Bellevue Hospital and Mount Sinai Hospital School of Nursing. Other classmates at Holyoke High School had applied to Massachusetts General, but Lillian recalls that she was the only student from there to be accepted. Her reason for applying was typical of a young woman her age. Many of her friends were going to Boston University, including the oldest brother of her "dearest friend," a young man to whom Lillian readily admits she was attracted. Because of this, Massachusetts General became her first choice. She submitted an application to Brown University since its four-year nursing program resulted in a college degree in nursing. At the time, however, Lillian knew that financially, attending Brown might be too expensive for her parents. Bellevue interested her because she had a friend who had begun her nurse's training there. After a visit to Bellevue, however, Lillian judged the nursing home where students lived as "old and decrepit." Her friend also discouraged Lillian from attending Bellevue because she felt that students did not receive enough training before working on the wards. Lillian applied to Mount Sinai due to the fact that Dr. Leibowitz, her brother Jerry's pediatrician, recommended it.

As it turned out, all four nursing schools accepted Lillian. She ended up at Mount Sinai because her parents asked her to go there. Esther and Adolfo decided to move back to New York City where he would go into business with Uncle Bernardo. Since Lillian preferred Massachusetts General, in her words she "rebelled a little" at their request. Yet as she explains, "I adored my parents" and wanted to honor their wish. At the same time, Lillian knew that she would be able to see her mother and father more easily if they all lived in New York City. (When she actually began her training at Mount Sinai, however, her parents had left that city for New Haven, Connecticut. Adolf's business venture with his uncle did not work out.) Lillian believes that the Krells' move to Holyoke when she was a child helped her gain admission to Mount Sinai's nursing school. "If I had not been living in Massachusetts, I would not have been accepted at Mount Sinai." Lillian explains that the New York school "prided itself in accepting students from across the country." Thus in a modern sense, she contributed to the school's diversity since she lived in a different state when she applied to Mount Sinai. Due to the fact that

Lillian did not possess a New York State high school diploma, she had to pass a State Board educational examination; in all probability, it was New York's way of verifying that she had a high school background equivalent to its graduating students. As Lillian began her studies at Mount Sinai in the fall of 1940, over three hundred thousand professionally trained nurses worked in the United States. She fit the profile of who became a nurse in the first half of the twentieth century--a native-born, white, single woman.[44] Where Lillian differed was in her religious affiliation. What is often surprising to people today is the amount of societal prejudices women, especially Jewish women, had to deal with in the early twentieth century if they wanted to become a nurse.

The cultural biases women confronted were rooted in some unseemly aspects of nursing. Lillian characterizes them as "unpleasant things" nurses dealt with on a daily basis. She graphically identifies some of these as "blood," "bedpans," and "death." One could add vomit, urine, and feces to her list. Nurses had to clean up all of this. They also administered enemas, changed soiled dressings, and catheterized female patients. Before the availability of antibiotics in World War II, nurses could become infected with serious diseases such as diphtheria or scarlet fever.[45] Lillian contrasted this medical world with the one her father had wanted her to work in after high school. It was the world of international business. As a secretary, in Lillian's words, she would have been in a "clean" environment, working with "paper and pencils." Those she interacted with would have been "business men" in suits, as she describes them. Lillian points out that nurses, however, would see "naked men." As if these aspects of nursing were not enough to make families question their daughter's choice of a vocation, Jewish women faced additional cultural prejudices that related to their faith. The Krells were Orthodox Jews. Lillian observes that, "It was an era where men and women did not sit together in an Orthodox Temple." In this religious tradition, any type of pre-marital intimacy was frowned upon. Even when they danced, she continues, Orthodox couples held a handkerchief between them. The Jewish bias against women entering the nursing field remained strong in the early twentieth century in spite of Scriptural references in the Old Testament to women as nurses. Even Jewish publications at the turn of the twentieth century that encouraged women to enter this field did not eliminate the community's reluctance to see their daughters become nurses.[46]

One reason for this relates to the association between trained nurses and Christianity. American Jews already lived in a society where Protestantism and Catholicism dominated many aspects of their daily lives. Parents would understandably have been hesitant to approve a career choice for their daughters that was said to originate in the Christian faith. Early twentieth century nursing textbooks made this connection. Authors of one prominent series wrote their publication from a clear "socio-Christian perspective." Nursing was said to come out of "Christian love and charity," a clear example of the "good works" one could perform. It was not unusual for hospital-based nursing schools, even Jewish ones, to require their students to attend prayer sessions where passages from the New Testament were read aloud. This custom persisted into the 1940s.[47] At Mount Sinai's Residential Facility, Lillian found out that Jewish students were not excused from such prayer meetings before breakfast each day.

In addition to the relationship between nursing and Christianity, elements within the Jewish culture reinforced a suspicion that nursing was not an acceptable career choice for young women. These included an economic consideration. Nursing required years of training, while other positions were open to young women that brought immediate income to her and the family. Parents held a gender bias, too, when it came to education that could intrude upon what they felt was their daughter's primary calling, that of a wife and mother.[48] While such considerations have been cited as relevant to why Jewish families did not readily accept a daughter's wish to become a nurse, these beliefs were held by Protestant families as well. They were simply part of the societal perceptions of women in the first half of the twentieth century. They existed in the culture as a whole, and especially within the Orthodox Jewish community in which Lillian's parents had been raised. Nursing was "not for a Jewish girl" became a refrain that young women of Lillian's generation heard again and again from their relatives.[49]

In this respect, however, Lillian's progressive parents were somewhat different. Esther and Adolfo had matured as "broad-minded people," to use Lillian's characterization of them. For example, rather than have their teenage daughter sneak a cigarette, Adolfo offered to leave some out on a table for her. And in respect to liquor, Adolfo made it clear to his daughter that if she was curious about its taste, he would pour her a drink himself. Lillian realized that her progressive parents would not stand in her way when it came to nursing school. Recall that her mother approved of her career choice. Perhaps the example set by Esther's Portuguese nursing friend Maria Urcelay influenced her. As for Adolfo, Lillian stresses that he never brought up such cultural prejudices when his only daughter told him she wanted to become a nurse. As explained earlier, he did not approve of her decision. But Lillian sees his reaction as one that related more to what she identifies as the "prestige" her father associated with international trade rather than any biases against nurses. As Lillian concludes, Adolfo judged the business world as a "nicer environment" than that offered by the medical field. She adds, too, that he also felt it commanded "more respect." Additionally, Lillian emphasizes that Adolfo "prized" trade between Argentina, his native land, and the United States, his adopted one. He wanted his daughter to be part of an international commercial relationship between the two countries that he felt would develop in the near future. Lillian also points out that her father's early life undoubtedly influenced his career choice for her. Adolfo believed women should be able to take care of themselves in case something happened to their husband. He had only to look at his own mother to see the value in this. Upon the death of Adolfo's father, Lillian reminds us that her grandmother had to turn her children over to her in-laws while she struggled to make a living. Understandably, Adolfo wanted his daughter to be able to provide for herself if such a need arose. He believed for more than one reason that the business world would allow her to do that to a greater degree than would the world of nursing.

Aside from any cultural or parental reservations Lillian faced, another unspoken obstacle confronted Jewish women who aspired to become professionally trained nurses. In the first half of the twentieth century, nursing schools had quotas as to how many Jewish and black women they admitted. Between 1875 and 1920, for example, two major training schools in New York City, Bellevue Hospital and New

York Hospital, graduated only four Jewish nurses. Such quotas still existed when Lillian applied to nursing schools. It seems that generally speaking, Jewish women attended nursing schools that operated as part of Jewish hospitals. It is not clear if this occurred because they thought they would be more comfortable at an institution tied to their religious community or if it was because they were excluded from other nursing schools.[50] Lillian's decision to study at Mount Sinai supports the general profile of Jewish women attending nursing schools at Jewish hospitals. Certainly Lillian chose Mount Sinai's nursing school because her parents asked her to, but she embraced the choice after visiting the hospital before she began her studies there.

In the judgment of one historian, in the early twentieth century New York City represented the "center of the nursing world."[51] Mount Sinai Hospital was part of that "center." It spread over three city blocks. Fifth Avenue and Madison Avenue bordered it on one side, while 99th Street and 101st Street did so on the other side. The hospital stood at the end of what New Yorkers called "Millionaire's Row." A contemporary description of that section reads, "It is a quarter of old mansions, air-conditioned apartments, exclusive clubs, luxurious hotels, fabulous penthouses; of great churches and museums; of art galleries, antique shops, and specialty stores."[52] Lillian admits to being "impressed by the surroundings" in that part of New York. In a city teeming with people, Central Park's open landscape lay right across the street from Mount Sinai. But Lillian stresses that the hospital bordered not only what she characterizes as "a very wealthy area," but also "a very poor area, Spanish Harlem." That neighborhood sat at the other end of the large medical complex. When Lillian began her nursing studies, eighteen buildings made up the hospital. She characterizes her room as "a delightful residence." The building she lived and studied in was relatively new when Lillian started her program late in 1940. It opened its doors in 1927. Fourteen stories in height, the nursing school building loomed as the tallest of all of the Mount Sinai structures. An underground tunnel connected it to other parts of the hospital complex. Reception rooms, offices, a four-hundred-seat auditorium, a living room, and a library comprised the first and second floors. The latter was the floor devoted to teaching, with triple the instructional space of the old nursing school building. Lillian remembers the classrooms as "very nice." Students lived in rooms on eight floors of the building. Lillian describes the living area as "the nursing home." Faculty and the supervisory nursing staff lived on the twelfth and thirteenth floors. A gymnasium and infirmary, where ill students or staff members received free medical care, took over most of the fourteenth floor. Altogether, nine hundred doctors, surgeons, and laboratory scientists joined over fourteen hundred administrators, nurses, and service personnel.[53] This was the world Lillian entered in September 1940.

When Lillian began her training, the Krells had not yet moved back to New York City. Esther and Adolfo, therefore, drove Lillian by automobile from Holyoke to the Mount Sinai Hospital School of Nursing. Esther borrowed money from her sister for the initial costs of her daughter's medical education. According to Lillian, the school required a one-time payment of about $250 for what she calls "an entry fee." An additional $50 dollars or so covered her probationary student uniform. Lillian explains that the nursing school accepted two classes each year, one that began in February and one that started in September. Lillian estimates that her fall class had between ninety and ninety-five students. Yet only about forty, in her estimation, graduated three years later. Some probably could not keep up academically. But Lillian attributes what she calls "the big drop-out rate" to Mount Sinai's rule that if a student nurse married, she had to leave the training program. The women who had been admitted with her that September came from many states. Lillian especially remembers some from Hazelton, Pennsylvania, a coal mining town. Soon after she arrived at Mount Sinai, the administration assigned another student nurse to act as Lillian's "big sister." She was Irene Mondik, who Lillian describes as "a delightful young woman from Hazelton." Irene had begun nursing school in February 1940, some six months before Lillian did so. As she settled in, Lillian was grateful that she had a private room. That meant, in her own words, that she would not have to "adjust to someone else," especially when it came to staying up past "lights out" so she could study longer.

Immediately, Mount Sinai introduced Lillian to the hierarchical nature of nursing school. To graduate, she would progress through three different levels of study as she spent time as a probationary nurse (known as a "probie"), a junior nurse, and, finally, a senior nurse. Basic to the medical hierarchy was the idea of deference. A student submitted to the orders of those nursing students who were above her, to the head nurse, and, most prominently, to the doctors. Obedience and strict discipline were basic to the hierarchy.[54]

Lillian spent six months as a probie. She recalls the uniform for that stage of her training as "not an attractive one." It consisted of a navy blue dress with a starched white collar and starched cuffs that the student attached to her upper arm. She also tied a starched white apron around her waist. Probies wore no caps on their head. Black oxford shoes and black lisle stockings completed the outfit. Esther had to go to the Italian section of New Haven to locate the stockings. (Mount Sinai was the only nursing school Lillian knew of that had not yet progressed to white stockings.) No make-up could be worn. Adolfo disagreed with such a regulation. He liked women to look their best, and he felt make-up helped them to do that. Following Mount Sinai's regulations made his daughter, Adolfo thought, look like "a washerwoman." It did not add to Lillian's appearance, either, that the school required students at all levels to wear a hairnet. That covering posed a special problem for Lillian. Her red hair was thick and, in her words, "it went through the hairnet." Once properly attired, Lillian began her months as a probie. During that time, she worked only on dummies, literally. Probationary nurses learned how to bathe patients and change their sheets using the mannequins. They worked on other inanimate objects, as well. For example, probies practiced injections on oranges.

A nursing instructor, Madam Gubursky, oversaw the education of the probie nurses. Some seventy years later, Lillian still recalls a song the students sang about her at their "Annual Show Performance" at the Guggenheim Auditorium following the "Capping Services":

"Six lessons from Madam Gubursky,
And you'll discover how to be a good nursky.
Those lessons won't make you,
They'll break you.
And making those beds won't make you,
They'll break you.

Pull tight on those corners,
Now don't pat that sheet.
Look out for those wrinkles,
You've got to be neat.
Six lessons from Madam Gubursky,
And you'll discover what practice can do.
It's step 1-2-3 girls, follow me.
It's bound to bring out the nursky in you."

After those first six months, Lillian passed a required exam to prove that she had mastered some of the basic skills students needed to move on to the next level of the nursing program. With her parents in attendance, she was officially admitted to the Mount Sinai Hospital School of Nursing at a formal ceremony where she was "capped." That day, Lillian received a nurse's distinct white cap to wear on her head, with the ever-present hairnet. (In her last year in nursing school, a black band was added to her nurse's cap to indicate her senior status.) Her student nurse's uniform now became a short-sleeved blue and white plaid dress. As with her probie outfit, Lillian attached a starched collar and starched cuffs (again worn on her upper arms) to the dress. The uniform also required a starched white bib and a big, starched apron. The bottom of the dress hung below the knee to calf-level. The black oxford shoes and black lisle stockings remained.

With her time as probie now over, Lillian became a junior student nurse, a status she would hold for one and a half years. In this new capacity, she could now go onto the hospital wards where she would "trade work for knowledge." Some of that learning took place on the wards, and some occurred in the classrooms. The days began early. Before any instruction took place, all student nurses had to go downstairs at 6:30 A.M. to collectively read portions of the King James Version of the Bible. This included women such as Lillian who were of the Jewish faith. "What bothered me the most," Lillian shares, "was that I had to get up early to read a Christian Bible." During her time at Mount Sinai, Lillian stresses that she did this "every day for three years." In this respect, the administration at a Jewish hospital made no religious allowance for its Jewish student nurses. Only after morning prayers were the student nurses allowed to go to breakfast. In the employee cafeteria, the insensitivity to religious beliefs continued.

Mount Sinai kitchen staff regularly served non-kosher dinner food to its student nurses and, on Sundays, non-kosher luncheon meals. Lillian further explains that on that day, the cafeteria frequently put out ham and pork as its main entrée. The hospital had a kosher kitchen, but it was only for the patients in private rooms, not for the staff. On many occasions, therefore, this left Jewish students raised in an Orthodox home with less than a complete meal. Lillian became friends with Doris Maslan, a Jewish student nurse from Maine whose father was a rabbi. He sent his daughter kosher salami, which Doris shared with Lillian. They ate the salami with crackers and sometimes, Lillian adds, "a nice Jewish rye" bread in their rooms.

Lillian & George at family's summer home

Lillian also recalls with regret how Mount Sinai's regulations prohibited her from attending in their entirety Sabbath Eve services. There was a Temple on 86th Street, ten blocks away. But Lillian could never stay for the whole evening's services. She had to leave to be back in her room at the nursing school by 9:30 P.M. If a student came in late, she would be restricted for a month. This meant, as Lillian explains, that the student lost her late pass for the next month. If any student failed three times to be in her room by curfew, a nursing board formally admonished her.

Lillian's formal education included both class and ward instruction. Classes ran for four hours, Mondays through Saturdays. Students met with instructional nurses or doctors who taught them in either one of the classrooms in the nursing building or in a laboratory. Lillian "loved the classes on the whole." She remembers one or two doctors as the primary instructors. Sometimes they heard a lecture from German-born physicians; their heavy accent could make the lesson difficult to understand. Lillian recalls one of those classroom sessions with pride. Dr. Schick, a German Jewish refugee who she identifies as "an elderly, dignified, well-known physician," walked into one of the dietician classes. According to Lillian, he was famous for the discovery of the smallpox vaccination. Dr. Schick turned to Lillian and asked her, "Young lady, can you tell me what a calorie is?" Lillian replied, "A unit of heat. We intake calories. What we eat provides us with the food and energy we need." Her response impressed Dr. Schick. Aside from the regular classrooms, sometimes the operating theater became the center for learning as students observed surgical procedures. The four hours of classroom instruction was accompanied by eight hours on the wards. A nursing student could be given the morning shift (7:00 A.M. - 3:00 P.M.), the relief shift (3:00 P.M. - 11:00 P.M.), or the night shift (11:00 P.M. - 7:00 A.M.).

A night shift proved especially difficult for the student nurse, a fact Lillian attests to. After eight hours on the wards, she was very tired. Yet she still had to show up for morning classroom instruction. On the wards and in the classrooms, the students learned firsthand what the professional responsibilities of a nurse entailed. Among these were taking a patient's vital signs (the temperature, pulse, and respiration), administering medications, bathing the patient, and inserting a catheter into female patients when necessary. (Male interns handled male patients for that procedure.) Student nurses also observed boundaries dictated by gender when it came to bathing male patients. The young women were not to wash the genital area. Instead, after they bathed the patient, they were to hand the man the washcloth and ask him to finish his sponge bath himself. One of Lillian's patients, who she identifies as "an elderly Jewish man," did not understand the implication of that directive. After giving him the washcloth, clearly telling him, "I want you to finish your bath," Lillian left his bedside. Some minutes later she was abruptly summoned by her graduate instructor who saw the gentleman shampooing his hair. When Lillian questioned him as to why he was doing that, he replied in a thick Jewish accent, "Darling, you did such a good job that the only thing I had left to wash was my hair." Decades later, she laughs at this incident.

Similarly, a smile appears on Lillian's face when she recounts a story of her time on the wards that involved a physician who became a world-famous doctor, Jonas Salk. When she attended Mount Sinai's nursing school, however, Salk was just an intern. According to Lillian, he did not communicate well with patients or with staff. He tended to mumble and hurriedly leave the patients' bedside. He also usually failed to sign his instructions for patient care. Lillian recalls having to "always chase him to get his signature" on those medical orders. One day when she came on duty, a Mrs. Goldberg was suffering abdominal pain following gall bladder surgery. Lillian offered to send for the intern on duty, Dr. Salk, but Mrs. Goldberg did not want to see him. She called him "*schtuma*," a Yiddish word for being silent or unable to speak. With amusement, Lillian recounts that when her student nursing class graduated in 1943, they voted Dr. Jonas Salk the physician least likely to succeed in the field of medicine.

Student nurses also assisted the doctors as they made their rounds. One day soon after she ceased being a probie, Lillian was on the gynecological ward. Dr. Isidor Rubin needed her assistance. He later became well-known for pioneering an examination, the uterotubal insufflation test, to help women who had not been able to conceive a child. This method of analyzing what appeared to be a female sterility problem focused on the woman's Fallopian tubes. It employed a non-surgical procedure to open them.[55] Lillian believes that the first time Dr. Rubin performed this procedure on a patient at Mount Sinai Hospital was early in 1941. When he did so, the doctor called upon her to assist him. Describing herself as "this little student who just got capped," Lillian concludes that she "was just lucky that day."

With wards that were, in Lillian's words, "constantly full," doctors and nurses kept busy. Lillian remembers about twenty-five beds on one side of a ward, and another fifteen to twenty on the opposite side. Student nurses raised and lowered the beds with an iron crank. Lillian observes that, "the bed often did not go down or come up easily." If that happened, she had to exert great physical effort to adjust it for patient comfort. Lillian describes herself as always "bending, bending, bending." Jokingly, she even ascribes her bent-over frame today as the result of her years as a student nurse. Large flasks used for patient infusions posed another problem for Lillian.

They resembled a big jug and weighed about five pounds. Hung from a metal stand near the bedside, nurses had to lift the flask up high to put it into place, turning it over as they did so. Lillian's short stature made that difficult for her, but, unlike the beds that always needed adjustment, not all patients received infusions. When asked about her most difficult and nicest patients, Lillian has a ready answer. Interestingly, both were entertainers. The actor Orson Wells proved the most demanding one. Lillian dealt with him when she was in her senior year at Mount Sinai. Wells was hard to please. As Lillian tells the story, one day, after giving him his breakfast tray, the actor threw it at her. She came to understand why Wells' wife Rita Hayworth, a Hollywood star in her own right, often left the hospital room in tears. In contrast, the famous singer and dancer Danny Kaye was Lillian's nicest patient. Hospitalized for pneumonia, he gave nurses free tickets for his Broadway show. Lillian recalls Kaye as "always charming and appreciative of the care his nurses gave him."

In addition to the patients on the wards, student nurses could also be assigned to rooms adjacent to the wards where the staff cared for the most critically ill patients. If the rooms housed people with contagious diseases, student nurses followed a lengthy procedure to protect themselves when they interacted with the patients. Vital signs, for example, had to be taken regularly. Lillian, or any nurse, removed her watch and put it on a table outside of the room that housed infected patients. She reached inside of the room to get what Lillian describes as "a white, surgical gown" that she put over her nurse's uniform; in so doing, the nurse took care only to touch the inside of the gown since the outside could carry germs. She then washed her hands in a Lysol solution to disinfect them. With a thermometer in her right hand and a watch in her left hand, the nurse was ready to enter the infectious room. She might have to repeat this procedure anywhere from six to ten times a day for each infectious patient.[56] Lillian describes medical gloves as "thick and heavy," making it difficult for the doctor or nurse to retain any dexterity. The eight hours on the wards along with the four hours of classroom instruction gave student nurses such as Lillian a twelve-hour workday. But even then, their labor did not end. In the early 1940s, Lillian points out that hospitals did not have what she calls "prepared central supply equipment" as they do today to, for example, remove sutures. Instead, after her twelve-hour day in class and on the wards, Lillian and other student nurses had to wash all of the medical equipment by hand before sterilizing it. This included rubber tubing, needles, and syringes. The cleaning and disinfecting took about ninety minutes according to Lillian. The nurses then set the items out for the next staff members who came on duty.

Lillian's three years in Mount Sinai's nursing program thus resulted in long days, weeks, and months of training. She stresses that for six days a week, her Monday through Saturday workdays lasted more than twelve hours as she attended classes, showed up for her shift on the wards, and then prepared the equipment for the next group. Since no classroom instruction occurred on Sundays, those workdays were four hours shorter. In her second year of the nursing program, Mount Sinai began paying Lillian a monthly stipend of nine dollars; the amount remained unchanged through her senior year. Additionally, her mother gave her five to ten dollars each month, and an aunt added to that as well. Lillian's expenses were not great since Mount Sinai provided her with room and board, but she did need some cash for incidentals. She went to a nearby coffee shop with friends, an ice cream parlor on Lexington Avenue, and small shops in Spanish Harlem. Lillian also had one clothing expense. Even though she wore a uniform every day, she needed to purchase undergarments on a regular basis. In addition to these small expenses, Lillian paid for roundtrip subway and train tickets when she had her day off once a month. She always spent as much of that day as she could with her parents in New Haven. Recall that "the nursing home" required students to be in by 9:30 P.M., but given the distance Lillian traveled to visit her family, even with a late pass she seldom made that curfew hour. She sighs when explaining, "I was always on restriction because I was late coming home from Connecticut." Lillian's tardiness was not her fault. The trains were, she explains, "often late during the war years." It was on one of those trips that the Krells learned together about the attack that brought America into World War II.

Chapter 4

America Enters the War:
A Dramatic Enlistment and Departure

The date was December 7, 1941. The war in Europe had been going on since September 1939. On one side stood the Axis powers, led by Adolph Hitler's German government, and on the other side the Allied nations, led by Great Britain. While President Franklin D. Roosevelt's administration clearly favored the Allies, at the end of 1941 America was not officially a belligerent nation. That changed on December 7th when Japan, one of the Axis countries, attacked the United States' Pacific fleet based at Pearl Harbor, Hawaii. The date fell on a Sunday that coincided with Lillian's day off. On those monthly visits home, Adolfo looked forward to a musical interlude with his daughter. Lillian played the piano for him. He followed that by putting some records on the Victrola. Adolfo especially enjoyed playing tango music as father and daughter danced together. On one such afternoon Harold, the son of a neighbor, came into the Krell home crying. Distraught, the young man complained to Lillian and her parents, "You're the only people dancing and singing in the United States today." Harold then proceeded to share the news of the Japanese attack at Pearl Harbor. Adolfo's initial reaction mirrored that of many Americans. He asked, "My God, where is Pearl Harbor?" Then Lillian and her parents did something else that others were doing across the country. They turned on the radio to hear the news reports. Lillian telephoned Mount Sinai and was told to return to the hospital as soon as possible. She quickly left New Haven. The trains were especially crowded, Lillian remembers, because servicemen home on Christmas leave were trying to report back to their duty stations. Everyone knew that there was no question the United States would now enter the war on the side of the Allies.

Mount Sinai Hospital had already been engaged in activities to support the war against Hitler's Germany. In 1940 it began collecting blood plasma to send to Great Britain. It could be used there not only for English soldiers, but for civilians as well. Germany had begun a sustained bombing campaign against the British Isles in September 1940. London was particularly hard hit. As in other locations throughout the United States, volunteers showed up to donate blood. At Mount Sinai, about two hundred and sixty people did so each week, coming into the medical center during one of its three weekly collection times. The hospital dedicated an entire floor to the "Blood for Britain" program. By the end of 1944, over sixteen thousand donors had shown up.[57] Lillian helped out at the blood bank, but always, she points out, after her regular eight-hour shift on the wards was over. Her twelve-hour plus day (classroom time, ward time, and clean-up time) became even longer. But it was in keeping with Lillian's nature to offer what little "free" time she had to help out in the war effort on the Home Front. Millions of other Americans did the same. Lillian did more than volunteer at the blood bank. In September 1940, the same year Mount Sinai began collecting blood plasma, Congress passed what was initially a one-year draft. This would create a pool of young American men in preparation for when, or if, the country entered the war. Lillian volunteered time there, too. She remembers the hospital staff assisting in the physical examinations for the inductees. According to Lillian, this happened in a room near the basement. One day when she showed up there, she saw a black doctor from Harlem, Dr. Payne, awaiting a nursing assistant. Lillian explains that the white nurses went past Dr. Payne. But Lillian "walked straight up to him." The two even spent some time together outside of the hospital at a nearby coffee shop.

In 1941, Mount Sinai added more of what was then called "National Defense Activities" to its war-related work. The United States exported military material to Great Britain. Many ships departed from New York City. Because of that fact, German submarines lurked off the coast. With this in mind, more defense preparations began in the city months before America entered the war. Mount Sinai offered First-Aid classes. It trained nurses' aides in conjunction with the American Red Cross (ARC), graduating several thousand. The hospital created a "catastrophe unit," to care for "disaster victims," obviously in case New York City itself was attacked internally by spies or externally by German military forces. In partnership with the Red Cross, the staff also oversaw "emergency ambulances operated by American Women's Voluntary Services." In such an atmosphere, it is telling that one other activity on the part of Mount Sinai Hospital was the creation of a course on "War Neuroses." Adding to an unsettling atmosphere, the institution had its employees practice air-raid drills. The eighteen hospital buildings had fifty-three different roof levels that volunteers guarded in air raid drills. Additionally, the staff learned the most efficient method to extinguish incendiary bombs. Mount Sinai also practiced blackouts. The entire hospital could cover its windows at night in a matter of minutes, no easy feat remembering the size of the Mount Sinai complex. Altogether, the hospital had more than nine thousand windows that had to be darkened in blackout drills.[58]

One role Mount Sinai played in World War II that it is especially proud of concerns its staffing of the Third General Hospital that operated within the United States Army. The history of that unit dates back to 1916, during the First World War. Doctors, nurses, and other staff members from Mount Sinai served in what the military identified as Base Hospital Number 3 in World War I. It treated the American wounded at Vauclaire, France. The flag flown by Base Hospital Number 3 was presented late in August 1942 to a newly activated Third General Hospital, its World War II counterpart. The ceremony took place at Mount Sinai's Blumenthal Auditorium. Just a few days later, the Third General Hospital, staffed by Mount Sinai's doctors, nurses, and technicians, left for basic training. It sailed for Europe in May 1943 where it treated American casualties in North Africa, Italy, and France. Almost nine hundred Mount Sinai doctors, nurses, employees, and even hospital trustees served in other medical military units aside from the Third General Hospital. [59] As a nurse in the Army Nurse Corps (ANC), Lillian became one of them after she graduated. The famous American General Jimmy Doolittle recruited Lillian toward the end of her second year in the nursing program.

In the aftermath of the attack on Pearl Harbor, Americans wanted to strike back at Japan. That included President Roosevelt. In January 1942 he approved a plan by which Army planes would take off from a Navy aircraft carrier to bomb Tokyo and other Japanese cities. The military charged a well-known Army aviator, then Colonel Jimmy Doolittle, with implementing the plan. The "Doolittle Raid" occurred in April 1942. The colonel returned to the United States in mid-May as a hero. At a White House ceremony, Roosevelt conferred the Medal of Honor upon him and promoted him to the rank of brigadier general. At the end of May, the government sent Doolittle on public relation trips to war plants. He left for military service in Europe the first week of August 1942.[60] Given those dates, Doolittle visited Mount Sinai Hospital sometime in June or July. He joined representatives from the ARC to recruit student nurses for the ANC. Before and during World War II, the Red Cross acted as the primary recruiter of nurses for the United States Army.[61] Its visit to Mount Sinai for this purpose was not, therefore, an unusual one.

Seventy years later, Lillian still regales listeners with the story of how Doolittle signed her up for the ANC. She describes him as "charismatic," "impressive," "dynamic," and "handsome." In addition to his charm, Lillian recalls him making an announcement that would certainly have made his Mount Sinai audience somber. "Young ladies, we anticipate a long war, one with many casualties." In all probability, Doolittle or the ARC representatives shared statistics on how desperately nurses were needed. When the war began in Europe in 1939, the ANC had less than seven hundred nurses. By December of 1941, the number had risen to over seven thousand.[62] But many more would be needed as millions of American men prepared to enter the military. They would fight overseas in a war that would not be over soon. Casualties would assuredly be high.

About six months before the ARC and Doolittle visited Mount Sinai Hospital, *Life* magazine ran a major story about the need for more trained medical workers. The cover of the January 5, 1942 issue carried a photograph of a nurse with the caption, "Wanted: 50,000 Nurses." *Life* reported that the United States had some thirteen hundred nurses' training schools in the United States. Yet even their twenty-three thousand yearly graduates would not, by themselves, be enough to meet the nation's needs in wartime. The story inside of the magazine called for one hundred thousand nurses' aides to relieve some of the workload of Registered Nurses (RNs), meaning graduate nurses who had passed the State Board exam. Lillian would be one of those RNs in about a year and a half. Caught up in Doolittle's forceful personality and by the military need the Red Cross stressed, Lillian promptly signed up to join the ANC after graduation in the fall of 1943. (Her induction into the ANC was predicated on her becoming a licensed RN.) As he did with the handful of other student nurses who volunteered that day, Doolittle signed Lillian's enlistment papers. She proudly points to this fact as well as to "a handshake and a hug" that the general bestowed upon her. As a result of this, Lillian confesses that she did not want to wash her hand or her arm. While the moment was an important one for her, she decided not to mention it to her parents on her next visit home. "I didn't say a word," Lillian explains. After all, the war might be over before she graduated. Lillian adds that there existed the possibility, too, that she would not pass her State Board exams. That appears to have been unlikely, though, given Lillian's dedication to her studies. But she rationalizes it as another reason for not telling Esther and Adolfo about her pending enlistment. "I didn't want to upset my parents for a year," she concludes.

Just months after that memorable day when Doolittle visited Mount Sinai Hospital, Lillian began her third and last year of nursing school. It was the fall of 1942. Soon after that there was a three month period when Lillian's schedule became significantly lighter. This happened when she went to New York City's Columbia Presbyterian Hospital for training in obstetrics. She found the change from Mount Sinai a pleasant one. There was not a requirement that she get up early for prayers, she sat in classes with pre-med students as well as nurses, and the hospital gave her a late pass each week so she could attend Temple on Friday evenings. If she had night duty, a nurse's aide brought her a snack. Whereas Mount Sinai allowed her one late pass a month, Presbyterian presented her with three a week. Lillian describes her experience at the Presbyterian hospital as "wonderful." She felt she had "more freedom," too, with her daily residency overseen by a "kind housemother." The staff also appeared to hold a favorable opinion of Lillian. When she left to return to Mount Sinai, her head nurse suggested that, after graduation, a position might be available for her at Columbia Presbyterian Hospital.

During her months at that hospital, Lillian was struck by how much less hierarchical it was than Mount Sinai. Regulations there, for example, required student nurses to give their place in an elevator or cafeteria line to a physician if one should appear. Lillian judged this rule to be part of a pattern in which the Mount Sinai administration "spoiled" its doctors. Privileges afforded to physicians even extended to the underground tunnels that connected the hospital's eighteen buildings. At various points in the tunnels, elevators carried the staff to the floors above. Protocol demanded that student nurses step back in the lines for the elevators if an intern, a physician, or a graduate nurse appeared. The elevators were usually crowded; giving one's place in line could mean waiting for another elevator. Student nurses were to follow the same policy in cafeteria lines. Columbia Presbyterian Hospital had no such deferential regulations. At Mount Sinai, Lillian encountered strict rules, too, in respect to relationships between students and more senior nurses. She became friends with her head nurse, Helen Glickman. They were so close that Helen often accompanied Lillian home when she visited her parents. (Raised in an orphanage in Joplin, Missouri, Helen must have appreciated spending time with a loving family). But Mount Sinai's rules did not allow Lillian to visit Helen in the latter's fifth floor room. Usually, the two women met at a local coffee shop.

Incidents such as these might appear on the surface to be inconsequential, but they spoke to a policy of deference that supported a hierarchy where those who held power over student nurses were not to be questioned. Recognizing this is basic to understanding the most traumatic event Lillian experienced during her three years at Mount Sinai. The episode almost led to her expulsion from nursing school just months before graduation. But note the word "almost." Drawing upon her determination to become a nurse, Lillian stood up to that power structure. At the time, however, she did not see her assertiveness as particularly brave. Instead, she felt no pride in her actions. Lillian stresses that, as a victim, she felt ashamed. What follows is Lillian's account of what happened to her.

The incident concerned Dr. A. A. Berg who received his medical degree in 1894. Lillian describes him as "an eminent surgeon." He was that. Berg's specialty was gastroenterology. Along with a colleague, he developed a surgical treatment in which doctors removed part of the stomach for patients who suffered from ulcers. Berg spent his entire professional life at Mount Sinai, having been appointed as an Attending Surgeon in 1914 and then retiring in 1934. Berg remained with the hospital in the years after that as a Consulting Surgeon. In his medical career, he held Honorary Fellowships in several European scientific organizations. From 1943-1947, Berg served as president of the International College of Surgeons.[63] As noted earlier, one historian identifies deference and hierarchy as fundamental to the world of the student nurse. Certainly if anyone expected submission from those with less experience, it was someone like Dr. A. A. Berg.

Lillian points to a reputation he had among student nurses. It was represented in what she calls "the dance." Nurses moved a certain way when Berg came near them. He was known for grabbing their breasts and buttocks. "The dance" was a way the young women tried to avoid his grasp. When Lillian was about four or five months away from graduation, she and others in her class prepared to leave for White Plains, New York, where they were to study psychiatry. A more senior nurse, however, told Lillian that she was to remain at Mount Sinai Hospital. The administration decided to put her in charge of a semi-private ward. Student nurses would work under her. Lillian explains that this was an unusual responsibility, even though she was a senior nurse. She believes that staff shortages due to World War II explain her new assignment.

One night Lillian sent the younger student nurses down to the cafeteria for their evening meal. She stayed on the ward, planning to eat her dinner after they returned. While they were gone, Lillian worked alone on the ward. Some of the patients were due for an infusion. She went to get the large flask containers needed for that procedure. They were kept on a high shelf. Lillian used a short stepstool to stand on. As she did so, she stuck one of her legs out to help balance herself as she reached up to get the flask. Suddenly, Lillian felt a pain in her genital area. She looked down and saw Berg with his hand under her uniform. Lillian ordered him, in her words, to remove his hand "from my private parts." He did not do so. She grabbed a syringe from a shelf and put a needle on it. Lillian threatened to stick it into his carotid artery if he did not take out his hand. Both nurse and doctor knew that would mean sudden death. Berg stepped back. When the student nurses returned from dinner, they found Lillian shaken and in tears. She explained what had happened, naming Berg as the doctor who had assaulted her. Within hours, Berg complained to the administration about Lillian, perhaps saying that she had threatened him.

The administrative nurse on duty summoned Lillian to her office where she proceeded to tell Lillian to pack her bags. She was being expelled. Lillian made it clear that she would not go home in disgrace. She had done nothing wrong. Lillian's refusal to leave the school was a threat to the power structure. She challenged it in two other ways as well. First, Lillian told the head nurse that if she was forced to leave, she would contact the *Daily News*, a New York City tabloid newspaper. She would explain to the paper how Mount Sinai failed to protect its student nurses. Second, she told the head nurse that she would pursue a lawsuit against the hospital, the Board of Trustees, and also against a member of the Guggenheim family who sat on the Board. This was no idle threat. One of Lillian's cousins was a lawyer who worked with Judge Samuel Leibowitz, a well known criminal attorney.

Another head nurse who liked Lillian, Miss Cell, interceded on her behalf. Cell diffused the situation with a suggestion that Lillian be assigned to a Mount Sinai outpatient clinic she oversaw, located in Spanish Harlem. The school accepted this compromise. Lillian thus spent her last months in the hospital's nursing program working in the outpatient clinic. This introduced Lillian to the world of public health nursing. The phrase originated with Lillian Wald, an American Jewish nurse. After graduating in 1891 from the New York Hospital School of Nursing, Wald witnessed early in her career the desperate plight of poor immigrants. She became a forceful advocate of the idea that trained nurses should visit, in the tenement buildings, members of the working class who were ill. Society on the whole came to see the benefits of such free medical care for its urban poor. It would not only help that population, but it would also cut down on the spread of contagious diseases throughout the city. An even larger societal benefit evolved as nurses in their visits consciously and unconsciously shared middle-class values with the immigrant population. What were primarily medical visits also came to further an acculturation process.[64] Wald's initial goal was a simple one, however, to help the poor.

That is probably what appealed to Lillian about working in the public health field. She was helping those who needed assistance the most, people who could not pay for medical care. In her own words, Lillian "loved making house calls." She "felt needed," she adds. Lillian also saw another side of medical care that was not taught at nursing schools. By the early 1940s, most American women delivered their babies in hospitals. A sterile environment had been a major factor in moving childbirth from the home to the hospital. But Puerto Rican women Lillian visited preferred to deliver their babies at home. Comparing the two experiences--hospital versus home--Lillian came to see advantages in the latter. As she explains, at Mount Sinai a new mother stayed in bed for about three days after the birth and remained in the hospital for one-two weeks, even with a normal delivery. The Puerto Rican woman was up and about soon after delivery. Lillian saw no negative consequences to the poor woman's actions, whereas she felt that the sedentary hospital policy might not be the healthier one. That is not to say that Lillian saw the benefits in other customs she encountered. One Puerto Rican woman, for example, used a red ribbon affixed to her baby's clothing to ward off evil spirits.

It could be that Lillian enjoyed her months as a public health nurse because of the autonomy that accompanied such a position.

When she started working at the clinic, an RN accompanied her. Eventually, though, Lillian made house calls by herself. Recall the rigid hierarchy she lived with at Mount Sinai Hospital's nursing school. Her outpatient clinic work gave her a freedom she had not experienced in the medical world up to that time. One scholar in the history of nursing argues that, "Public health allowed for the most independent judgment and autonomy of all the nursing practice fields."[65] Nurses who went out into the community relied on their own conclusions as to what type of care should be given to their patients. Doctors or head nurses did not accompany the public health nurse on her visits. Lillian was so much in her element in these last months of nursing school that she admits she would have gone into the field of public nursing after graduation if she had not made that prior commitment to the ANC. In fact, Lillian at first forgot about her enlistment. Before graduation, she considered applying for a scholarship to Peabody College in Nashville, Tennessee. It had a prominent public health nursing education program. Lillian would have graduated with a college degree in that field. If Peabody College had not worked out, Lillian thought of working in Appalachia.

In November 1943, Lillian's time as a student nurse came to an end. Officially, her three years in the nursing program had been over in October. Early that month, Lillian took the State Board exam in nursing at St. Vincent Hospital in New York City. She knew that if she passed it, the Army would send her orders to report for duty per her enlistment in the summer of 1942. Even though she took the Boards in October, Lillian did not receive her diploma and the white uniform of a graduate nurse. Before that could happen, she had to make up days she had missed due to illnesses. They totaled close to a month. Most occurred in her first year as a student nurse. Lillian points out that it was not unusual for beginning students to miss many days of training after being exposed to various germs for which they did not have immunities. In her case, she recalls her illnesses as basically being "colds and earaches." After she took her State Boards, Lillian worked on a hospital ward until mid-November to satisfy what she calls her "make-up time." With the rest of her class, she had already gone through a graduation ceremony in February. It was customary for the fall class to participate in the February commencement for students who had entered training earlier in the year. This saved the school from having to schedule two graduation ceremonies, one in the winter and one in the fall. While Lillian and others were recognized in the winter ceremony, they still had several months of training left before they were officially "graduated."

Nine months after the February recognition for the two "Class of 1943" nursing students, Lillian officially graduated, but not at a formal ceremony. Rather, one morning after prayers her classmates gathered around her. She stood before them dressed for the first time in her white, graduate nurse's uniform. A corsage of roses added a celebratory note to the outfit. The nurses congratulated Lillian. Because this was "her day," Lillian was asked to choose a song for the morning's gathering. From a limited list of musical choices, she selected an early nineteenth century one, "Believe Me, If All Those Endearing Young Charms." The Director of Nursing, Grace Warman, affixed an RN pin to her uniform and gave Lillian her diploma. As she did so, Grace told Lillian that she had received one of the highest scores on the State Board nursing exam. That is how Lillian found out that she had passed the test. On that same November day, Lillian wore for the first time the white cap of an RN. She describes it as cone-shaped, similar to an inverted dunce cap. The material was organdy; ruffles stood out around the edges of the cap. Like the one she wore as a senior-year nurse, the cap of Mount Sinai's graduate nurses had a black band around it.

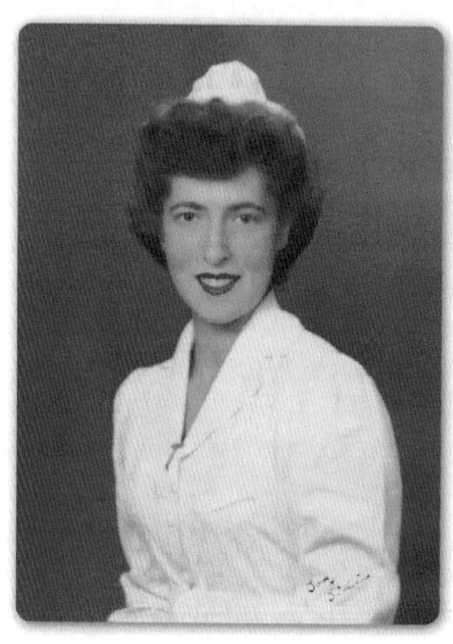

Lillian's time at Mount Sinai ended in a dramatic way. She explains that traditionally, graduate nurses stayed on at the hospital for anywhere from six months to a year. When a nurse did that, according to Lillian her nine dollar a month stipend became a ninety dollars a month salary; she received room and board in addition to her pay. But on Lillian's November graduation day (when she had officially finished her "make-up time"), she describes herself as "marching" into the head nurse's office to turn in a letter of resignation from the hospital. Lillian does not believe anyone had ever resigned before like that, so soon after graduation. She explains that the hospital "was not too happy" about her decision. (It was short of nurses because so many staff members had entered military service.) By mid-November, Lillian had received her Army orders to report for induction on February 1, 1944. As she gave the head nurse her resignation letter, Lillian announced that she would be reporting for military service soon. First, however, she wanted to spend some time with her family. Lillian agreed to stay on for about another month before she left for New Haven.

Arriving home in mid-December, Lillian stayed with her parents for about six weeks. She never told them about Berg's assault. If she had, Lillian believes Adolfo "would have killed" the doctor. In spite of what had happened to her at Mount Sinai, Lillian still credits the nursing school with giving her what she classifies as "an excellent background." Esther and Adolfo urged her to apply to a hospital in New Haven for a nursing position. Lillian knew then that it was time to tell them about her enlistment in the ANC. As she recalls, she announced, "I might as well tell you. I signed up for the Army." Her mother and father were, as Lillian puts it, "shocked." She understands their reaction, "I had always discussed things with them." But Lillian had changed in more than one way from the eighteen-year-old girl who had left for nursing school. She returned home as a twenty-one year old woman, confident in her skills as a graduate nurse. The next two years increased her professional confidence even more as she served overseas in the United States Army from D-Day until the end of the war in Europe.

Chapter 5

"This Man's Army"
An Overseas Assignment

Lillian describes the Army she joined early in 1944 as "this man's Army." By the numbers, it was that, although some three hundred and fifty thousand women served in the American military during World War II. (Overall enlistment in all branches of the armed forces during the war totaled about sixteen million.) Women joined the Navy, the Marine Corps, the Army, and the Coast Guard. "Free a Man to Fight" became the recruiting phrase. Although there were some exceptions, women basically served in support positions, far from the combat zones. Nurses were one of those exceptions, but even then, they constituted only twenty percent of all military women. About fifty-seven thousand nurses enlisted in the Army and some fourteen thousand in the Navy. Those numbers represented approximately one-third of all practicing nurses in the United States at that time. Over seventy Army and Navy nurses, assigned to the Philippines and Guam before December 7, 1941, became prisoners of war (POWs). The Japanese held them for about three years. In Europe, the Germans captured only one American Army nurse, and they kept her for just four months. Sixteen nurses from both theaters died as a result of enemy action.[66]

Like the men who joined the United States military, nurses served for "the duration of the war plus six months."[67] Their formal time in the armed forces began with basic training (BT). For nurses, however, their BT was less intense for a simple reason--the military needed them in active duty as soon as possible. In the first eighteen months after the nation entered World War II, an enlisted nurse's introduction to Army life proved to be superficial. Some were not even taught how to properly salute a superior officer, and they could not execute the simplest close order drills. Additionally, the Army originally did not explain the Articles of War (which governs military conduct) to newly inducted nurses. It was not until July 1943 that the first mandatory BT centers for Army nurses opened. One of them was the England General Hospital in Atlantic City, New Jersey.[68] That is where the Army ordered Lillian to report for her BT on February 1, 1944. A few days before that, Lillian took the train into New York City from New Haven. She stayed with her best friend Matilda ("Maddy") Glass, who she had gone through the nursing program with at Mount Sinai. They initially met when an instructor paired them together to practice putting bandages on each other. Maddy's family lived in the Bronx. It was a large brood; in addition to her parents, she had five sisters and a brother. They all took Lillian and Maddy to Penn Station on February 1st. Lillian remembers how the Glasses cried so much at the station that, she recalls with amusement, an observer would have thought the two women were leaving forever. Yet their destination, she points out, was only about a ninety minute train ride from New York City.

George and Lillian

Atlantic City is a barrier island off the coast of New Jersey. It offers beaches, hotels, and gambling to its visitors. That carefree atmosphere dramatically changed in World War II when the Army took over the city. Lillian points out that England General Hospital had been a large hotel before the military converted it into a hospital. Other buildings in Atlantic City were used as training centers as well as living quarters. She remembers seeing American casualties arriving from Italy where a major United States offensive, at Anzio south of Rome, had begun in January. The Army used one of the premier hotels of Atlantic City, the Chalfonte, as what Lillian calls the "nurses' home." It is where the women stayed during their BT. Lillian stresses how impressed she was with the housing the Army requisitioned for the nurses. She describes herself at that time as "a Depression kid who had never stayed at a hotel in her life," and the Chalfonte was such a luxurious one.

Upon Lillian's arrival at what was known as Camp Boardwalk, she immediately confronted a major problem. Knowing that the Army would clothe her, she did not take a suitcase. Lillian had, however, packed a briefcase with what she calls her Army "paperwork." It served a utilitarian purpose since she knew she would accumulate many military documents. The briefcase would be a logical place to put them all. At the same time, Lillian felt it would make her "feel more professional." She carried the briefcase with her on the trip to the Glass' home and then on the train to Atlantic City. Imagine Lillian's surprise when the sergeant who greeted her at Camp Boardwalk asked to see her orders, and, upon opening her briefcase, they were not there. Lillian knew she had not lost them. She distinctly recalled putting them into the briefcase. To the dismay of the sergeant, she spent some minutes rummaging through the bag. In so doing, Lillian held up a long line of nurses reporting for duty. With a degree of exasperation, the sergeant sent her away. Lillian went back to the Chalfonte and used one of its phones to call her parents, probably "collect," she adds with a laugh. Over the telephone, her mother solved the mystery of the missing orders. Adolfo, obviously proud of his daughter's enlistment, had "opened up the briefcase," Lillian explains. She continues. Her father "took out my orders that said Lt. Lillian Krell." Adolfo then "framed them and hung them on the living room wall." Esther promised to mail them to her. Lillian thus had to await the arrival of the orders before she could start BT.

The Chalfonte

Adolfo was justly pleased with Lillian's commission as an officer in the United States Army. What he probably did not understand was that all nurses in the ANC held what was known as "relative rank." From 1901, when the military established the ANC, through the World War I period, Army nurses held no rank at all. This did not change until 1920 when an Army Reorganization Act instituted relative rank for members of the ANC. This meant that nurses received a military title and their uniform displayed the insignia of an officer. From 1920-1942, however, a member of the ANC could rise no higher than the rank of captain. In 1942, over ninety percent of Army nurses held the rank of a second lieutenant. For the women, years in the military obviously did not easily lead to even the rank of first lieutenant. And for those years, the pay of nurses was less than that of male officers of equal rank. This changed in December 1942 when officers in the ANC could now rise to the rank of colonel; at the same time, the pay of Army nurses was to be the same as male Army officers of equal rank. Lillian points out that she entered the ANC early in 1944 as a second lieutenant. She still held that rank when she received her discharge at the end of 1945.[69]

Lillian remembers her Army training as taking thirty days. That was typical for nurses. During that time, the Army spread one hundred and forty-four hours of instruction over a four-week period. Lillian and other nurses were taught military conduct as well as military law. They learned how to care for their equipment and uniform. They also studied topics that must have given the women pause--how to dig a foxhole, use camouflage, pitch a tent, and read maps. Classes covered how nurses were to protect themselves from a chemical attack. At that point, Lillian remembers being introduced to the gas mask. Physical exercises were basic to BT. In Lillian's view, this part of training was "strenuous." The nurses drilled and performed calisthenics on the

boardwalk. As Lillian describes the scene, they sounded off, " 'hup, two, three, four' on the boardwalk of Atlantic City."[70] A sergeant complained to her during one drill, "Lieutenant, you are not marching. You are bouncing." They went out on bivouacs and forced marches.[71] Lillian characterizes her BT weeks as "very difficult for me." Weighing about one hundred and fifteen pounds with a "slight build," she had a hard time fulfilling the physical demands placed upon her. On a five-mile forced march, the weight of her forty-pound backpack slowed her down. Lillian directed the others to go ahead of her. An ambulance driver took pity on the young nurse and gave her a lift. She got off before the sergeant in charge of the march saw her leaving the vehicle. Lillian also describes how she had difficulties "crawling under barbed wire," getting over fences, and climbing up cargo nets to board a ship. The sergeant who oversaw her BT, she recounts, "always criticized me. I never had problems with officers, only with sergeants."

Lillian did not endure the embarrassments of BT by herself since Maddy was always with her. The two new RNs went through Camp Boardwalk together for those four weeks, sharing the high and low points. In fact, Lillian and Maddy were under the impression that they would be able to stay together after their training. But the two newly commissioned 2nd Lieutenants received different assignments when their month in Atlantic City ended. Lillian stresses their "disappointment" at their orders. The Army had eighty hospitals within the United States. Lillian and Maddy ended up at two different ones.[72] As Lillian explains, "I was to report to Tilden General Hospital at Fort Dix, New Jersey, while my friend and classmate would be going to Halloran General on Staten Island in New York. Of course, we reasoned, this had to be a 'gross mistake.' After all, the Army had promised when we joined they would keep us together!"[73] They decided to appeal their assignments. While in BT, one of the subjects Lillian and Maddy had studied was what Lillian recalls as "Army Grievance Procedures." The two nurses decided to act on what they had learned. Lillian wrote a letter that Maddy joined her in signing. They sent it, she adds, to "the Nurse Corps Adjutant of the First Service Command. We requested a hearing relating to our complaints." She concludes, "Apparently our letter did make some waves."[74] After mailing it, the two friends dutifully reported to their respective Army hospitals.

Lillian believes that only a few weeks passed before she received a special delivery letter from the First Service Command. The communication directed her "to report immediately" to the Adjutant's office in New York City. Maddy received similar orders. Once there, Lillian and her friend met face to face with a high ranking "tough Army gal," as she describes the Adjutant. She adds that the woman was "old Army," indicating that the officer was a firm believer in following orders. Lillian recalls the Adjutant "hitting the desk," informing the two second lieutenants, "You go where the Army sends you." Furthermore, according to Lillian, the Adjutant judged the appeal she and Maddy had sent as "the most nervy letter I've ever read." As the ANC officer lectured the two young nurses, Lillian remembers herself and Maddy standing before the Adjutant "shivering, with our heads down." Emphatically, the senior nurse made it clear that, "You go where you are assigned." Orders are not to be questioned. At the same time, the Adjutant told Lillian and Maddy that she was not done with them. In Lillian's recollection, the officer announced, "You're going to hear from me again." Before the two young nurses left, the Adjutant asked them if they would be open to an overseas assignment together. They replied in the affirmative.

But for the moment, the two lieutenants were to report back to their respective hospitals, Lillian to Tilden General and Maddy to Halloren General. Lillian recalls that she and her friend left the Adjutant's office "completely crushed." To use Lillian's description, however, Maddy's family was "thrilled," at her assignment to Halloran General Hospital since it was only a twenty-minute ferryboat ride from their home. Lillian remembers herself as "happy at Fort Dix" where she worked as a surgical nurse. Their respective stays at those two Army bases were not long ones, though. Recall that Lillian and Maddy completed BT early in March. If Lillian's timetable is correct, their meeting with the Adjutant took place sometime in mid-March. Lillian distinctly remembers that it was on her twenty-second birthday, April 1, 1944, that she received a new set of orders. She happened to be off duty that day. Along with some friends, Lillian went into a nearby town where she enjoyed a hot fudge sundae as a birthday treat. She found a telegram waiting for her when she arrived back at her quarters. It ordered her to report to the 297th General Hospital, affiliated with the Cook County Hospital in Chicago. The unit would be arriving soon at Fort Dix. After telephoning Maddy, Lillian found out that her friend had received the same orders. Lillian explains that originally the Army planned to send the 297th to the South Pacific, but the High Command changed its destination to the European Theater where it was to be based in England. The Army sent the hospital unit to Fort Dix before its Atlantic crossing. It appears, as Lillian came to understand it, that the 297th found itself two nurses short as it prepared to ship out for the ETO. The Army used Lillian and Maddy to fill those two openings. Lillian's Commanding Officer (CO) told her that she had never heard of such recently inducted nurses being sent overseas. The CO tried to keep Lillian at Fort Dix where she was needed, going so far as to contact the First Service Command. But the CO's appeal was to no avail. As such, on May 30, 1944, Memorial Day weekend, Lillian and Maddy boarded a troop transport ship with others in the 297th General Hospital, bound for the British Isles.[75]

Maddy & Lillian before they shipped out

Between mid-1942 and May 1945, approximately four and a half million American military personnel crossed the Atlantic, bound for the ETO. They embarked from four ports--New York City, Boston, Hampton Roads (Virginia), and Charleston. Seventy-five percent of those who sailed left from New York City, making it the busiest port in the United States. The allied navies did not have vessels that could function as troop carriers for very large numbers of the military. That is why the Allies enlisted the service of American, British, and French passenger liners to transport troops across the Atlantic. Two of them, the *RMS Queen Mary* and the *RMS Queen Elizabeth*, were the only eighty-thousand-ton ships in existence. Before World War II began, publicity releases described "the *Queens*" as "Floating Palaces," a reference to the luxurious accommodations the ships offered to wealthy passengers. But when war broke out in Europe, the Allies converted the *Queen Mary* and the *Queen Elizabeth* into troopships. On one trans-Atlantic trip alone, each could carry up to fifteen thousand members of the military. The *Queen Mary* made fifty-six Atlantic crossings and the *Queen Elizabeth* sixty-four. It is estimated that each transported a total of some four hundred thousand troops to the ETO.[76] Two of them were Lillian and Maddy. With the rest of the 297th General Hospital, they shipped out on the *Queen Elizabeth*.

The very beginning of the trans-Atlantic trip still holds a vivid memory for Lillian. As she describes it, she found herself "struggling up the gangplank" of the *Queen Elizabeth*, "burdened" with a forty-pound field pack. When she was about halfway up, Lillian remembers that someone yelled at her through a bullhorn, "Lieutenant, please move, you're holding up the loading of the troopship." Lillian confesses that she is not sure if the backpack was too heavy or if she was too scared. When asked if there was any one time when she regretted enlisting in the ANC, Lillian said just once--the moment she was struggling to make her way up the gangplank. She thought to herself, "Where am I going? What am I doing here?" Seeing her distress, a chaplain came down to help her make it onboard the ship. With a clear sense of humor, Lillian's recollection of that departure day continues--"I would not describe this trip as exactly a 'pleasure cruise.' We were packed in like sardines: 10,000 battle ready troops and 75 nurses! Despite tight security in rerouting our troop transport train from New Jersey and boarding ship after midnight as a big 'security secret,' we sailed from New York Harbor at high noon on Memorial Day 1944, with all [of] New York standing

Army nurses & a troopship prepare to depart

dockside on this bright, clear sunny day to wave 'good-bye' to our troop laden ship. (By now we were sure that all [of] Germany knew we were on the way.)"[77]

When the *Queen Elizabeth* pulled out, Lillian admits to being "upset" that it was not part of a convoy. As she explains her concern, the ship was "alone on this great big ocean." Convoys offered protection to troopships, especially to slow-moving vessels. But the *Queen Elizabeth* did not fall into that vulnerable category. Like the *Queen Mary*, she could move at almost thirty knots, outrunning any German submarine.[78] In spite of the relative security her speed afforded the *Queen Elizabeth*, the Army issued each person a life vest. Regular drills occurred during the crossing, too. Such practices would never have been enough, though, to guarantee everyone's survival in case a German ship would have sunk the *Queen Elizabeth*. She simply did not carry enough lifeboats or rafts to hold all of the passengers, which could be as many as fifteen thousand souls. At best, they could have held about eight thousand individuals.[79]

In spite of the ship's speed, the next week probably passed slowly for most of the military personnel on board. They spent their days waiting to reach the ETO. Eating and sleeping became two central events. Lillian remembers two daily meals, one in the morning and one in the evening. The food portions were what Lillian characterizes as "moderate," so much so that she sometimes "conned a British waiter" into giving her an extra sandwich that she in turn gave to a soldier who appeared especially hungry. Lillian recalls soldiers sleeping in large areas, such as the luxury liner's ballroom. Nurses, however, were assigned to staterooms or cabins. She judges the room she shared with ten nurses as one built to accommodate perhaps four people. The Army furnished a hammock. But the movement of the ship made Lillian feel, in her word, "insecure" as she tried to sleep suspended above the floor. Instead, she found a small mattress and laid on it near the cabin's door.

Lillian kept professionally busy during the trip. Early in the voyage, she volunteered to help out in the ship's hospital. She was the only Army nurse to do so. A Canadian doctor and nurse staffed the unit. As Lillian recalls it, they mainly treated cases of venereal disease, contracted, she stresses, by soldiers before they boarded the ship. The hospital's nurse taught Lillian how to administer antibiotics, a first for the newly minted second lieutenant. While in transit, the American nurses received what would be their assignments within the 297th General Hospital once it arrived in England. Lillian was to work on the psych ward. She did not look forward to that, in part because she had missed psychiatric training at Mount Sinai. (Recall that the administration decided to put her in charge of a ward just as her class began that phase of its education.) Faced with an assignment that she felt she had no background in, Lillian offered instead to work with a senior member of the ANC, 1st Lieutenant Lillian Cameron. Rumor had it that Cameron was difficult; the other nurses dreaded an assignment in orthopedics, the first lieutenant's specialty. Lillian, however, offered to work with Cameron, a woman she describes as "dynamic." There would be no friction between the two Lillians as they cared for patients together in the orthopedic wards of the 297th.

the troopship the *Queen Elizabeth* in New York City

The trip across the North Atlantic took seven days. The last few proved memorable for the wrong reasons, all of them tied to the weather. Departing New York when it did, the *Queen Elizabeth* could have struck an iceberg. That danger existed beginning each April for all ships in the North Atlantic; it lasted until August by which time any icebergs would have melted. Since Lillian left at the end of May, the *Queen Elizabeth* had to be on the lookout for that danger. As the ship neared the British Isles, another threat loomed--German U boats. To confound the enemy, the *Queen Elizabeth* approached Scotland in a "zigzag" fashion. It was standard practice for Allied ships to cease their straight forward movement once they neared the end of their voyage. The sharp turns of the zigzag approach made it more difficult for German submarines to get a fix on Allied vessels. But it did increase the distance traveled. The shortest route between New York City and Scotland measured some three thousand miles. The zigzag approach added on about five hundred more miles. The left, then right, movements of the ship must have unnerved the military personnel on board even more as gales struck the surrounding waters. The strong winds hit the North Atlantic regularly for at least six months out of every year, and Lillian sailed in one of those months.[80] She later observed, "Unfortunately, we hit stormy weather in the Mid-Atlantic with gale winds increasing as we neared the Irish Sea."[81] As she recalls, gales struck with particular force the day before the *Queen Elizabeth* landed in Scotland. She confesses that she thought, "This is the end." Lillian estimates the waves that crashed on the deck had to have been thirty-six to thirty-eight feet in height.

The bad weather continued the day of the landing. Even though it was June, a month Lillian associated with summer, off the coast of Scotland it was "cold, rainy, and dark." Given the weather they encountered, Lillian concluded, "It seemed like a sheer miracle when we safely arrived in Gourock, Scotland hours before dawn broke through the mist on June 6th, 1944..."[82] According to Lillian, the nurses had been ordered to be on deck at 3:00 A.M. to disembark. Officers told them that they would be the first group to leave the ship. That did not, however, prove to be the case. The nurses, Lillian recalls, "were kept waiting on deck as infantry and paratroopers" made their way into small boats that took them to shore. "We waited on deck," she later wrote, "for hours in a cold light drizzle to be taken off the 'Queen' by tender and put ashore. We were all deeply grateful to the British Red Cross Volunteers waiting for us dockside in the wee hours of the morning with sandwiches and hot coffee."[83]

The *Queen Elizabeth* disembarked its thousands of military personnel at the Clyde Estuary at Gourock, a small resort town about twenty-five miles west of Glasgow. The ship had been built just miles away, at the John Brown shipyards.[84] In Gourock, members of the 297th General Hospital boarded a train to take them to their next destination. Upon landing, and even during the train ride, the High Command did not announce to the recent arrivals the significance of the day. It turned out that June 6, 1944 was the date the Allies chose to invade the Normandy coast of northern France. In the history of World War II, it became the most famous on-shore landing of ground forces in all of the Pacific and European campaigns. Such an infusion of Allied forces was thought to be the beginning of the end of Nazi occupation of northern Europe. Once the Allies took back northern France from the Germans, they were only some five hundred miles from Berlin, the headquarters of Hitler's government. So in spite of the fact that World War II saw many amphibious landings, none became more famous than the one that occurred on the beaches of Normandy on June 6, 1944. The date became known simply as "D-Day." American and British infantrymen began setting foot on the beaches at 6:30 A.M. At that hour and the ones that followed, the medical personnel of the 297th was making its way to England. Eventually, they would treat some of the casualties incurred in the next days. The train that carried the 297th took the doctors, nurses, and technicians to Llandudno, North Wales. They stayed there, as Lillian explains, for a "few days awaiting and assembling our medical supplies. It was at our Llandudno stop-off when we first learned of the D-Day invasion."[85]

a 1998 picture Lillian took of Llandudno

The military boarded the nurses at some private homes. Lillian stayed with Maddy at the residence of the Edwards family. They are the ones who told her about the Allied invasion of Normandy. After its short stay in Llandudno, the 297th began what Lillian calls "another long train ride across Wales and the cold grey English countryside to

Stourbridge on the Severn River."[86] The waterway took the medical staff to Camp Bewdley which would be its post for over a year. The largest nearby city was Birmingham.

When the 297th arrived at its final destination, it became one of approximately six hundred overseas Army hospitals. Members of the ANC, of course, staffed those medical units. Late in January 1942, two and a half years before Lillian's debarkation, the very first nurses had arrived in the ETO. The island of Great Britain originally acted as the staging area for ANC arrivals. From various British military installations, the Army sent nurses to North Africa, Sicily, Italy, and, after the Normandy landings, to France, Belgium, and Holland. Toward the end of the war, nurses served in Germany, as well. They worked at various types of Army hospitals--a field hospital, an evacuation hospital, a convalescent or rehabilitation hospital or, like Lillian, at a general hospital. Field hospitals, some set up in tents with just a dirt floor, were the ones closest to the front lines. The Army Medical Department placed evacuation hospitals miles from the front, sometimes as close as twelve miles and other times as far as one hundred. If a doctor estimated the recovery time of a soldier to be just a few weeks, he was sent to a convalescent hospital in the area. If, however, the medical staff thought his recovery time would be longer, the soldier ended up at a general hospital, such as the 297th. On average, patients remained in a general hospital for around ninety days.[87]

Upon its arrival at Camp Bewdley, the 297th immediately set itself up to receive incoming casualties from the D-Day operation. Although the atmosphere among the staff would have been a somber one, Lillian supplied some levity. The nurses had thought that the buildings assigned to the 297th would be ready for them. This did not, however, prove to be the case. At Camp Bewdley, the unit found itself at an old British Army base. Lillian describes the structures as "decayed." She "teased" her supervisors, to use her word, about the poor conditions, joking that the English gave them a building with dust that had lain there since 1918, the World War I era. Lillian describes their initial plan of action--"The first order of the day was to clean, sweep, scrub and whitewash walls until some sense of order made it possible to set up hospital beds and unpack medical supplies.

a 1998 picture Lillian took of where the 297th General Hospital had once stood in the English countryside

I remember our nurses cutting up their cotton petticoats to provide much needed cleaning cloths."[88] Because of the incoming casualties from Normandy, Lillian believes the staff of the 297th set up hospital facilities "in record time." At English ports, the military transferred the wounded from ships that had been anchored off of the French coast to railroad cars. The trains, in turn, transported the injured to railroad stations near general hospitals. Ambulances picked the men up at the station and brought them to the medical units. For the 297th, Lillian points out, "We barely had time to organize and setup our hospital when our first wounded patients arrived in convoy after convoy from the Normandy invasion combat area. In no time at all we were operating at full capacity…"[89] According to Lillian, the arrival of large numbers of casualties "did not let up" until early December 1944, six months after D-Day. This is a very telling statement. For the 297th, that equates to six months of an unceasing influx of wounded. As an orthopedic nurse, Lillian attended to patients for twelve to fifteen hours a day, seven days a week. When large numbers of casualties arrived, she helped with general patients as well as those in her specialty. Lillian had one day a month off, but if ships carrying casualties from the continent had recently landed, she had to forego even that. According to Lillian, "convoys always seemed to arrive" on that one special day.

For all of the hours Army nurses put in, their salary had only recently been raised from that established by federal legislation passed in 1922. In June 1942 Congress passed a Pay Readjustment Act to increase their wages. (Due to the Great Depression, throughout the 1930s members of the ANC did not receive a raise.) In the summer of 1942, Congress set the annual base salary of an Army nurse at $1,082.[90] When she reported to BT in Atlantic City, Lillian filled out Army forms to designate that a portion of her monthly check be sent to her parents. The Krells deposited the so-called "allotment" into a savings account they created for their daughter. She kept only a small amount of her salary, about twenty-five dollars, for her expenses. The PX at Camp Bewdley sold shampoo, soap, and cologne at reasonable prices. Lillian also spent her money in some of the local towns on the rare occasions when she could get away from the camp.

When not on duty, Lillian stayed in what she calls "a hut" that she shared with five other nurses. They named it the "Last Chance." Made of wood, the small, one-room building was not well-sealed. Lillian explains that "rain, snow, and wind" came in through the sides of the hut. A potbelly stove heated the room. The nurses had to keep reminding each other, however, not to put too much coal into it because excessive heat was starting to melt the stove. Each lieutenant had her own narrow cot to sleep upon. Lillian remembers with gratitude the homemade, knitted blankets that the Chicago branch of the Red Cross sent the 297th. Aside from the cots, there was no room for any other pieces of furniture. Someone had affixed a metal bar on a wall from which the nurses could hang their uniforms. A shelf hung from the wall above each cot; the women put personal belongings on it. Because of the limited space, the nurses "tried to get everything under the bed." They put items that could not

fit on the shelf into boxes that slid under the cot. This included their uniforms.

Lillian judges the ANC uniform they wore while on duty to be "ridiculous." She explains that the Army designed it for the nurses who served in the South Pacific. Made of seersucker, it was one piece of material that did not need to be ironed or starched. (Even the cap could be laid out flat, unlike some of the hospital nursing caps stateside that had ruffles on the edges.) The pattern on the uniform's material was one of brown and white stripes. The outfit wrapped around the nurse's body, tying on the inside; buttons were not necessary. A sash insured that the uniform would not easily open up. This on-duty outfit was standard issue by the end of 1943.[91] Because the seersucker was so light weight, and the sleeves short, Lillian adds, "We were freezing in those uniforms." On the wards, the only heat provided to patients and staff came from potbelly stoves. One stood in each ward.

During a day shift, Lillian oversaw the care of between fifty and seventy-five patients. Additionally, she was responsible for seriously ill patients in a separate room adjacent to the wards. These could include men recuperating from surgery. (The 297th did not have recovery rooms.) Night duty meant more wards and more patients. When on that shift, she oversaw patient care in five wards located in different buildings on the hillside. (The wards were spread out, Lillian explains, in case of German bombing.) On such evenings, "I walked in the snow, the rain, and the wind," she recalls, going from ward to ward. As she rotated between the wards, she depended on the corpsman in each one to contact her if there was an emergency. When Lillian checked on patients in the dark, she used a flashlight to provide illumination. She laughs when she remembers that some of the soldiers called her Florence Nightingale, her flashlight being the modern day equivalent of the lamp Nightingale carried. When Lillian drew night duty, after eating breakfast she slept not in the Last Chance, but in a special hut for the night nurses; this guaranteed them uninterrupted sleep after their time on the wards. Regardless of her shift, Lillian remembers that "the days went by fast." That would have been especially true when a large influx of casualties arrived. Even after the Allies secured the Normandy beaches on June 6th, it took the invasion force almost three months to reach Paris in the face of heavy German resistance. By early September, American and British forces began moving toward Berlin, liberating cities in Belgium and Holland as they neared Germany's western borders.

a 1998 picture Lillian took of the path she walked between the wards

As the Allied lines moved east, so did the medical units. Once the United States controlled northern Europe from France to Belgium, the Army's medical department established a system to move casualties from the battle zones to the general hospitals in England. Their first stop was at "air and rail holding units" that gathered the wounded for transportation to some general hospitals the Army set up at Liege in Belgium and at Verdun in France. Once doctors deemed soldiers ready to leave those facilities, planes or trains carried the men to "the hub of the [medical care] system," located in Paris. That city became home to seven United States Army general hospitals and one convalescent camp. American casualties that were destined for England left on ships from the French port of Cherbourg to the English port of Southampton. From there, the Army sent the wounded to American general hospitals that had been set up throughout the midlands countryside in the southern part of England.[92] Lillian credits, in her words, "the Army's amazing transportation system" that moved the casualties "from the battlefield to Army base hospitals in England so quickly." As she concludes, "This, above all, saved many lives."[93] Lillian explains that some reached the 297th within twenty-four hours of becoming a casualty. When large groups of wounded arrived, she points out that the 297th worked around the clock. Lillian agrees with a conclusion drawn by one historian of Army nurses in World War II, a colonel herself in the ANC. The officer argues that during the war, nurses overseas performed work that back in the States would have been done by an intern. They "ordered lab work, independently started IVs and medications, changed dressings and assessed and treated wounds…"[94]

Lillian characterizes her time as a member of the ANC in the European Theater as "a remarkable experience." Even so, she sometimes found it hard to function on a daily basis without showing her emotions as casualties came in from the continent. In honestly recalling those months, Lillian confesses, "I held up very well when I was on duty, but I cried when I got off duty. I never told anyone. I would have my cry. [Yet] I was always strong [while] on duty." Although she admits, "It was a shock seeing the boys wounded, in the condition they were," the treatment the soldiers received before they arrived in England saved many lives. In particular, Lillian praises sulfa powder and the antibiotic drug penicillin. Together, they contributed to the survival rate before the patients reached the 297th and the other general hospitals in England. Soldiers within each Army company had been trained as

medics or aidmen. Usually one of them reached a wounded member of their unit within thirty minutes from when the solider became a casualty.[95] The medic or aidman applied sulfa powder to the wound. Sulfa drugs appeared in Europe in the mid-1930s. They "stopped bacteria from multiplying, allowing the body time to assemble its defenses and attack the invaders."[96] For her patients, Lillian credits sulfa powder with "controlling infection, in the process saving a lot of limbs."

Once the soldier reached a hospital unit on the continent, another new miracle drug could be administered to him, penicillin. This antibiotic also fought bacterial infections. Army hospitals in the United States had begun experimental use of penicillin in the spring of 1943. One of them had been Halloran General Hospital where Maddy had been assigned after BT.[97] According to Lillian, civilian hospitals in the United States did not have access to this new drug. In the ETO, penicillin was not available until D-Day in June 1944.[98] Lillian describes the drug as resembling brown sugar, but with "tougher grains." Nurses had to dissolve, in a sterilized container, the thick granules before injecting the penicillin into the muscle area. Formal studies on survival rates mirror the conclusion Lillian holds on the importance of sulfa powder and penicillin. One study notes that their use soon after a soldier became a casualty "kept the incident of serious infection low, in spite of surgical backlog [in the field], and in spite of the fact that many casualties occurred on pastures and farmland contaminated with animal and human feces."[99]

Lillian identifies triage as one of the hardest duties she had. She decided which patients took precedence over others after a quick evaluation of their medical status. Put another way, Lillian determined which men were in the most critical condition and which ones could wait for treatment. She stresses that there was no time to run tests to type the blood for each patient. Instead, blood plasma was used when possible. (Plasma is the liquid part of the blood apart from the cells.) No compatibility tests for blood type were needed for its use since plasma contains no red blood cells. Scientists had discovered that plasma could be stored for long periods of time and that it also could be dried into a solid substance. During the war, liquid plasma was used in the States and the dried form sent overseas. As long as the patient had not lost a large amount of red blood cells, the plasma "filled the veins and arteries, preventing a disastrous fall in blood pressure until the body could regenerate red cells in normal quantities." Lillian stresses that the nurses administered the plasma infusions, another of their many responsibilities. To this day, she is grateful to the ARC for its role in gathering plasma on the Home

Front. In the States, the Red Cross collected more than thirteen million pints of blood; it processed over ten million into dried plasma for use in the war theaters.[100] In Lillian's opinion, plasma was "the lifesaving grace of the medical teams."

While most of the patients who arrived at the 297th were soldiers, an occasional member of the Navy or Air Corps was brought in. With amusement, Lillian observed firsthand the age-old rivalry between the services. Members of the Air Corps' medical staff visited the hospital to check on its men; they tried to get the pilots transferred to one of their hospitals. Lillian concluded that the Air Corps "did not trust the Army to care for its wounded." But whether the patient was Navy or Air Corps, such men were usually too ill to be moved. Sometimes the patients were civilians, members of the French underground; this would have been especially true in the months during the Battle for Normandy (June-August 1944). Lillian judges them to have been "charming," often kissing her hand. While the Frenchmen did not realize it, that gracious act posed a health problem for the nurses. According to Lillian, "almost all" of the Frenchmen arrived with tuberculosis, which some of the ANC women then contracted.

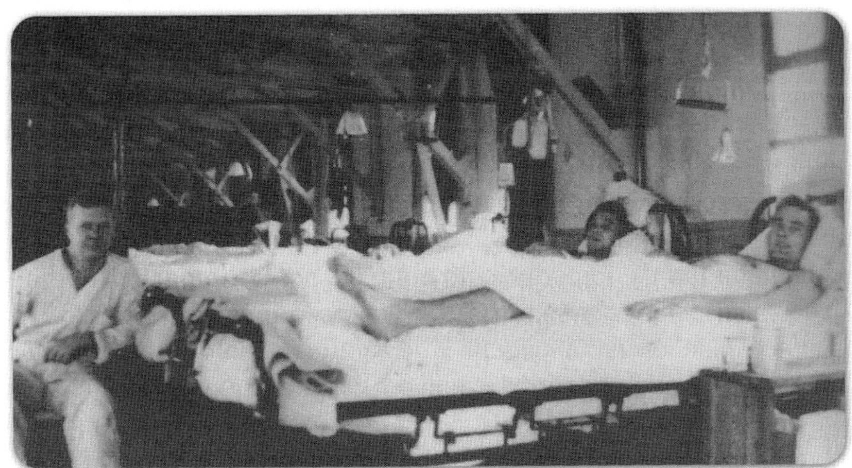

Lillian's patients at Camp Bewdley

Regardless of whether the patients were Army, Navy, Air Corps, or from the French underground, Lillian emphasizes that, "We gave our boys the best care we could." Note her use of the word "boys." She refers to them that way throughout any discussion of her time with the

297th at Camp Bewdley. In her mind, then and now, they were so young. On rare occasions when the mess hall received some real eggs instead of the powdered ones, Lillian and the other nurses used the potbelly stove in the ward to make each "boy" eggs the way he liked them, scrambled or soft. Two of her easiest tasks as a nurse were to give sponge baths and back rubs to "the boys." Still in keeping with the modesty considerations she first met at Mount Sinai, on the wards of the 297th, male members of the hospital staff washed the patient's genital area if he could not do that himself.

As a surgical orthopedic nurse, Lillian dealt with what she calls "some sad cases." She remembers boys who "limped" around the wards, on "a cane or on crutches." Many lost a limb. She credits one of the doctors, Hampar Kelikian, with saving many arms and legs. Lillian identifies him as the Chief Orthopedic Surgeon with the 297th. Because she became the Lead Nurse of the Orthopedic Surgical Unit, the two worked closely together. Lillian speaks of him with great reverence, calling him "a wonderful, wonderful man." She insists that his story with the 297th at Camp Bewdley is very much a part of her story with the unit. Kelikian pioneered in performing bone grafts on patients. This was when, surgically, pieces of bone from other parts of the patient's body were put into the spaces between or around broken bones. Lillian explains that the 297th became the first Army hospital in the ETO to perform bone grafts. She points out that English and American doctors visited the 297th to observe Kelikian's technique that, Lillian believes, saved "many lives and limbs." One soldier who benefitted from Kelikian's skill is a patient with whom Lillian remains in touch, almost seventy years after they met on a hospital ward.

His name is Al Bressack. At age nineteen, he clearly could be classified as one of the "boys" Lillian referred to when she used that title. Al arrived at the 297th toward the end of February 1945. He hailed from the same New York City borough as his nurse. Decades later, Al fondly describes his first meeting with Lillian--"I heard that Brooklyn voice and I immediately fell in love with her."[101] Shrapnel from a German shell that landed near him resulted in severe injuries to his lower limbs. By performing bone grafts, Kelikian avoided having to amputate one of Al's legs. When some of Lillian's "boys" arrived back in the States, they contacted Esther and Adolfo to tell them that their daughter was well. Some even visited the Krells. The soldiers did this not at Lillian's request, but on their own. Like her concern for Al, such contacts testify to the personal involvement that Lillian displayed in her nursing. Perhaps one reason she admires Kelikian so much relates to his interest in the patients, something they shared. Late at night he visited soldiers on the wards, checking in on them more, in Lillian's estimation, than other doctors did. In a thick Armenian accent from his homeland, Kelikian asked the men his stock question--"So Sonny boy, can you wiggle your toes?" But with the doctor's accent, the "wiggle" came out "viggle," to the amusement of the patients. If the soldier could move his toes, the affirmative answer usually indicated a successful operation. In Lillian's recollection, the young men "loved being called 'Sonny Boy.' " Kelikian had a nickname for Lillian, too, "Little Girl."

Patients from the 297th at the Red Cross' Donutmobile

In addition to his surgical skill, Lillian also admired Kelikian's personal history. It was one of overcoming great odds to achieve a dream. He lost his parents in the Armenian genocide that occurred in the Ottoman Empire during and after World War I. Kelikian immigrated to the United States as, to use Lillian's characterization, "a poor Armenian refugee." According to Lillian, he worked for years as a bricklayer before he completed his medical studies. While in England with the 297th, his wife mailed him packages that contained Armenian food. Kelikian shared the items with Lillian, Maddy, Lillian Cameron, and a corpsman who worked the orthopedic ward. (Maddy joined such gatherings. In Lillian's words, the staff nicknamed the two nurses "the twins," meaning, where Lillian went,

Maddy was often there, too.) It was at such social moments that Lillian learned the details of the doctor's life before he immigrated to America.

Perhaps because of the friendship between the physician and his nurse, the commander of the 297th, Colonel Francis Pruitt, asked Lillian for her help. Kelikian always carried an onion in one of his uniform pockets and a piece of bread in another. Pruitt asked Lillian to try to convince the doctor to cease this habit. Yet when she broached the subject with Kelikian, his explanation made her "burst into tears," as Lillian puts it. She recounts his reply to her request, "Little Girl, if you knew starvation as I did, you would understand." The doctor reminded her about his experiences during the Armenian genocide when he went without food. But "if you have bread and an onion," he told Lillian, "you will never be hungry." That was the only time she brought up the subject of what he carried in his pockets. One can still easily see Lillian's admiration for Kelikian today, almost seven decades after they worked together. "As Dr. K's surgical nurse," Lillian concludes, "I literally loved him for his unique surgical skills and [for] his fatherly kindness. He will forever be my God-Given Hero."[102] Another individual who Lillian came to love while at Camp Bewdley was a person not associated in any way with the United States Army. She was a local Englishwoman, Mrs. Winifred Mann, who became, in Lillian's characterization, "like a grandmother" to the young nurse.

In the evenings, after working a day shift at the hospital, Lillian often visited the local English countryside, dotted with small villages and towns. She explains that during the late hours of the day, there still could be enough light to allow this type of adventure because of "British Double Summer Time." In the war years, the English moved their clocks forward in the summer months by two hours. Lillian took advantage of that extra daylight.

She rode a three-speed bicycle she bought from an Englishwoman who worked at the hospital. It served as her method of transportation. (Lillian received her first bike when she was fifteen years old; she describes it as a "two wheeler with balloon tires." She had never ridden a three-speed bicycle, with her emphasis on the word "speed,"

a 1998 picture Lillian took of the English town of Bewdley

until Camp Bewdley.) The fact that it was a woman's bike accommodated her Class A uniform (a cap, jacket, shirt, tie, and skirt). Regulations required that when a member of the Army left camp, he or she had to be in uniform. While the military issued trousers to the nurses, they could be worn only for night duty on the wards. Once properly attired after her shift ended, Lillian was ready for some "down time." She often ended up in the nearby town of Bewdley, about a twenty-five minute ride from the camp. Lillian met Mrs. Mann there because of a cat. One day, while approaching the Mann residence, Lillian spied a cat sitting on a table in the garden. Since she "loved" such animals, as she puts it, she got off her bike. Coming outside to greet her was the owner of the garden, cat, and house--Winifred Mann. The older Englishwoman immediately began calling Lillian "Ginger" because of her red hair. (Redheads in Britain often received that nickname.) As a widow, she lived alone. Her only child, a son, served in India as part of the British Army. (Laughing, Lillian explains that in an attempt at matchmaking during and after the war, Mrs. Mann wanted him to meet Lillian. It did not concern her that her young American friend was Jewish.) The Englishwoman's warm manner and her inviting fireplace on cold evenings made the Mann home act as a magnet for Lillian's bicycle.

Due to the British government's rationing program, families had little extra food to offer Americans who visited them. The United States Army understood this, so it urged members of its military to first make a stop at the Army's mess kitchen before going to an English home. The staff there had orders to give the serviceperson some canned goods to take as a contribution to the meal. Lillian did this before she got on her bike to visit Mrs. Mann. She often took peaches. Lillian also wrote her parents to ask them to mail some nonperishable food items directly to Mrs. Mann. As for herself, she requested that Esther and Adolfo send her some personal items the Army did not issue to the nurses, such as nylons. In respect to specific foods she craved, Lillian asked that they include chocolate, graham crackers, and marshmallows in their packages to her. She took the latter item with her on trips to visit Mrs. Mann. Sitting in front of the fireplace, the American nurse introduced the Englishwoman to roasted marshmallows. The two became close on such evenings as they shared stories of their lives, their families, and observations on the war. Put simply, Lillian admits, "I really loved Mrs. Mann."

an English cottage during the World War II years

Because of this deep friendship, Lillian willingly consented to, in her word, "spy" for Bewdley's vicar. He had given Mrs. Mann a list of names belonging to some American soldiers who were dating local girls. The clergyman wanted to insure that the men were single. Could the nurse find out if they really were? Lillian enlisted the help of an Army Protestant chaplain who had, months earlier, helped her up the gangplank of the departing *Queen Elizabeth*. In other ways, the chaplain had showed kindnesses to her, unlike a certain Catholic chaplain. That priest made fun of Lillian's Jewish, New York accent. He called her "Sadie" even though he knew her given name. While

Lillian does not ascribe such behavior to anti-Semitism, that could have been the case. However out of character it may sound today, anti-Semitism pervaded American society, including the enlisted and officer ranks of the military.[103] The Catholic priest, in Lillian's estimation, also drank too much. Obviously, not all chaplains lived up to the high standards associated with their office. Ignoring him, Lillian instead recruited her Protestant chaplain friend to carry out the request made by Bewdley's vicar. As a result, she explains that she "helped to end some romances" by unmasking the duplicity of more than one American soldier.

In addition to Lillian's trips to the surrounding English countryside, on some rare occasions she also went to Birmingham. These excursions usually occurred on High Holy Holidays when her nursing schedule allowed her to attend Temple there. The kind Protestant chaplain who became her friend arranged for a car to carry Jewish soldiers to the city's synagogue on such special days. If Lillian was free, she went with them. But it generally proved easier for her to go to Friday night services at Camp Bewdley. Enlisted men organized and conducted these religious gatherings. Lillian and Maddy were the only two officers present. A soldier by the name of Bernstein seemed to be in charge of the Sabbath service. Much to her surprise, Lillian recognized him as the older brother of one of her high school classmates from Holyoke, Massachusetts. While it was sometimes possible for her to attend religious services, it proved impossible to adhere to a kosher diet due to the lack of choices given to her by the Army mess. By December 1944, six months into her overseas service, Lillian had lost so much weight that it became obvious to her superiors that she needed a leave to regain her strength. Dietary religious considerations were not responsible for the weight loss. She explains it by pointing to how

Lillian and Maddy

tired she usually was, too tired to eat well, and how Army food was not the most appealing. For example, Lillian could not acquire a taste for the powdered eggs the mess hall usually served. She craved real eggs. At first, her superiors thought that perhaps she had contracted tuberculosis, as some of the other nurses had. But that proved not to be the case after being tested for the disease. Lillian clearly needed more relaxation than her bicycle tours of the English countryside, her visits with Mrs. Mann, and the few journeys to Birmingham could give her. Her CO approved a week's leave for Lillian. Maddy also qualified.

Chapter 6

A Romance Begins and A War Ends

Initially, Lillian thought she and Maddy would spend their time in London. Maddy's boyfriend Gene intended to meet them there. After their arrival, however, things did not go as planned. Gene had not made it to the city, which put Maddy in a bad mood. Additionally, Lillian could not relax as German rockets hit the city on a regular basis. She recalls the British people called them "pilotless planes." They were also known as "buzz bombs." As she remembers, "they sputtered all over London, making a 'sput' sound before hitting the ground or a building." Sightseeing became impossible since the buzz bombs rained down upon the city day and night. In the evenings, she and Maddy sought safety from the bombing in underground shelters. Lillian recalls with sadness the faces of crying babies in the shelter. She felt an empathy with them. "Uncomfortable" is the word Lillian chose to describe her feelings on what was supposed to be a respite for her from the war. She told Maddy that she wanted to leave London, but her friend wanted to stay. On her own, Lillian visited the city's ARC office. She confessed to the staff there that she was "tired, I needed to rest, and I wanted to get out of London." The Red Cross recommended a stay at a hotel in Edinburgh, Scotland that the Army had taken over. The representative even offered to arrange transportation for Lillian from her London hotel to the train station. When Lillian shared news of this opportunity with Maddy, her friend made it clear that she did not want Lillian to leave. Determined, though, Lillian announced that she was going to Scotland.

Reluctantly, Maddy accompanied her. The two nurses arrived at the Princess Hotel in Edinburgh late at night. It was filled with American soldiers doing what Lillian and Maddy were, trying to get away from the war.

The next morning, December 5, 1944, happened to be Adolfo's birthday. Although she did not realize it when the day began, it would be a life altering one for her. After breakfast, a group of hotel guests left on a tour of Edinburgh Castle. Lillian remembers that December 5th as one of "freezing cold." It had snowed in the days before. In spite of the weather, Lillian focused on having a good time. She took pictures of the castle, but a problem persisted as she snapped various shots. A certain sergeant kept on getting in her way in spite of

a 1998 picture Lillian took of the Princess Hotel

Lillian's protests. After arriving back at the Princess Hotel, Lillian went to her room to freshen up for dinner. When she returned downstairs to the dining room, she could not easily find a place for her and Maddy to sit. She asked two soldiers to save two seats she spied. Once the nurses got to them with their food trays in hand, Lillian heard a voice ask, "Do you really think your photos will come out?" The question came from the "pesty" sergeant (her description) who had obstructed some of her shots. A conversation with him ensued. He introduced himself as Len Swerdlow. Once they finished their meal, he mentioned a dance in town. "How about going with me?" Len asked Lillian. "No, I do not know you," she responded. Len openly accused Lillian of prejudice, arguing, "If I was an officer, you would go." She assured him she was "a liberal" and would never discriminate. GIs around them, according to Lillian, took bets on, "Would she or won't she go to the dance?" The soldier and nurse reached a compromise. If Len got a date for Maddy, then the four of them would go out that night. He did so. That is how, on her father's birthday, Lillian met and had her first date with the man who she would eventually marry.

That evening, as they danced, Len tried to find out about Lillian's background. Phrased in a modern way, he wanted to know her ethnicity. Len had a flare for acting, Lillian explains. As such, he spoke in various accents, trying to tease a response out of his date. Because of Lillian's red hair and freckles, Len first thought she might be Irish, so he used a brogue accent. Lillian did not indicate any sign of identifying with that culture. (She thought he was Italian because of his "dark hair and Mediterranean skin.") Len tried other accents, English and Scottish ones, for example, but without success. Finally, Lillian recalls, he "spoke in a low voice in Yiddish." Lillian answered in such a way that Len realized she was familiar with Yiddish. It turned out that Len was Jewish, too, and, they both came from New York City. Lillian and Len spent the rest of the week together enjoying the sights Edinburgh offered. More importantly, though, they got to know each other. She found out that he was assigned to the 379th Bomb Group where he worked in purchasing. When asked what attracted her to Len, Lillian explained that "he was fun to be with. He had a good sense of humor." But, she adds, she did not feel then that Len was the "love of my life." They parted Edinburgh as friends.

Soon after Lillian returned to Camp Bewdley, the most emotionally taxing period in her overseas service began. She confesses that after receiving D-Day casualties in June 1944, she thought they would be "the worst I ever saw." Unfortunately, that did not prove to be the case. "The worst" began arriving less than a week after she reported back. Far from the front lines, the 297th General Hospital went about its duties on December 16, 1944 as it would have on any other day. Yet hundreds of miles away, a German counteroffensive began on that date. It became known as the Battle of the Bulge. The name comes from the fifty-some-mile "bulge" enemy forces penetrated into the Allied line that stretched across the Belgian part of the vast Ardennes Forest. It took American and British troops six weeks to push the enemy forces back. The fighting in that month and a half resulted in casualties that, for Lillian, proved to be the most distressing for her. One day in mid-December, as Lillian remembers it, the COs announced to the personnel in the 297th that a large contingent of wounded would be arriving. The staff received no other information as to what they would be dealing with. It could very well be that the enormity of what they faced was not known that day to the hospital's High Command.

One military historian, who served as a company commander in this campaign, judged the fight in the Ardennes between the Allies and the Germans to be "the greatest battle ever fought by the United States Army."[104] For the Americans alone, approximately six hundred thousand fought in the Battle of the Bulge. Of that number, about forty-seven thousand were wounded and nineteen thousand killed.[105] In the weeks that the two armies clashed, about forty percent of the personnel that composed the United States' Medical Department was based in the ETO, including 15,612 nurses. And every one of them was needed given those high casualty numbers.[106] Lillian describes how the "troop trains brought in hundreds and hundreds of wounded." Their injuries were, she adds, "so severe, so bad." As the men arrived at the 297th, she concluded that the casualties from the Battle of the Bulge seemed "worse than those from Normandy."

Lillian thought the men "looked terrible." They were, she adds, "so beaten up and dirty." She describes them as "full of mud and dirt." In her capacity as an orthopedic nurse, Lillian saw amputation after amputation, although bone grafting saved some limbs. What became the bane of so many soldiers, and the medical staff who treated them, was a condition that developed in the Ardennes because of the severe winter--trench foot. American field shoes and combat boots did not protect the soldiers' feet from the wet woods and fields. (Because the High Command expected the war to be over before the harsh weather hit, proper winter uniforms and boots had not arrived at the front.) Wet socks and freezing temperatures combined to create circulation problems in the soldier's feet. As Lillian explains the condition, "the capillaries froze so the bone was not getting proper circulation." Toes could turn black due to the lack of blood flow. If the case of trench foot or frostbite became an extreme one, the pain could be excruciating. This foot condition plagued the men beginning in November, weeks before the Germans attacked. The situation became worse during the six-week battle.

a December 1944 magazine cover Lillian has kept

As one Army historian concluded, "Trench foot put far more men out of action in the Bulge than the Germans did."[107] Lillian points out that frostbite could damage the capillaries, blood vessels, and bone. Consequently, the orthopedic wards saw many cases. Just getting the wet socks off of the frozen feet proved difficult. The socks were, literally, attached to the skin. Lillian remembers how the staff received orders not to pull the socks off. If anyone did that, the skin would come off with the socks. The feet had to be allowed to defrost naturally. Once that happened, as Lillian explains, the nurses "slowly, slowly" used a sterilized medical instrument to take off pieces of the sock until they removed all of the material. While the 297th continued to receive casualties from the continent in the winter months and into the spring of 1945, none equaled what its staff dealt with from the Battle of the Bulge.

Lillian at Camp Bewdley

For Lillian, a deepening relationship with Len marked the months after the last enemy offensive. The war against the Nazis was winding down at the same time. On the military front, in March the allied forces crossed the Rhine River into Germany. It was only a matter of time before a surrender would be forced upon Hitler's government. On the personal front for Lillian, Staff Sergeant Swerdlow was clearly serious about the Army nurse he had met in Edinburgh. From December 1944 until May 1945, the two saw each other three times. Once Len took a train to Bewdley; he stayed in a hotel there. The two also met in the English town of Lester, which Lillian estimates to have been about halfway between Camp Bewdley and London. Lillian took a train to Lester and stayed with the British Red Cross that had set itself up in one of the town's buildings. They met for a third time in Nottingham where Len, in Lillian's word, "billeted" her in a private home. She characterizes all of these as short visits. Given their Army responsibilities, they were never able to spend days together as they had in Edinburgh. But they wrote each other many letters, and Len even used his superior officer's name to telephone Lillian. That man was Colonel Jakequist. From his airbase in Kimbolton, Len placed calls to the 297th. Camp Bewdley's loudspeaker announced that "Colonel Jakequist" was on the phone for "Lieutenant Krell." Lillian took the call wherever she was, be it on the wards or in the dining room. When a colonel wants to speak with a lieutenant, it is incumbent on the lower-ranking officer to do so immediately. Lillian received some good-natured ribbing from the medical staff about her "colonel friend," an Air Corps officer, no less. In truth, it was Len on the other end of the phone. Once, however, to Lillian's surprise, Colonel Jakequist's voice really was the one she heard when she picked up the phone. The Colonel had found out about how Len was using his name. Amused, he actually made a call to Lieutenant Krell.

In one of his conversations with Lillian, Len told her that he wanted to become "formally engaged," as she explains it. Her reply to him was a simple one. She thought they were moving "too fast." Understanding how serious Len was, Lillian asked him in writing for what she calls "letters of recommendation." She admits he telephoned her once he received that request. Somewhat exasperated, he wanted an explanation. In the end, Len had people contact Lillian attesting to his character. She remembers getting a letter from Len's sister Muriel who was a social worker. Recall Lillian's desire to help families in poor neighborhoods when she worked in Public Health for Mount Sinai Hospital. Perhaps Len thought that a good word from a social worker might carry some weight; it could have been secondary in his mind that the woman was his sister. One of Len's cousins, a high school principal, also wrote Lillian as a witness to his high character. The letter that stands out in Lillian's mind is from musical star Eddie Cantor. He was famous in the United States as a Broadway and radio performer. Len met Cantor at a Hollywood canteen for servicemen before Len shipped out for the ETO. The soldier and the star both hailed from Cherry Street on the East Side of New York City. This served as the basis of more than one invitation Len received from Cantor to spend time with the star outside of the canteen. Len even went to Cantor's home. Knowing that a letter from such a celebrity would impress Lillian, Len wrote Cantor who in turn wrote to Lillian. By early May 1945, Len received word that the Army was sending his bomb group to France. She, too, was due for a move. The 297th had been told that it would soon return to the United States where members of the hospital unit would be given a thirty-day leave. After that, orders called for the 297th to be shipped out to the Pacific as the war against Japan continued. The Allies planned an invasion of the Japanese homeland. Tens of thousands of casualties were predicted.

Understanding that they both would be based elsewhere in the near future, Len contacted Lillian to arrange a date with her in London on Tuesday, May 8th to say goodbye. His departure from England was imminent. Len and Lillian decided to eat at Izzo's, an establishment that she describes as "a kosher-style restaurant." Located in the basement of a building, Lillian points out that Izzo's was one "of the few places in the city where one could get Jewish food." They planned to have an early dinner there before each went back to his/her Army base. The blackouts that London still enforced made a late dinner date problematic. As Lillian recalls it, "We were in the restaurant awaiting dinner and discussing our departure plans from England when a crowd of people suddenly burst into the restaurant shouting and crying, 'The war is over! The Germans have surrendered. The Germans have surrendered.' How we managed to get out to the street so quickly, I will never know. We were encircled by throngs of people as sirens and horns in the city began to blow. Double-decker buses were stopped on the street and taken over by the frenzied mob. People were crying and yelling; everyone, both friends and strangers, were hugging and kissing." As Lillian humorously adds, "We never did get our dinner." Somewhat taken aback by the energy of the crowd, Lillian explains what happened next. "We managed to safely maneuver to a side street, holding hands tightly in an effort not to get separated, when we again found ourselves encircled by people singing and dancing to the tune of 'Roll Out the Barrel.' " Also known as "The Beer Barrel Polka," the lyrics of this popular World War II song included the words, "We've got the blues on the run." Certainly based on Lillian's description of that May 8th day in London, the whole city agreed with those words. She adds, "Someone had pushed a piano out to the middle of the street and was madly pounding out popular songs of the wartime era. It was truly a day to remember."

For the children, May 8th held an added significance. Lillian explains it. "As darkness descended on London, the lights went on for the first time since 1939. The amazement of the children and adults was profound; so many of the children had never seen or remembered London's city lights at night. Their eyes opened wide in wonderment of the fairyland about them. It was a moment I will treasure forever! The tears of joy flowed freely as friends and strangers embraced each other and sang, 'When The Lights Go On Again All Over The World.' " The song envisioned a day when the war would be over. That day had finally come to Europe after six long years.

With the crowds that converged in the streets, cars and buses could not move. Len, however, had to get to the train station so he could report back to his Army base in Kimbolton. The only way to get to the station was by foot. Lillian remembers walking "all night, for miles." Once there, in her words, they "bid each other an emotional goodbye, not knowing when or if we would ever see each other again." At the station, they located the platform where Len's outgoing train stood. He boarded it, but Lillian recounts how "he kept getting on and off," seemingly torn between his Army orders and his desire to stay with his girl. In what Lillian judges to have been a spur-of-the-moment decision, Len proposed to her, "literally seconds before the train departed." Her reply was a surprised, "What?" to which Len countered, "Oh, come on, marry me." Lillian responded with a "yes." Years later, she observed, "I do believe our decision…[in] the aftermath of a very emotional day…surprised both of us. Needless to say, at this moment we had nothing more than faith in each other and uncertain hope for a future life together." While May 8th for the Swerdlows became the date of their engagement, it also became known as V-E Day (Victory in Europe Day). At one point hours earlier, before they went to Izzo's, Len and Lillian had stopped at a photographer's studio. Len wanted a picture of them together, before he left for France. He bought two copies, one for each of them. That photograph became both a snapshot of them on V-E Day as well as one of them on their engagement day.

After Len left the station, Lillian made her way back to the British Red Cross building where she was staying. (Only military women, she explains, could lodge there. Lillian was the only American guest.) She did not have to return to Camp Bewdley for several days. Since Lillian was still in London on Friday night, she went to the West London Synagogue to attend Sabbath Eve services. There she experienced what she judges to have been, "the most memorable Sabbath of my life." Arriving at the Temple, Lillian joined what she recalls as "an overflowing crowd of worshippers." She intended during the service to thank God for his blessings, including the end of the European war as well as the promise of her new life with Len. Lillian describes the Sabbath service as reflective of the "mood of all [of] Europe--Peace and Hope for the future…it was an almost overwhelming experience as we embraced fellow Jews and wished each other Peace, Love, and a happy Shabbat. As the tears flowed, I realized that as Jews, we were all one family." Certainly the thankfulness for the end of the war resonated especially strong within Jewish communities because of the Holocaust. In the last weeks of the war, Allied armies liberated one concentration camp after another. The world then knew the true horror of the war for the Jewish community--Hitler's murder of six million Jews. The emotional outpouring of the Sabbath service was not over, however.

The rabbi introduced some prominent guests, Rabbi and Mrs. Stephen S. Wise and a former governor of New York, Herbert Lehman, and his wife. According to Lillian, these individuals were in London to represent the World Jewish Congress. On this Sabbath after V-E Day, Rabbi Wise and Governor Lehman asked the congregation for donations to, in Lillian's words, "purchase the ships that would be needed to transport displaced Jews from Hitler's death camps to Palestine," an area of the Middle East that became known as Israel. Before everyone left the synagogue, Lillian had the opportunity to personally meet the Wises and Lehmans. (Dressed in her American Army nurse's uniform, she undoubtedly stood out in the crowd.) Unknown to Lillian, in just three months she would meet them again on her voyage home to the States.

The next four months at Camp Bewdley held much less drama for Lillian than earlier ones. Records indicate that on V-E Day, the number of Army nurses in the ETO totaled more than twenty thousand. They were there to care for over three million members of the Army should the need arise.[108] With the war over in Europe, however, that many men and nurses were no longer necessary. Incoming patients from the continent destined for the 297th had slowed down so much that in the middle of the summer, the Army closed down the unit completely. The General Hospital moved to some buildings in Wolverly, near Kidderminster in Worcestershire. Those quarters had been occupied by the 52nd General Hospital before the Medical Department transferred it to Bristol.[109] Lillian stresses that the new housing accommodations proved much more satisfactory than those in Camp Bewdley. The nurses, for example, slept in a large Quonset hut on what Lillian recalls as "very comfortable beds" instead of the cots they had used in the Last Chance, their small wooden hut at Bewdley. The 297th spent several weeks packing their equipment. The staff itself literally lived out of their packed bags in the last few weeks. Lillian explains that they had to be ready at a moment's notice to leave for the States. While she and others awaited transportation to move them to the English coast, news came that the Japanese had surrendered on August 10, 1945, after American planes dropped atomic bombs on two Japanese cities.

By the end of August, the 297th General Hospital had packed and was ready for its return to the States. Staff members looked forward to their thirty-day leave, although they knew that after it, the unit reported to Camp Sibert in Alabama. (With the war over now even in the Pacific, the 297th would not be needed in that theater.) The ship that took them home was the same one that had brought them to the ETO, the *Queen Elizabeth*. The hospital unit boarded her at Southampton. Before Lillian left the dock, she sent a telegram to her parents in New Haven informing them of her immediate departure. "Please meet me," she recalls, was her simple request. The ship left England on August 26, 1945.[110] It proved to be a tranquil voyage. No gales struck the vessel as it left European waters, and the zigzag approach the *Queen* had observed fifteen months earlier was no longer necessary. Lillian remembers the ship as being crowded, so much so that she "stepped over bodies" when walking on the deck. She also recalls the excitement she felt at finally going home. Lillian slept once again on the floor, near the door, in a cabin she shared with other nurses. As she had on the voyage over, she volunteered to work with the Canadian doctor and nurse in the ship's hospital. The lounging accommodations there, Lillian explains, were much more comfortable than in other areas of the ship. She could rest on "small couches" instead of trying to find a place to sit down in other parts of the packed vessel. Lillian characterizes her stay in the hospital area as "a relief" given the human density elsewhere on the ship. In spite of the thousands on board the *Queen Elizabeth*, five passengers especially drew Lillian's attention. Four of them were ones she had met at the London Sabbath Eve services following V-E Day, namely the Wises and the Lehmans. Mrs. Wise sat down with Lillian and Maddy more than once during the crossing. She stressed the dire need for nurses to accompany Jewish refugees on the ships heading for Palestine. Both lieutenants diplomatically reminded the rabbi's wife that, for now, they still belonged to the ANC. One last notable passenger who Lillian encountered was the Hollywood movie star Jimmy Stewart, himself a returning Army veteran. Stewart dutifully posed for a picture Lillian took of him on deck.

Lillian's picture of Jimmy Stewart

When the *Queen Elizabeth* sailed into New York City on Thursday, August 30, 1945, according to Lillian it was "one of the first peacetime, large passenger ships to arrive home from Europe."[111] Just as Lillian had departed her hometown some fifteen months before to crowds of well-wishers on the docks, the *Queen* arrived on August 30th to a similar tumultuous welcome. "It was," Lillian wrote decades later, "a homecoming celebration to be remembered forever…Fireboats streaming fountains of water came out to meet us. Tugs were whistling. Sirens were blowing. People were lined up wall to wall from the Battery to Dockside waving and shouting. 'Welcome Home' banners were everywhere as thousands of balloons festooned the sky!"[112] Crowds might have been especially large in New York City that day since the coming Saturday-Monday was Labor Day weekend.

When the *Queen Elizabeth* landed, Lillian expected to somehow find her parents in the crowd. She did not know it, but Adolfo and Esther were at their summer home in Westport, Massachusetts. The residence had no telephone or electricity. The telegram Lillian had sent from Southampton arrived at the Krell home in New Haven, but to an empty house. Her parents, therefore, were not at the pier to greet her. Lillian explains that she "stayed dockside until everyone had left." Almost all of the money she carried was English, but she took a few of the American coins she had and telephoned an aunt who lived in Brooklyn. No one was home. "I felt stranded and alone," she admits. A taxi cab driver saw her. He probably took pity on the wayward looking lieutenant. The man asked Lillian if she had just returned to the States. She replied in the affirmative, pointing out that she had planned on her parents meeting the ship. The taxi cab driver offered to drive her to the Algonquin Hotel in the city, even though Lillian stressed she only had English pounds to cover the fare, not American dollars. The New Yorker obviously did not care about being paid. Once they arrived at the hotel, the driver spoke to the front desk while Lillian stood nearby. At the urging of the taxi driver, the management took over the situation. The man at the front desk declared to her, "You must be tired and hungry." The hotel gave her a suite, urging her to go up to it and rest. They would send a dinner to her room. Once in her suite, Lillian showered, something she really needed after five days on the *Queen Elizabeth*. The hotel staff even sent her heavy uniform, appropriate to English weather but not to the milder, summer climate of New York City, to the cleaners. Lillian donned her much lighter summer uniform; she had never worn that outfit while in England because of the colder climate.

The next day, after breakfast at the Algonquin, she telephoned Len's parents, Morris and Lillie Swerdlow. (No one was still at the Krell's New Haven home to answer Lillian's phone calls.) Len had given Lillian a telephone number to call. Unknown to her, it was the number of an upstairs' neighbor. The Swerdlows did not have a phone. After a woman answered the ringing, Lillian heard her yell down the stairs, "Len's girl is on the phone." His parents knew their son had become engaged, but he had not given them much personal information about Lillian, aside from the fact she was an Army nurse. Lillian characterizes the Swerdlows as "very religious." Interestingly, Len had not told them she was Jewish. Certainly the name "Krell" gave no indication of her Hebrew background. Len's mother invited Lillian to Friday night dinner; she did not explain to her on the phone the significance of that meal for Jewish families. Lillian offered no hint she understood it, either. By the time she left for the Sabbath Eve dinner, the hotel had pressed her summer uniform for her. "It looked stunning," she recalls. Her gold lieutenant bars and campaign ribbons added even more of a military look to her outfit. Lillian had visited the hotel beauty salon where she had her hair and nails done. Applying new make-up, she was ready to meet her future in-laws. Very familiar with the New York subway system, Lillian had no problem finding the Swerdlow home in Brooklyn.

When she arrived, Len's parents and his sister Muriel greeted her. They expected Muriel's husband soon. Len's brother Monroe would also join the family for dinner. As the Swerdlows undoubtedly looked Lillian over, they still had no idea she was Jewish. Her red hair and freckles, like her last name, gave no evidence of that. Even when Mrs. Swerdlow, in Lillian's recollection, announced, "I am going to light the candles because this is what Jewish people do on Friday nights," Lillian gave no indication she understood the custom. It was only during the meal that she shared her identity with her hosts. The family started to tease Len's brother-in-law about his parents' Austrian background. One of the Swerdlow's used a word, *glitzeiana*, to describe Jews from that area of Europe. Lillian joined the conversation, using the same word to describe her maternal grandmother who had also emigrated from Austria.

Relieved to know that her son would be marrying a Jewish woman, Mrs. Swerdlow still had some concerns that she posed to Lillian in the form of three questions. "Is your mother kosher? Do you keep the Sabbath? Do your parents have two sets of dishes?" Lillian answered that "yes," her mother prepared proper meals, and "yes," she tried to always keep the Sabbath, even though her three years at Mount Sinai and eighteen months in the Army made that sometimes difficult. In respect to the query on the number of dish sets the Krells had, "yes," they had more than one. As Lillian puts it, that affirmative answer meant that her parents "kept kosher." (The tradition of two sets of dishes relates to the Torah prohibition on allowing contact between meat and milk. Lillian explains that, health-wise, such contact is a concern. In generations past, wooden dishes were the norm, but blood from the meat could seep into the cracks in the wood. Milk later put into the dish would curdle, leading to, as she adds, infections.) Mrs. Swerdlow must have been pleased with Lillian's answers.

Mr. Swerdlow seemed taken with his future daughter-in-law, too. He appears to have been proud of her military service. Would Lillian please accompany him to Temple the next day, wearing her uniform? Len's father was president of the conservative Temple. He must have wanted to show off his son's fiancé. When Lillian went with him, the rabbi told the congregation that Lieutenant Krell had just returned from overseas service. He added that she was the future wife of Len Swerdlow. That night, some of Monroe's friends came over to the Swerdlow home. One of them owned an old jalopy. The group offered to take Lillian wherever she wanted to go. She admitted that she would like to drive to Coney Island. It had a kosher hot dog stand that she would love to visit. (Recall that Lillian had been away from her old haunts for one and a half years, ever since she had reported for duty at Atlantic City on February 1, 1944.) Before the young people left the apartment, Mr. Swerdlow insisted on two things. Concerned that Lillian's Army uniform might get dirty in the jalopy, he spread a beige sheet on the seat where she would sit. Additionally, he cautioned Monroe, "You remember, this is Lenny's girl."

Once back at the Hotel Algonquin, Lillian finally connected with her parents by telephone. Adolfo and Esther found their daughter's telegram awaiting them when they returned from their summer home. After a New York City bank converted her English pounds to American dollars, Lillian paid her hotel bill. She admits to being surprised at the small amount the management charged her for all of the services she received at the Algonquin. Once checked out, Lillian boarded the subway for the ride to New Haven where she reunited with her family. Her thirty-day leave coincided with two Jewish Holy Days, Rosh Hashanah on September 7th and Yom Kippur on September 16th. Lillian chose the word "special" to describe their observance with her parents. It must have been that for Adolfo and Esther. Jerry, Lillian's brother, recalls even today how his father and mother waited anxiously for Lillian's telephone calls from England. There were not that many, but when she could, Lillian wrote her parents to tell them when to expect a call from her. Jerry remembers all of this, but, interestingly, Lillian does not. That might be more indicative of the excitement on the New Haven end of the connection than the Camp Bewdley one. How the Krells must have anticipated those few times when they could speak with their beloved daughter. Jerry picked up on that expectation, probably forming the basis of his strong memory of the calls. Lillian, daily surrounded by the war, has other recollections that take precedence over telephone conversations with her parents. During her September leave, aside from the Holy Days' observations, Lillian remembers spending days visiting friends. The New Haven Temple organized what she describes as "a big party for veterans" arriving home. Lillian went to it, the only nurse in attendance.

As it turned out, her thirty-day leave became one that lasted about ninety days. In October she reported to an Army office in New York City. Lillian's orders, received in England before the 297th's departure, indicated that she would be sent to Camp Sibert. Originally, her general hospital unit was to gather at the Alabama base for its next assignment. But once she reported in, Lillian found out that the Army decided to disband the 297th, probably due to Japan's surrender. With the war over in the Pacific as well as in Europe, Lillian anticipated a discharge from her military service in the immediate future. It would still be one as a second lieutenant, however. She held that rank throughout her eighteen months in the ANC. While in England, Dr. Kelikian kept putting her in for a promotion to first lieutenant. Nothing came from his recommendations, through no fault of Lillian's. The ANC, she was told, already had its quota of first lieutenants. Once back home in the States, a sergeant at the New York City's Army office similarly felt Lillian should be promoted. He even wanted to get her back pay to the point where she qualified for the status of a first lieutenant. (Lillian defines this as anytime after her first six months in the ETO.) But Lillian wanted to end his talk of a promotion and a retroactive pay raise. She had no desire to report to Camp Sibert. With the disbandment of the 297th, Lillian did not know where she would end up. Len was also due home from France.

In Lillian's recollections, by the fall of 1945 she "wanted out" of the Army. "I had seen enough and done enough," Lillian explains. "I was ready for marriage. I also wanted to get credentialed in Public Health." Once the sergeant who wanted to help her get a promotion heard this from Lillian, he put his energy into helping her get a discharge. Thus she remembers spending October and November going "back and forth from New York City to New Haven." During those months, the Army did not assign her to any of its hospitals. The paperwork for her discharge that the sergeant initiated in October finally reached fruition. The Army released her from active duty on December 8, 1945 at Fort Dix in New Jersey.[113] Lillian's departure from the ANC in the months right after World War II ended was not unusual. In August 1945 when Japan surrendered, over 57,000 women served in the ANC. Demobilization proceeded in a rapid fashion for both the men and the women in the armed forces. By the end of September 1946, only 8,500 nurses remained in the ANC.[114]

When Lillian left the Army Separation Center as a civilian, she was not far from her parent's New Haven home. On that December day, however, she was a world away from the war she had experienced in England. One could argue that combat is the most powerful human experience an individual can go through. For Americans, the natural borders of the United States had protected them from outside attack throughout most of their history. As such, men experienced war more than women did because they served in combat, usually overseas. During the American Civil War in the mid-19th century, soldiers used a phrase to identify those who had been intimately touched by war. Such individuals had "seen the elephant."[115] The men understood that the enormity of what they had witnessed would never be surpassed. In World War II, as an Army nurse, Lillian, too, had "seen the elephant."

Although not on the front lines, Lillian witnessed war close up, in the most personal way. She dealt with its casualties. On the orthopedic ward of the 297th General Hospital at Camp Bewdley, she saw the traumatic responses of "boys" when they realized that a limb had been amputated. As best she could, she comforted them. The positive attitude of many gave her strength to go on every day. And those days were long ones, recall--twelve-hour shifts, seven days a week. Emotionally and medically, one of the hardest tasks Lillian confronted was triage. She had just moments to assess patients who arrived by convoy from the continent, just minutes to check their vital signs to determine who needed to be seen first by the doctors. Lillian would have looked into their faces as she did that. Some feigned a strength they may not have had; even these "boys" would have touched an emotional chord in her. But feelings must be checked at the door, so to speak, if a nurse is to function while on duty. In a moving confession, Lillian shared how she remained strong while on the wards, but how she cried after her shift ended. While most patients who reached the general hospitals survived, some did not. Lillian saw a handful of them die, young men just a few years older in many cases than her brothers.

During her time in England, the convoys that brought casualties from the continent did not allow for very much "time off." By her own estimation, from her arrival in June 1944 until early December 1944, there was no let up in the seemingly constant arrival of patients. American forces moved through northern France, Holland, Belgium, and, finally, western Germany. Such progress in the war meant thousands of American casualties. Some of them ended up at the 297th General Hospital in England. The few hours spent with Mrs. Mann in front of the fireplace in the Englishwoman's home gave Lillian a short respite from the horrors of war, but just a short one. On the one-week leave she did receive, it began on anything but a tranquil note. Lillian planned to spend it in London, but there, too, she confronted the horrors of war. German bombing forced her into underground shelters. The look on the faces of beleaguered children huddled with her became a sight she could never forget. Once she returned to duty after that short leave, the Battle of the Bulge again resulted in large numbers of incoming casualties. Lillian experienced war in a different way than combat soldiers. She confronted it close up through her patients. Seeing the mangled bodies of "boys," day after day, month after month, impacted Lillian in ways she could not show, or even articulate after she left the war zone. She had certainly "seen the elephant."

As Lillian insightfully concludes, "In retrospect, I would like to feel that I, as well as my fellow nurses in the U.S. Army Nurse Corps, served our wounded men and country well." She adds, "As women, we played an important and needed role in the services of the Armed Forces."[116] Regardless of which war historians study, the critical role played by nurses who treated its casualties must be acknowledged. The emotional cost of that war for them should also be recognized. Although it impacted Lillian in ways that are difficult for her to discuss, the enormity of her time in the ANC is not lost on her. Lillian uses the word "destiny" to explain her military service in World War II. She traces her fate to the grievance letter she wrote protesting the Army's orders after boot camp to send Lillian to one Army hospital and Maddy to another. If not for that letter, and what she believes was "an irate response" to her protest, Lillian probably would not have seen overseas duty.[117] That duty changed her life in two significant ways--she served in a war zone and she also found love while stationed there. Both of those dramatically altered her life forever. As such, her World War II experience was both professional and personal.

Epilogue

After her discharge from the Army, Lillian felt sure of two things. First, she intended to become better acquainted with Len. His ship landed in New York City on December 31, 1945. He wanted to marry soon, but Lillian preferred a somewhat longer engagement so they could get to know each other more. Second, she planned to use the GI Bill to further her formal education in Public Health. Since she could pursue both of these interests in New York City, it became home early in 1946. Lillian's parents asked her to settle in New Haven, but professional and personal loves drew her to the city where she had been born. She stayed at the home of an aunt and uncle.

The first six months of 1946 proved difficult ones for Lillian and Len's relationship. In her words, he "could not seem to find himself." Len had served in the Army for four years, having enlisted on January 9, 1942, just one month after the United States entered the war.[118] He spent most of that time with his bomb group. Although Len was not part of a crew, he nonetheless had friends who died on bombing missions. He witnessed such losses for a few years. As such, Len experienced firsthand the human cost of war. Lillian stresses that he served in the ETO for a much longer time than her fifteen months at Camp Bewdley. With Len's return to the States and subsequent discharge, Lillian believes he "just could not seem to fit in." He had, again in her words, "a hard time adjusting to civilian life." Len toyed with the idea of re-enlisting in the Army. That resulted in a serious discussion between the engaged couple on their future together. Lillian made it clear that she did not want to be "an Air Force wife," moving from one base to another. She wanted to work in Public

Health, and she did not want to move far away from her parents. Len also talked about relocating to California where he had trained and where some of his Army buddies lived. But Lillian honestly told him that she preferred to stay in the New York-Connecticut area where her family lived. The time after Len came home was one marked by what she characterizes as "a lot of ups and downs" in their relationship, At one point, Lillian even considered returning her engagement ring to him. The months before their marriage were, in her conclusion, "the worst time" in their relationship. Len encouraged Lillian to return to school, but that educational path did not seem to be the one for him.

Passed unanimously by Congress in 1944, the GI Bill of Rights thanked veterans in more than one way for their military service. Lillian took advantage of its offer to pay tuition for a college or university education. Over one million veterans went to such institutions in the years right after the war ended, Lillian being one of them.[119] Initially, she intended to enroll in New York University's Public Health Program. But during the interview process, Lillian confronted a not-so-subtle form of discrimination. The woman who interviewed her fixated on Lillian's engagement ring. She openly concluded that Lillian would marry and eventually have children. "Where would that leave you?" she queried Lillian. "We would be wasting our money to give you an education." Turned away from New York University, Lillian applied to Columbia University where she had received her training in obstetrics. Learning from her last experience, Lillian deftly removed her ring before the interview. Additionally, she points out that a man conducted the question and answer session, a fact she saw as one in her favor. Columbia accepted her into its Public Health Program. She took classes on campus while also working at a Public Health clinic

associated with the university. At the end of two years, she would be certified in the field of Public Health. Len, too, had planned to return to school. (He had been attending Brooklyn College when he entered the Army.) Heavy enrollment at the school of his choice combined with a decline in his father's health made that problematic. Early in 1946 when Lillian began her Public Health program at Columbia, Len began working with a cousin who had a graphics arts business in New York City. Len and Lillian married on June 2, 1946 in Brooklyn. Unfortunately, Morris Swerdlow died from a heart attack just a few weeks after the wedding. The newlyweds moved in with Len's mother, who had an empty house now with the loss of her husband.

After Lillian earned her credential from Columbia, the couple moved to New Haven. She secured a position at Yale University's hospital, and Len opened a variety store with one of Lillian's uncles. Following the birth of their first child, Barbara, in 1948, Lillian temporarily retired from the work force. A son, Michael, followed in 1952. Len "was not happy," as his wife puts it, in the family business he managed. He still wanted to move to California. When an opportunity arose, he decided to act on his postwar dream to relocate to the West Coast.

50th Wedding Anniversary

Building on his Army background in purchasing, in 1955 Len took a job with a motor home company, Vacation Industries in El Monte, California. He was in charge of purchasing everything from stationary to mechanical parts for the recreational vehicles. With their daughter and son, the Swerdlows moved to La Puente in the San Gabriel Valley outside of Los Angeles. They had their third and last child, Ellen, in 1958. When this youngest daughter entered preschool, Lillian returned to the world of nursing. For twenty-five years, she worked with La Puente's Rowland Unified School District as a nurse. With his business expertise and community ties, Len helped his wife raise money for a school clinic in a poor neighborhood. Lillian ran it. She oversaw federal and state funded programs such as ones for migrant children and those in special education. (The clinic still stands today, renamed the "Lillian Swerdlow Children's Clinic" in her honor after she retired.) Once Adolfo stopped working, he and Esther moved to La Puente to join their daughter and her family. (They died in 1979 and 1987, respectively.) After their arrival in the San Gabriel Valley, Lillian and Len did not move for thirty-six years. It was only his retirement that prompted a relocation, this time to Oceanside in northern San Diego County. For several years after that, Lillian and Len enjoyed the company of their three children and five grandchildren. In 1999 Len passed away from a heart problem.

Since then, aside from extended visits by family members, Lillian has lived alone. She points out that she wondered what that would be like because she had never been by herself. Throughout her childhood and teen years, of course, Lillian resided with her parents. While she had a room of her own at Mount Sinai's School of Nursing, the living situation still remained a communal one with its shared bathrooms and dining halls. For a few months after graduation, she lived at home with her parents. During her basic training in Atlantic City, another Army nurse served as her roommate. Her short stay at Tilden General Hospital meant more Army-style living. Once in England with the 297th, Lillian shared a hut with five other nurses. Upon her return home and subsequent military discharge, she either lived with her parents in New Haven or her aunt and uncle in New York City. Married to Len for fifty-three years before his death, it was only at the age of seventy-seven that Lillian lived by herself.

But do not think of Lillian as anything but a more mature version of the woman who displayed so much strength at critical points in her life. She dutifully but firmly made it clear to her father that nursing, not business, was the career she wanted to pursue. In the Berg incident just months before graduation, Mount Sinai's hierarchical structure threatened her dream to become a nurse. Yet in response, Lillian stood up to power. Told to pack her bags, she refused to go quietly. Instead, she asserted her right to be there. "I had done nothing wrong," she forcefully states. Even though at the time she did not see her stand as a courageous one, it was that, especially for the era. Lillian drew on her strength again while in England. She held herself together when caring for patients who looked "so terrible" upon their arrival at the hospital. Even today, decades after the war, her ninety-year-old body belies the strength within it.

Lillian fills her home with the family heritage that she passionately shares with visitors. Shelves and walls abound with photographs of the Krell and Ernst side of her family, most notably Adolfo, Esther, and Basha. Pictures from the war years are similarly prominent--Lillian's graduation portrait from Mount Sinai hangs in a hallway with photos of her and Len. She placed an enlarged snapshot of herself and Maddy sitting on the hood of a jeep in England on a wall near the front door. Paintings from Argentina, inherited from her parents, decorate the living room walls. And, of course, there are photographs of the children and grandchildren at various ages. Lillian keeps family heirlooms nearby, too. Stored in a closet is one of her most treasured items, the uniform Adolfo had on when he "jumped ship" in 1918. A large shadowbox hangs on a wall in the entryway. It holds a golden apron Esther received from a friend on the Krells' fiftieth wedding anniversary. Lillian still has the uniform she wore as an Army nurse. This is just a representative accounting of the heritage Lillian surrounds herself with. Her entire life can be surveyed by studying each photograph, painting, and heirloom. A visitor to this home will learn about Lillian's heritage, training as a nurse, and military service during World War II by just studying her possessions. Living alone? No, not really. Lillian Krell Swerdlow is surrounded by the history she has witnessed.

Endnotes

---

[1] Quotations from Hirsch and information on his work are taken from http://www.jewishencyclopedia.com/view.jsp?artid=771&letter=H, accessed May 16, 2011.
[2] The history of the Krells in Argentina is taken from Lillian's unpublished story of her father, *The Little Jewish Gaucho* (1999) and from a conversation with this author on May 11, 2011. Other details on the family history of the Krells and the Ernsts (Lillian's maternal grandparents), as well as stories of Lillian's life, are also taken from information she shared with the author in May-June, 2011. Unless otherwise indicated, all quotations from Lillian are from these interviews.
[3] Lillian is quite clear on Esther's birth year since her mother told her she was born at the beginning of the new century. The 1910 and 1920 Censuses, however, lists her birth year as 1901 as does the California Death Index, 1940-1997. www.ancestry.com (accessed May 21, May 22, and May 28, 2011 respectively).
[4] The 1900 and 1910 Censuses list Isidor's birthplace as Austria. www.ancestry.com (accessed May 23 and May 22, 2011 respectively).
[5] The 1900, 1910, and 1920 Censuses respectively. www.ancestry.com (accessed May 23, May 22, and May 22, 2011 respectively).
[6] The 1910 and 1900 Censuses respectively. www.ancestry.com (accessed May 22 and May 23, 2011 respectively).
[7] The Federal Writers' Project Guide to 1930s New York, *The WPA Guide to New York City* (New York, 1939; 1992 edition), p. 308.
[8] The 1910 Census. www.ancestry.com (accessed May 22, 2011).
[9] The 1920 Census. www.ancestry.com (accessed on May 22, 2011).
[10] http://www.vny.cuny.edu/blizzard/stories/stories.html (accessed May 26, 2011).
[11] Statistics on mortality rates in the flu pandemic are taken from John M. Barry, *The Great Influenza: The Epic Story of the Deadliest Plague in History* (New York, 2004), p. 4.
[12] Carol R. Byerly, *Fever of War: The Influenza Epidemic in the U.S. Army during World War I* (New York, 2005), p. 4.
[13] Byerly, *Fever of War*, p. 5 (number who became ill) and p. 33 (population of the United States).
[14] Ibid., p. 5.
[15] Barry, *The Great Influenza*, p. 276.
[16] The 1920 Census, www.ancestry.com (accessed on May 22, 2011).
[17] http://www.history-of-tango.com/couple-dancing.htnl and http://www.history-of-tango.com/tango-origins.html (accessed May 22, 2011).
[18] Linda Kerber, *No Constitutional Right To Be Ladies: Women and the Obligations of Citizenship* (New York, 1998), p. 41. Kerber points out that even into the 1950s, some American-born women were denied passports because they had married aliens before 1922 (pp. 42-43). Most women whose lives had been affected by the Expatriation Act had their citizenship restored in 1922 with the Cable Act (p. 42).
[19] Writers' Program of the Works Projects Administration in the State of New York, *New York: A Guide to the Empire State* (New York, 1940; 1955 edition) p. 489.
[20] *The WPA Guide to New York City*, pp. xviii, 431, 433.

[21] Ibid., p. 497.
[22] Ibid., pp. 455, 461, and 476 respectively.
[23] Information on the origin, symptoms, and treatment of pertussis can be found at http://www.ncbi.nlm.nih.gov/pubmedhealth/PMH0002528/ (accessed May 23, 2011).
[24] The detailed description of the ferry ride is from *The WPA Guide to New York City*, pp. 410-412.
[25] U.S. Naturalization Records Indexes, 1794-1995, www.ancestry.com (accessed May 14, 2011). On his naturalization papers, Adolfo Anglicized his first name, signing as "Adolph."
[26] The 1930 Census, www.ancestry.com (accessed May 25, 2011). It lists, along with Basha, her thirty-two year old daughter Elizabeth, her twenty-one year old son William, and her sixteen year old son Abraham. Since these three family members lived with Basha early in 1930 when the census was taken, they probably resided with her the prior year when the three Ernsts lived there, too.
[27] New York Passenger Lists, 1820-1957, www.ancestry.com (accessed May 28, 2011).
[28] The Federal Writers' Project of the Works Progress Administration, *The WPA Guide to Massachusetts* (New York, 1983), p. 230. Originally published in 1937 as *Massachusetts: A Guide to Its Places and People*.
[29] The 1930 Census, www.ancestry.com (accessed May 23, 2011).
[30] Information on Maria and Leandro is taken from the 1930 Census, www.ancestry.com (accessed May 28, 2011).
[31] *The WPA Guide to Massachusetts*, p. 248. One-third of the population in Holyoke was Irish, and a large number of French Canadians added to the Catholic influence that could be seen throughout the city. Poles constituted ten percent of the population, with the rest of the residents having English, Scotch, German, Italian, Greek, Scandinavian, and Jewish roots (p. 248).
[32] Unless otherwise indicated, all quotations from Lillian regarding her training as a nurse, her service in the United States Army Nurse Corps, and her life after the war are taken from interviews with the author in February-April 2012.
[33] Patricia D'Antonio, *American Nursing: A History of Knowledge, Authority, and the Meaning of Work* (Baltimore, Maryland, 2010), p. 3. D'Antonio also cited the figure of twenty thousand American women who volunteered their nursing services during the Civil War (p. 9). Mary T. Sarnecky makes a very clear connection as to how "good nursing could save lives" in *A History of the U.S. Army Nurse Corps* (Philadelphia, 1999), pp. 22-23. For the idea that it was a woman's duty to nurse her family and community, see also Susan M. Reverby, *Ordered to Care: The Dilemma of American Nursing, 1850-1945* (New York, 1987; 1990 reprint), p. 11.
[34] Joseph Hirsh and Beka Doherty, *The First Hundred Years of The Mount Sinai Hospital of New York, 1852-1952* (New York, 1952), p. 66.
[35] For the establishment of the hospital-based nursing school in the United States, see Reverby, *Ordered to Care*, p. 47 as well as Hirsh and Doherty, *The First Hundred Years*, pp. 65-68. Additionally, Hirsh and Doherty powerfully describe the

unsanitary living conditions in New York City (pp. 4-7). For the establishment of the Mount Sinai Hospital, see Hirsh and Doherty, *The First Hundred Years*, p. 287.
[36] For the idea of "trading work for knowledge," see D'Antonio, *American Nursing*, pp. xiv, 1 and Reverby, *Ordered to Care*, pp. 3, 47. The idea of nurses' training schools being based in hospitals can be found in D'Antonio, *American Nursing*, pp. 29, 67,169. This remained the norm even in the 1960s when 80% of all nursing students were still trained in hospital-based schools; the proliferation of community colleges after that decade moved the training away from the hospitals and into those two-year institutions. The curriculum of scientific nursing is taken from D'Antonio, *American Nursing*, p. 19.
[37] Reverby, *Ordered to Care*, pp. 97 and 103 contrasts the changing social status of hospital patients. Hirsh, *The First Hundred Years*, pp. 212 and 214 explains the emphasis on nursing as a profession and the increased training time.
[38] D'Antonio, *American Nursing*, p. 163.
[39] Both quotations on this change in employment after graduation come from Reverby, *Ordered to Care*, pp. 179-180 respectively. See also p. 3.
[40] Both quotations on relieving students of the complete responsibility for patient care and on the economic benefit to hospitals in doing so are from D'Antonio, *American Nursing*, p. 165.
[41] Reverby, *Ordered to Care*, p. 170 on the 1928 report.
[42] Ibid., p. 182 and D'Antonio, *American Nursing*, p. 161 on the increasing complexity of medical care by nurses.
[43] On the 1940 high school requirement, and the percentage who had such a degree in 1940, see D'Antonio, *American Nursing*, p. 163.
[44] The total number of nurses in 1940 is taken from D'Antonio, *American Nursing*, p. 187. D'Antonio also profiles some characteristics of the average nurse on p. 162; a more complete profile is in Reverby, *Ordered to Care*, pp. 80, 85.
[45] For the "intimate body work" nurses dealt with, see D'Antonio, *American Nursing*, pp. 3, 30, 47.
[46] An invaluable book that deals with this religious prejudice within the Jewish community is Evelyn Rose Benson's *As We See Ourselves, Jewish Women in Nursing* (Indianapolis, Indiana, 2001). For the Judaic roots of women as nurses, see pp. 4, 7; for turn-of-the-century publications that urged women to become nurses, see pp. 23, 25.
[47] For the relationship between Christianity and the new concept of professionally trained nurses, see, ibid., pp. 2, 26, 46, 59. See also, Susan L. Mayer, "Nursing in the United States," (March 20, 2009) *Jewish Women: A Comprehensive Historical Encyclopedia* at http://jwa.org/encyclopedia/article/nursing-in-united-states (accessed February 13, 2012).
[48] Mayer, "Nursing in the United States."
[49] Benson, *As We See Ourselves,* devotes as entire chapter to the prejudice Jewish women who wanted to become nurses confronted. For recollections from women who were contemporaries with Lillian, see pp. 60, 85, 107-108, 110-114.
[50] Benson, *As We See Ourselves*, p. 46 and Mayer, "Nursing in the United States" on the quotas.

[51] D'Antonio, *American Nursing*, p. 60.
[52] Federal Writers' Project, *The WPA Guide to New York City*, p. 233.
[53] On the number of buildings that comprised the hospital and on the nursing school's building, see Hirsh, *The First Hundred Years*, pp. 297, 295, 214-215 respectively.
[54] D'Antonio, *American Nursing*, pp. 29-30, 42.
[55] Hirsh, *The First Hundred Years*, pp. 183-185 describes Rubin's association with this test and what it consisted of.
[56] D'Antonio, *American Nursing*, p. 47 on the care of infectious patients. Lillian agreed with this description.
[57] For information on the Blood for Britain program at Mount Sinai Hospital, see Hirsh, *The First One Hundred Years*, pp. 258, 297.
[58] On Mount Sinai's National Defense Activities, see ibid., pp. 260, 297.
[59] On the Third General Hospital, see ibid., pp. 261-262, 294, 297.
[60] General James H. "Jimmy" Doolittle, *I Could Never Be So Lucky Again* (New York City, 1991; 1992 Bantam paperback edition), pp. 268, 271, 277.
[61] Barbara Brooks Tomblin, *G.I. Nightingales, The Army Nurse Corps in World War II* (Lexington, KY, 1996), p. 210. By the end of World War II, the American military took over its own recruitment efforts.
[62] Benson, *As We See Ourselves*, pp. 177-178 cites the statistics on the number in the ANC.
[63] Hirsh, *The First One Hundred Years*, pp. 187, 281-282, 294. Berg died in 1950 (p. 282).
[64] D'Antonio, *American Nursing*, pp. 64-66 on the benefits of public health nursing to the larger society. For background on Wald, see Benson, *As We See Ourselves*, pp. 48-51.
[65] Reverby, *Ordered to Care*, p. 110.
[66] Statistics cited in this paragraph can be found in Tomblin, *G.I. Nightingales*, pp. 204, 209; Albert E. Cowdrey, *Fighting For Life, American Military Medicine in World War II* (New York, 1994), pp. 105-106; Evelyn M. Monahan and Rosemary Neidel-Greenlee, *And If I Perish, Frontline U.S. Army Nurses in World War II* (New York, 2003), p. 6. Tomblin mentions Army 2nd Lt. Reba Z. Whittle as a POW held by the Germans (*G.I. Nightingales*, p. 140); the most complete story of Whittle's time as a prisoner can be found in a February 1990 U.S. Army War College "Study Project" by Lieutenant Colonel Mary E.V. Frank. Frank's forty-two page paper is available on the Internet. The number of ANC nurses who died while in the service is taken from Mary T. Sarnecky, *A History of the U.S. Army Nurse Corps* (Philadelphia, 1999), p. 278.
[67] Kathi Jackson, *They Called Them Angels, American Military Nurses in World War II* (Westport, Connecticut, 2000; 2006 edition), p. 4. The "duration of the war plus six months" went into effect for nurses by November 1942.
[68] For the evolution of nurses' BT, see Sarnecky, *A History of the U.S. Army Nurse Corps*, pp. 275-276.
[69] For explanations of relative rank, see Sarnecky, *A History of the U.S. Army Nurse Corps*, pp. 268, 394-395; Tomblin, *G.I. Nightingales*, pp. 4-6; Graham A. Cosmas

and Albert E. Cowdrey, *United States Army in World War II, the Technical Services, The Medical Department: Medical Service in the European Theater of Operations* (Washington, D.C, 1992), p. 120.
[70] Almost all of the quotations regarding Lillian's time in the ANC are taken from conversations between her and the author in March-April, 2012. Some are drawn, and cited, from the four pages of text Lillian wrote for a small booklet she put together in February 1996, *A Destiny to Fulfill, My Story as a W.W. II Army Nurse*.
[71] BT for nurses is detailed in Sarnecky, *A History of the U.S. Army Nurse Corps*, p. 275 and Jackson, *They Called Them Angels*, p. 9.
[72] Jackson, *They Called Them Angels*, p. xviii.
[73] Swerdlow, *A Destiny to Fulfill*, page unnumbered.
[74] Ibid.
[75] Departure and arrival dates for Lillian's trip to the ETO in May 1944 and her return home in August 1945 are taken from her War Department "Certificate of Service." Copy.
[76] Statistics on troop transportation, and the two *Queens*, is taken from Alister Satchell, *Running the Gauntlet: How Three Giant Liners Carried a Million Men to War, 1942-1945* (Annapolis, 2001), pp. 19, 9, 68, 24, 52, 69, 70, 230, and 224 respectively.
[77] Swerdlow, *A Destiny to Fulfill*, page unnumbered.
[78] Satchell, *Running the Gauntlet*, p. 11. Thirty knots equates to thirty-four and a half miles per hour.
[79] Ibid., p.71.
[80] Ibid., p. 27 on the climatic conditions the *Queen Elizabeth* confronted and pp. 9, 26, and 79 on the zigzag approach.
[81] Swerdlow, *A Destiny to Fulfill*, page unnumbered.
[82] Ibid.
[83] Ibid.
[84] Satchell, *Running the Gauntlet*, pp. 96 and 102 on the Clyde Estuary and on the shipyards.
[85] Swerdlow, *A Destiny to Fulfill*, page unnumbered.
[86] Ibid.
[87] Jackson, *They Called Them Angels*, pp. xviii, 180-181; Sarnecky, *A History of the U.S. Army Nurse Corps*, pp. 212, 229.
[88] Swerdlow, *A Destiny to Fulfill*, page unnumbered.
[89] Ibid.
[90] Sarnecky, *A History of the U.S. Army Nurse Corps*, pp. 266-267.
[91] Lillian vividly recalls the seersucker outfit and it is also described in Jackson, *They Called Them Angels*, p. 13.
[92] The transportation system by which American wounded were moved from the battlefield to the general hospitals in England is described in Cowdrey, *Fighting for Life*, p. 268.
[93] Swerdlow, *A Destiny to Fulfill*, page unnumbered.
[94] Sarnecky, *A History of the U.S. Army Nurse Corps*, p. 398.

---

[95] Cosmas and Cowdrey, *Medical Service in the European Theater of Operations*, pp. 360-361 on aidmen.
[96] Cowdrey, *Fighting for Life*, p. 29.
[97] Sarnecky, *A History of the U.S. Army Nurse Corps*, p. 231.
[98] Cosmas and Cowdrey, *Medical Service in the European Theater of Operations*, p. 619.
[99] Ibid., p. 234.
[100] Quotation on plasma and statistics are from Cowdrey, *Fighting for Life*, pp. 165-167 and p. 171.
[101] Phone conversation with Al Bressack, May 1, 2012. Al still vividly remembers what he calls, "the worst day of my life," namely February 23, 1945 when a German shell landed near him.
[102] Swerdlow, *A Destiny to Fulfill*, page unnumbered.
[103] For the discrimination American Jews confronted in the military, see Deborah Dash Moore's *GI Jews: How World War II Changed a Generation* (Cambridge, 2004).
[104] Charles MacDonald, *A Time for Trumpets: the Untold Story of the Battle of the Bulge* (New York, 1985; 2002 edition), p. 11.
[105] Ibid., p. 618.
[106] Cosmas and Cowdrey, *Medical Service in the European Theater of Operations*, pp. 440-441.
[107] Geoffrey Perret, *There's A War To Be Won, The United States Army in World War II* (New York, 1991), pp. 434, 490-491.
[108] The number of nurses and soldiers in the ETO on May 8, 1945 is taken from Sarnecky, *A History of the U.S. Army Nurse Corps*, p. 229. In comparison, Sarnecky states that 1.2 million Army men served in the Pacific at that time (p. 229).
[109] The 52nd General Hospital left Wolverly on June 26, 1945. http://library.upstate.edu/collections/history/local/52nd.php (accessed May 3, 2012).
[110] Departure date entered on Lillian's War Department "Certificate of Service." Copy.
[111] Arrival date entered on Lillian's War Department "Certificate of Service." Copy.
[112] Swerdlow, *A Destiny to Fulfill*, page unnumbered.
[113] Discharge date entered on Lillian's War Department "Certificate of Service." Copy.
[114] Tomblin, *G.I. Nightingales*, p. 204.
[115] For examples of how soldiers used the phrase, see, James M. McPherson, *For Cause & Comrades, Why Men Fought In the Civil* War (New York, 1997), pp. 31, 33.
[116] Swerdlow, *A Destiny to Fulfill*, page unnumbered.
[117] Ibid.
[118] U.S. World War II Army Enlistment Records, 1938-1946, www.ancestry.com (accessed May 7, 2012).
[119] On the GI Bill of Rights, see, David M. Kennedy, *Freedom From Fear: The American People in War and Depression, 1929-1945* (New York, 1999), pp. 786-787.

Y0-CCN-647

Nursing Ethics in the Life Span

SOUTHERN MISSIONARY COLLEGE
Division of Nursing Library
711 Lake Estelle Drive
Orlando, Florida 32803

2013
DF

Nursing Ethics in the Life Span

Elsie L. Bandman, R.N., Ed.D., F.A.A.N.
Professor of Nursing
Hunter-Bellevue School of Nursing
Hunter College of the City University of New York

Bertram Bandman, Ph.D.
Professor of Philosophy
Brooklyn Center, Long Island University

WY
85
B214N

11239

APPLETON-CENTURY-CROFTS/Norwalk, Connecticut

SOUTHERN MISSIONARY COLLEGE
Division of Nursing Library
711 Lake Estelle Drive
Orlando, Florida

0-8385-7026-7

Notice: The author(s) and publisher of this volume have taken care that the information and recommendations contained herein are accurate and compatible with the standards generally accepted at the time of publication.

Copyright © 1985 by Appleton-Century-Crofts
A Publishing Division of Prentice-Hall, Inc.

All rights reserved. This book, or any parts thereof, may not be used or reproduced in any manner without written permission. For information, address Appleton-Century-Crofts, 25 Van Zant Street, East Norwalk, Connecticut 06855.

85 86 87 88 89 90 / 10 9 8 7 6 5 4 3 2 1

Prentice-Hall International, Inc., London
Prentice-Hall of Australia, Pty. Ltd., Sydney
Prentice-Hall Canada, Inc.
Prentice-Hall of India Private Limited, New Delhi
Prentice-Hall of Japan, Inc., Tokyo
Prentice-Hall of Southeast Asia (Pte.) Ltd., Singapore
Whitehall Books Ltd., Wellington, New Zealand
Editora Prentice-Hall do Brasil Ltda., Rio de Janeiro

Library of Congress Cataloging in Publication Data

Bandman, Elsie, L.
Nursing ethics in the life span.

Includes index.
1. Nursing ethics. I. Bandman, Bertram. II. Title
[DNLM: 1. Ethics, Nursing. WY 85 B214n]
RT85.B33 1985 174'.2 84-3029
ISBN 0-8385-7026-7

Design: Jean M. Sabato

PRINTED IN THE UNITED STATES OF AMERICA

To some significant people
in our lives

Lea Le Clair Lucier
Nancy Bandman
Gunter Magnus
Alice Gregoire
Malvina Kremer
Edwin S. Robbins
Edith Schick
Catherine P. Murphy

Contents

PART TWO: Ethical Decision Making in Nursing

PART THREE: Nursing Ethics Through the Life Span

Preface

This book is about the moral problems of everyday nursing practice. These problems occur throughout the life span of clients. Emphasis is on the nurse's role in moral reasoning and evaluation of these problems, leading to effective and justified decision making.

As clinicians, managers, patient advocates, counselors, and teachers in health care delivery systems, nurses are key figures in developing a moral climate for health consumers and providers alike. This book provides a developmental framework for the application of relevant ethical principles. This framework consists of models of nurse-patient-physician relationship, and of guidelines to decision making and critical reasoning as the foundation of nursing practice. Ethical frameworks and decision making guidelines are essential to the nurse practitioner who cares for clients receiving complex technology, radical surgery, and potent drugs.

Among important values affecting clients and nurses are their rights. Human rights are not artifacts to be left in the reception rooms of clinics and hospitals. Everyday problems show that rights are morally significant to health care participants. Rights in health care are individual passports, permits and licenses to acceptable health care standards which promote maximal self-determination and well-being. To paraphrase John Rawls, as truth is to the realm of facts and descriptions, so rights based on justice are to social institutions. Human ideas and institutions without truth and rights are empty. Applying rights to nursing practice, persons are regarded as centers of self-determination and well-being. Concepts of universality, justice, utility, and altruism, complement rights at the core of client-nurse-physician relationships.

Selection of one principle over another for a given case is less a matter of preference than of careful weighing of relevant diagnostic, prognostic, and treatment data in the context of the client's goals, values and rational life plans. These considerations merge into the more general concern for the client's well being expressed in shared decision making. This work applies nursing strategies, guidelines, and canons of critical reasoning to the making of ethically justifiable decisions. Due regard is given moral assumptions, inductive and deductive inferences, and exposure of fallacies in argument as keys to sound and justifiable conclusions.

The organization of this book is intended to serve a variety of institutional purposes. First, the book can serve as the basis for a complete course on nursing ethics. Each chapter can be used for one, two, or three classes a week dealing with the topic, themes, and cases of the chapter. The book will cover a whole semester, giving the student a deepening understanding of the moral problems relevant to each developmental epoch of the life span. The role of the nurse is extensively developed.

A second use of the book is as a companion text in the core nursing courses of the integrated curriculum. However the curriculum is formulated, whether from a human-development, adaptation, crisis, systems, research, or health-deviations perspective, this text is useful for developing the ethical aspects of nursing care throughout the life span. Thus, the book can be used profitably throughout the entire curriculum over several years.

A third use of this book is in courses that examine the foundations and trends in nursing from a broad social and historical view. Knowledge of the ethics of nursing fulfills the essential criterion of a professional as one practicing within the framework of an ethical code based on moral principles. This book aims to provide a beacon for future development of the role of the nurse as patient advocate in health care policy formulation.

The fourth use of this book is to provide practitioners with essential knowledge relevant to the ethical problems that arise in everyday practice. Actual cases are presented with discussion aimed at showing the relevance of ethical principles to nursing practice. The roles of nurses are developed in relation to each developmental epoch in the life span.

The book is organized into three major divisions and may be used in any sequence. Part One discusses the moral significance and foundations of nurse-client-physician relationships. Nursing models, roles and professional codes are analyzed and evaluated. Part Two focuses on models of morality, values and priorities, and critical reasoning as worthy guidelines to effective decision making. Resulting principles and guidelines in nursing ethics are then put to work in the third and largest part of the book, the application of nursing ethics throughout the life span. The third part begins with the procreative family and progresses through the life span. Systematic moral-philosophical consideration is given to nursing problems in the procreative family, abortion, infancy, childhood, adolescence, adulthood, the aging and the dying.

Each chapter presents actual cases which are typical of those encountered in each developmental stage. Analysis of the ethical issues and problems is designed to help connect the underlying ethical principles with nursing practice as a basis for problem resolution. These features point to an enriched role for the place of reason in nursing ethics.

In Part One, Chapter 1, the moral foundations and significance of nursing as a humanistic profession are explored. Chapter 2 examines and analyzes models of patient, nurse, and physician relationships. Chapter 3 evaluates the ethical codes of nursing and medicine. Part Two, Chapter 4, can be used first, since it presents an orientation to the dominant ethical principles and values relevant to health care. This is followed by two chapters on decision making. Chapter 5 deals with nursing strategies and guidelines, and Chapter 6 with critical reasoning. Both chapters bear directly on facilitating shared decisions of the client with the interdisciplinary health care team. Part Three can be used first for provoking student thinking about specific ethical problems relevant to particular developmental epochs from infancy to death. This can be interspersed with examination of Chapter 4, "Models of Morality in Everyday Nursing Practice," and with the chapters on ethical decision making, followed by chapters in Part One. We are suggesting that at most points, the book moves freely from the general to the particular and vice versa. This maximizes its flexibility for use.

In closing, we wish to express our appreciation to Richard Lampert, editor-in-chief, for his interest and helpfulness throughout the development of this work and to Marion Kalstein, Kathleen Kelly, and Kevin McKenna for its successful completion. Moreover, we appreciate the works and encouragement of colleagues and friends in nursing ethics, most notably Catherine P. Murphy, Philip Pecorino, Arthur Caplan, Anne J. Davis, Mila A. Aroskar, Leah Curtin, Josephine M. Flaherty, James F. Childress, Myra Levine, James L. Muyskens, Andrew Jameton, Rick Moody, Sally Gadow, Stewart Spicker, and Sister Marie Celeste Allen.

New York City

Elsie L. Bandman
Bertram Bandman

PART ONE

Moral Foundations of Nurse-Patient–Physician Relationships

CHAPTER 1

The Moral Significance of Nursing

Through study of this chapter, the student is enabled to:

1. Give reasons for the importance of moral education for nurses
2. Justify the participation of nurses in moral decisions affecting individuals, groups, families, and health care delivery
3. Understand definitions of nursing as premises for reasoned arguments and choice in nursing ethics

INTRODUCTION

The art and science of nursing is a proud chapter in the history of humankind. Primary commitment to the health and well-being of the client and family is a characteristic of nursing. Nurses respond to the health needs of people in an evolving scientific and technological society.

The persistent thread that runs throughout nursing history is the continuity of care and nurture of human beings regardless of status or diagnosis.[1] In return, society recognizes the profession's authority and expects members of the profession to act responsibly. Self-regulation is a characteristic of an accountable, therefore mature, profession.[2] The nurse's interaction with the patient is guided by moral principles of "respect for human dignity and the uniqueness of the client."[3] The nurse seeks to meet the patient's health needs with concerns for the client's safety and best interests uppermost. The nurse's diagnosis of the patient's health needs is based on assessment processes of physical, psychological, and social responses of the client as well as perception of the individual as a whole human being who values life.

WHY NURSING ETHICS?

Through advances in medical technology, the opportunities for intervening in patient destiny by restoring heartbeat, respiration, kidneys, hearts themselves, and possibly optimum genetic composition are many. The future promises even more ways of controlling vital functions and altering body parts. Nurses are part of these interventions. At the primary level of prevention and care, patients and families look to "their" nurses for information, advice, and support when facing difficult decisions of this nature. At the secondary level of curative care, nurses are actively involved in monitoring and sustaining treatment modalities such as life-support systems. At a societal level, nurses are or expected to be actively involved in policy formulation within the health organization, in professional societies, and in legislative bodies.

Thus, nursing is part of the health care delivery system. More than in any other discipline, the practitioner of nursing is in continuous contact with the patient and the family. This position offers unique privileges and responsibilities. Nurses are privy to the patient's most intimate fears, hopes, and regrets. The family's relationship to the patient becomes vividly clear as the illness strips interactions of veneer and superficiality. The depth of the family's care or lack of concern and respect for the patient is revealed as illness progresses. By word and deed, the nurse manifests to the family a sense of caring and of fundamental human dignity. Thereby, the nurse contributes to a positive change in the immediate family relations with the patient and with other members of the interdisciplinary health team.

Nurses strive to meet universal human needs for care in illness and for the prevention of disease. Nurses seek to conserve that which is of value to every individual—the optimum functioning of all body systems and of the whole as an integrated unit. Above all, nursing is a human health service that has the quality of mercy and the potential for ennobling both the provider and the recipient. Nursing's practice "is concerned with humans and is humanizing."[4] A central concern of this practice is to enhance the personhood and the humanity of all involved in care.[5]

Indeed, we identify the nursing of the well and the sick with doing good. But why is nursing good? It is good because there is not an act of nursing that does not aim at what we identify as the good in commonsense terms. For example, when we say "Nurse Smith is giving nursing care to Mr. Jones," we mean that Nurse Smith is doing good by providing whatever nursing assistance is of value to Mr. Jones in gaining health. In fact, we identify nursing with the good so naturally that it becomes both a contradiction and morally reprehensible to say, "Nurse Smith aims to harm Mr. Jones." If, then, nurses' intent is to do good, why do we need nursing ethics? Is good intent not enough?

Good intent is not enough, since knowledge or ignorance of alternatives is a cause of good or harm. Reasons for choosing one alternative over another, or refusing treatment altogether, need to be critically examined in relation to other possibilities. Moreover, nurses wish not to impose their treatment choices on other persons whose autonomy is to be supported. The nurse's beliefs concerning the good life may differ from those of the patient. It is precisely this difference that needs to be acknowledged and respected as a mark of personhood and separateness. Knowledge, therefore, of the ethical views that support reasons for one choice over another are indispensable to the nurse in daily practice and in everyday life. Thus, the function of nursing ethics is to guide the activity of nursing on behalf of the good.

THE IMPORTANCE OF CLARIFYING AND JUSTIFYING VALUES

Nurses have special opportunities to educate persons and families on health matters of vital importance. A decision represents a choice among alternatives. The particular choice represents a selection among competing values. The nurse's participation is influenced by the nurse's own values and depends on the elements in the situation to which the nurse is responding. The nurse's values are related to the nurse's experiences of family life, school, peer relations, religion, economics, and culture. Values are guides to behavior.

Values have been said to have definable characteristics. These are the qualities of:

1. Free choice without coercion
2. Choice among alternatives
3. Choice with knowledge of the consequences
4. Choice on the basis of merit
5. Choice that is publicly affirmed
6. Choice upon which action is based
7. Choice that is repeated[6]

Although values contribute to the development of goals, attitudes, and feelings, they are often not selected on the basis of free choice, but rather grow out of experience that is particularly intense and meaningful. Religion, schools, friends, and eating, sleeping, and activity patterns were thrust upon us as children. Consequently, all humans are subject to influence by past experience of which the individual has little knowledge or memory. Therefore, choice is sometimes less than free and is too often heavily determined by forgotten early experience.

Moreover, choice among alternatives is only possible if alternatives are present, feasible, known, and understood. Nurses play a significant role in presenting alternatives to the client and family. Nurses are helpful to the extent that they are open to and have knowledge of the full range of options. Otherwise, choice is an illusion.

Obviously, the personal dimension of values is paramount. Therein lie the limitations of values as guides to choice and to action. It is good for individuals to know the nature and extent of their personal values, even if unaware of their source. Unexamined values alone are insufficient as grounds for ethical choice for both patient and nurse.

Beliefs concerning what is the good are so important in their effect on human life as to warrant critical examination. This is the function of the particular branch of philosophy called *ethics*: It deals with the good and the "ought" component of human thought and behavior.

WHAT IS ETHICS? WHAT IS NURSING ETHICS?

A preliminary but useful definition of ethics is that it is concerned with doing good and avoiding harm. Nursing affects people. Nursing has the power to do good or harm. Nurses also have an impact on larger groups of people and on the formulation of health policy affecting the whole of society.

Possibilities of good or harm depend partly on knowledge and partly on values. Both must be consciously and critically evaluated for their potential of good or harm to human beings, well or sick.

There are many opportunities to do good or harm to the patient. An example of good is to educate the patient to continue taking medication and to follow the prescribed diet. An example of harm is to avoid and thus deny the nursing needs of a difficult patient or one who does not conform to the nurse's values. Another example is to withhold information and counseling needed by the patient to make a decision with which the nurse may not agree.

WHAT IS GOOD OR HARM?

The question arises: What is good and what is harmful? Good for whom? Harmful to whom?

Sometimes it is not possible to do good to someone without also avoiding harm to that person. This has the earmarks of a dilemma, defined as a problem none of whose solutions is satisfactory. For example, a 38-year-old primipara has an amniocentesis that reveals the fetus as having Down's syndrome. The woman wants very much to give birth. Whereas "good" and "harm" are not always so easily defined, we can find a clue to the good in the example of what the pregnant woman wants, namely, to give birth. The dilemma involves her thwarted will: she cannot give birth to a normal child from this pregnancy. In her thwarted will, we find a clue also to the meaning of the harmful and bad. The mother considers the destruction of the fetus as a harmful act that destroys a life. The woman's husband rejects the possibility of a retarded child and feels the marriage will be destroyed as a consequence. This example gives us still another insight into the problem of defining good and bad.

HEALTH AS A GOAL OF THE GOOD LIFE

The practice of nursing is concerned with doing good. One of the goods and one of the highest values of nursing is its concern with the goal of the good life. Health is conducive to and is part of the good life. On this, Aristotle seems to have had a far better argument than Kant, who held that even good health may inspire pride and thus detract from a person's "good will," which, he argued, is the only unconditional good.[7] Aristotle had argued that health is a necessary condition of a completely happy life.

WHAT IS THE GOOD LIFE?

The good life is a lot of things—activities, processes, and goals pursued and achieved, obstacles removed, all without harm to anyone. We have seen that one of the necessary conditions of a good life is health. A means to health is achieved through nursing. But what is nursing?

WHAT IS NURSING?

Virginia Henderson was among the first of 20th-century scholars to seek a definition of nursing as

> . . . primarily assisting the individual (sick or well) in the performance of those activities contributing to health or its recovery (or to a peaceful death) that he would perform unaided if he had the necessary strength, will, or knowledge. It is likewise the unique contribution of nursing to help the individual to be independent of such assistance as soon as possible.[8]

To Henderson, nursing is essentially intervention on behalf of a disabled, dependent, and unhealthy person. Nursing is designed to compensate for a deficit on the basis of appropriate scientific and medical warrant for the treatment given. Unhappily, this definition seems too broad to distinguish nursing from other health professions, such as medicine or physical therapy.

The difficulty with a definition that is too broad reminds us of the attempt by early Greek philosophers to define humans. One proposed definition was that a human was a featherless biped. The philosopher Diogenes thereupon plucked the feathers from a chicken and threw it over the walls of the Academy, refuting that definition.[9] Whereas it is said that in ethics there are no final or absolute answers, there are refutations such as Diogenes's.

Recent Definitions

A review of definitions shows that the concept of nursing is changing. However, questions of authority among nursing, medicine, and science still need to be worked out. We may look to nursing definitions, then, as attempts to draw lines between nursing and allied health fields.

A more recent departure from the medical model as a source of authority is the independent nurse practitioner movement, which identifies nursing as independent community health practice with selected target populations such as the aged.

Another nursing movement that attempts independence from the medical model is identified with the wellness model. Thus, Martha Rogers in 1970 writes that

> nursing aims to assist people in achieving their maximum health potential. Maintenance and promotion of health, prevention of disease, nursing diagnosis, intervention and rehabilitation encompass the scope of nursing's goals.[10]

This definition of nursing attempts to identify nursing as treating the whole person on a continuing basis with the goal of restoring health and defines medicine as treating disease processes.

Another recent definition of nursing is:

> The diagnosis and treatment of human responses to actual or potential health problems.[11]

Marjory Gordon states that "nursing diagnoses or clinical diagnoses made by professional nurses describe actual or potential health problems that nurses, by virtue of their education and experience, are capable and licensed to treat."[12]

The concept of nursing diagnosis—despite some misleading and circular features of the definition, in addition to its being excessively broad—opens the possibility of a distinct nursing function and presents an important defining condition of nursing, namely, that nursing as well as medicine makes diagnostic judgments. Needed still is a further differentiation between medical and nursing diagnosis.

WHAT IS THE RELATION OF NURSING TO OTHER HEALTH PROFESSIONS?

The definition of nursing as diagnosing human responses does not clearly differentiate nursing from medicine and other health fields, for physicians and others could claim that they too diagnose and treat human responses. The questions that nursing definitions have not answered, then, are:

1. What is the relation among nursing, medicine, other health professionals, and patients?
2. How are the rules that identify the nurse's role similar to and also different from the rules that mark the roles of other health professionals and patients?

The issue remains whether nursing is relatively independent of medicine and/or of science, whether nursing may even be identified as a form of healing, or whether nursing is defined as working "under qualified instruction and direction." Nursing texts aim to specify the functions of nursing that mediate between the narrow and classical and the broader concepts of nursing.

Clearly, definitions do not authoritatively settle disputes. One person's definition of nursing may be another's antithesis. But the definitions reflect attempts to stake out the turf that belongs to an autonomous, yet interdependent, and dynamically changing field of nursing.

If a definition of nursing is acceptable to all nursing viewpoints formed, it is possible that it will be a synthesis of the old and the varying contemporary conceptions of nursing. A definition of nursing needs to answer the question as to how nursing is related to medicine, science, and other health fields and, most importantly, how it specifically serves the health needs of people.

CONCLUSION

Throughout the historical evolution of nursing, health has been regarded as a primary value, with nurses playing a central role in helping individuals, families, groups, and society to achieve maximum health potential. Nurses accord high value to the concept of total well-being. Nursing care presupposes the value of health as essential to a conception of the good life. However nursing is defined, the central question of nursing ethics remains. "How ought I to do good and avoid harm to my clients?" A further question is: "How shall I best work with physicians and other health professionals to implement nursing goals, such as restoring health?"

REFERENCES

1. American Nurses' Association: Nursing: A Social Policy. Kansas City, Mo., The Association, 1980, p. 9.
2. Ibid., p. 7.
3. American Nurses' Association: Code for Nurses with Interpretive Statements. Kansas City, Mo., The Association, 1976, p. 4.
4. Patridge K. B.: Nursing values in a changing society. Nursing Outlook 26(6): 356, 1978.
5. Ibid.
6. Raths L. E., Harmon M., Simon S. B.: Values and Teaching: Working with Values in the Classroom. Columbus, Ohio, Merrill, 1966, p. 28-29.
7. Fundamental Principles of the Metaphysics of Morals, Abbott T. K., Fox M., (trans). Indianapolis, Bobbs-Merrill, 1949, p. 11.
8. Harmer B., Henderson V.: Textbook of the Principles and Practices of Nursing. New York, Macmillan, 1955, p. 4.
9. Copi I.: Introduction to Logic, 5th ed. New York, Macmillan, 1978, p. 156.
10. Rogers M.: An Introduction to the Theoretical Basis of Nursing. Philadelphia, Davis, 1970, p. 86.
11. American Nurses' Association: Nursing: A Social Policy. Kansas City, Mo., p. 9.
12. Gordon M.: Nursing diagnosis and the diagnostic process. Nursing 76, (8):1299, 1976.

CHAPTER 2

Models of the Nurse-Patient-Physician Relationship

Through study of this chapter, the student is enabled to:

1. Evaluate models of physician-patient relationships for their relevance to nursing practice
2. Analyze Peplau's interpersonal, therapeutic model of the nurse-patient relationship
3. Utilize the interpersonal model of the nurse-patient relationship as the basis for implementing the nurse's role as patient advocate
4. Justify the role of the nurse as patient advocate

INTRODUCTION

Models are idealized patterns, greatly simplified, for looking at complex events in terms of their essential qualities. A model is an abstract representation of a significant portion of reality. Models essentialize the most general aspects of a given phenomenon. They have been called "candidates for reality,"[1] conjectures of what reality is like. A model is an abstract representation of reality, and is not necessarily pictorial or visual.[2] A model both simplifies and highlights "important features of the subject."[3]

Models oriented by values show different perceptions for understanding the health care process. The use of models refutes the conception that health care is value free and helps to identify clashes of values as they occur in practice between health professionals.

MODELS OF PATIENT-PHYSICIAN-NURSE RELATIONSHIP

Szasz and Hollander

Three models are defined by Szasz and Hollander, as the basis of the physician-patient relationship with recognition that these models of interaction are present in all human relationships.[4]

Activity-Passivity Model. The model of activity-passivity is that mode of interaction in which the physician is active and the patient is passive. This is an entirely appropriate orientation for infants, comatose and anesthesized patients, and patients in situations of emergency. It places the physician in absolute control, supports feelings of physician power, and minimizes identity with the person of the patient.[5] It is authoritarian and paternalistic.

Guidance-Cooperation Model. The guidance-cooperation model is the basis for most medical practice. It consists of a patient with symptoms seeking help from a physician who possesses knowledge relevant to the patient's needs. The physician offers guidance in the form of treatment. In return, the patient is expected to cooperate by obeying the orders received. The presupposition in this model is that the physician knows what is best for the patient, holds the patient's interests foremost, and is free from other priorities. The patient must be equally convinced of these aims.[6] This model is still paternalistic, although to a lesser degree.

Mutual-Participation Model. The third model is one of mutual participation, based on the premise that equality among human beings is of high value.[7] It is the central assumption of the democratic process as well. This kind of interaction presupposes that the participants have nearly equal power, that they need each other, and that the shared activity will be satisfying to both.[8]

This model is characteristic of concepts of self-help considered important in current health care practice. It also recognizes the patient's experience as an important factor in self-care, especially in chronic illness. The role of the physician in this model becomes one of helping patients to help themselves.[9] It is an interdependent, therefore more complex way of relating on the part of all participants. Szasz and Hollander view this model as both necessary and more appropriate for educated and intellectual patients similar to the physician. They see this model as "essentially foreign to medicine"[10] and point out that, as a principle, with improvement of the patient's health status, the physician-patient relationship should change. It is at this point that psychological needs for domination are likely to interfere with the patient's self-determination. The authors view the physician-patient relationship as being like the changing relationship of the parent to the growing child. As the offspring grows in responsibility and maturity, the parent-child relationship becomes increasingly egalitarian.

From a nursing perspective, the mutual-participation model is essential to the self-determination and autonomy of the patient as endorsed by the American Nurses' Association.[11] This model presupposes that human beings have the capacity for growth and change. Nursing that is based on respect for individual differences recognizes and supports the possibility of choice and self-direction as a value of high priority.[12]

Robert Veatch

Within Veatch's four models of physician-patient interaction are the possibilities for either facilitating or inhibiting an ethical relationship.[13]

The Engineering Model. In his engineering model, Veatch denies any possibility of value-free "pure" science or medicine. Choices are made continually among facts, observations, research designs, and statistical levels of significance within a frame of values by supposedly "pure" scientists. An even larger number of choices of value and significance must be made by persons in an applied field such as medicine in which, unlike engineering and plumbing, values cannot be eliminated in favor of technical advice to a human being.

The Priestly Model. In Veatch's priestly model the physician assumes the posture of a moral expert who presumes to tell the patient what he or she ought to do in the specific situation. This tradition is based on the ethical principle of "Do no harm." It is expressed in the paternalistic practice of withholding bad news from the patient and giving unrealistic reassurance. It takes away the decision from the patient, and gives freedom to the physician instead. It does not permit competent persons to refuse blood transfusions on the basis of religious beliefs, for example. Paternalism lessens the patient's dignity by reducing his or her control over body and life. Truth-telling and promise-keeping become arbitrary individual decisions on the basis of "Do no harm." Deception is similarly rationalized.[14]

The Collegial Model. In Veatch's collegial model, the physician and patient are "colleagues pursuing the common goal of eliminating the illness and preserving the health of the patient."[15] Trust and confidence are central. There is equality. Realistically, however, Veatch contends that there is no basis for equality in the physician-patient relationship since social class, economic status, and educational and value differences make the assumption of common interests an illusion.[16]

The Contractual Model. In the contractual model, Veatch defines the participants as interacting with expectations of obligations and benefits for each. Commitment to moral principles is essential. Moreover, the contract recognizes the patient's ultimate control of his or her own destiny. Therefore, there is a "sharing of ethical authority and responsibility" without the moral abdication of either physician or patient.[17]

Veatch sees the advantages of the contractual model as avoiding the moral abdication of the physician in the engineering model and the patient's moral abdication in the priestly model. Nor does the contractual model contain the false equality of the collegial model. The contractual model provides the patient with freedom of choice and control over significant options, with the physician free to decide the details within that reference frame. Furthermore, this model allows either participant to withdraw from the contract if necessary to retain personal moral integrity.[18]

Edmund D. Pelligrino

This physician says that the traditional, sacred relationship between physician and patient is changing and will be transformed within the next few years. The old simple one-to-one relationship is subject to the impact of increasing technology in medicine, the increasing sophistication of the public in health matters, the movement of medicine into institutions, and the insistence on democracy. The public is demanding more medical information, greater medical competence and accountability, and much more regulation.[19]

Emerging demands for patients' rights call for the concept of "valid" consent as a moral basis for decisions. The patient wants to know what is being done, why it is being done, the alternatives, and what the future holds for him or her. Each individual wants the utmost protection of rights to self-determination. This task may be an easy one in specific cases, but extremely difficult with an indefinite diagnosis or general treatments with uncertain outcomes and undesirable side effects. The patient has the right to know this. This enables the physician to function as a technical expert and adviser in working with the patient toward forming a decision and looking at its consequences.

With the expansion in numbers and kinds of health professionals and the movement of medical practice into hospitals, groups, teams, and organizations have formed. Thus, comprehensive medicine is now delivered by a broad spectrum of services in which the patient is shared. The team itself changes in response to the needs of the patient. This changes the position of the physician from the sole authority figure to a member of a group in which negotiation, analysis, and compromise processes are important. If, for example, the physician has no time for more than a diagnosis and a standard explanation, Pelligrino says that "the first rule of humanness [is] to see that other members of the health care team are permitted to answer the personal questions that lie at the root of the patient's plea for help."[20] Secondly, if a physician wishes to help an individual, there must be an acceptance of the human being as he or she is. Pelligrino's third point is that the physician's authority must be handled in a humane way without extension into the patient's belief and value system. The wise physician admits to not knowing all the answers. Lastly, institutionalization of care should work to the benefit of the patient, with more protection of patient's rights, professional accountability, and a physician-patient relationship between trusting adults in which ethical issues may be resolved.

A MODEL OF NURSE-PATIENT RELATIONSHIPS

Hildegard E. Peplau defined nursing as first a process, one that is both therapeutic and interpersonal. The process is goal-directed and occurs in steps, operations, and interactions between individuals in need of health services and the nurse.[21] Nursing is both an educative and a maturing force for helping individuals, groups, and communities to change in the direction of improved health. This happens on the basis of mutual respect, and "as persons who are alike, and yet, different . . . share in the solution of problems."[22]

Peplau sees the nurse-patient relationship on a continuum beginning with the relationship of stranger, moving through stages of problem and role definition to the achievement of mutual understanding, and ending in collaboration directed toward problem solution.[23] Skill in helping people toward resolution of problems while using old skills and developing new ones is a major criterion of the worth of nursing and what it can become. Nurses, along with other health professionals, facilitate "forward movement of personality and other ongoing human processes in the direction of creative, constructive, productive personal and community living."[24]

Peplau's fundamental view of the nurse-patient relationship is one that builds upon the worth and dignity of human beings, the development of trust, problem-solving measures, and collaboration. The nurse may function as a resource person who supplies information relevant to the patient's problem, as Pelligrino suggested. The nurse may also function in a counseling relationship, while the patient reviews feelings and events connected with illness. He or she may function as a surrogate parent, sibling, or significant other, permitting the patient to explore and examine feelings associated with these relationships. Finally, the nurse may function as an expert who understands the technical matters associated with the patient's illness. Thus, the relationship between nurse and patient is interpersonal, therapeutic, and authoritative to the extent of the nurse's knowledge on technical matters related to the illness. The process is educative and egalitarian, avoiding the nurse's imposition of his or her values on the patient. The aim is for patients to experience their illness as a way of reorienting feelings and strengthening the personality in positive ways.[25]

Nurses help to reduce the threat of illness to individuals by accepting people as they are and helping them through stress. Together, patient and nurse move through stages of patient dependence, independence, and into the stage of interdependence when both are engaged cooperatively in problem-related tasks. At this point, the patient may utilize available services fully in the service of problem resolution and of moving on to new goals and to new relationships.

Peplau's view of the nurse-patient relationship is one akin to a partnership of individuals willing to engage in collaborative relationships of trust and problem solving.

Peplau defines roles in nursing as emerging from demands on nurses made by patients, by the profession itself, and by society. She identifies nurses' roles as those of stranger, resource person, teacher, leader, surrogate, and counselor. She defines the role of stranger as occupied by a person who accords positive interest, courtesy, and respect to the other as the other is at that time. The nurse must establish the patient relationship as a helping one. As a resource person, the nurse functions as a source of knowledge on health matters related to the patient's needs. The role of teacher combines all the other roles in the service of patient learning and growth. The role of leader can be exercised in the clinical situation as well as at the local, national, and international level. Peplau raises the issue of democratic nursing practice as one in which the patient becomes an active participant in developing the nursing care plan.[26] The nurse as leader does not dictate patient goals or require that the patient give up independence and submit to the domination of the nurse. Basic feelings of respect for the worth of each individual are necessary for a democratic relationship to be operative.

The surrogate role of the nurse is one in which the patient views the nurse as a person from the past—a parent, a sibling, a significant other.[27] The therapeutic task for the nurse becomes one of helping the patient identify and clarify similarities between the past and the present situation—the nurse as a person from the past and as him- or herself in the present. Peplau sees the relationship as moving on a continuum from mother authority and child dependence to that of fully interdependent adults, depending on how ill the patient may be.[28] The nursing goal is to increase patient awareness of the experience of old feelings without imposing goals of the nurse that force the patient to function at a fully adult level at all times.

Similarly, the physician's and the nurse's relationship with the patient is affected by the presence or absence of mutual respect, trust, the sharing of authority, and freedom from surrogate miscasting—a physician misperceived as a father or husband figure and a nurse misperceived as wife or mother.

The role of counselor is intertwined with all other roles. In the clinical situation, Peplau defines counseling as "the way in which nurses respond to demands made upon them, rather than to what those demands are."[29] The process includes examining experiences, feelings, and problems associated with health. The aim is to help patients understand the current situation of health in relation to other experiences of life. Intrusive and other anxiety-provoking health care measures require nursing assistance to the affected individual in identifying, exploring, and accepting associated feelings. Thus, the meaning of the event will be clearly related to goals of health. The emphasis is solely on helping the individual to understand and to deal more effectively with concerns of health.

This model of the nurse-patient relationship may, more than any other nursing model, contain the foundation for a democratic, egalitarian relationship of mutual trust and respect between nurse, patient, and physician compatible with the model of nurse as patient advocate. Peplau's model is also compatible with Veatch's contractual model. Peplau insists on the full participation of the patient, with the selection of goals and problem definition solidly in the patient's control. The nurse facilitates, strengthens, and educates the patient's processes of defining the problem, along with analysis, implementation, resolution, and evaluation of the process and goals. Choices and values supported are those of the patient, with the nurse utilizing Peplau's various roles to enhance the patient's sense of worth and autonomy. The composite of the roles as Peplau defines them is the basis for a nursing role as patient advocate.

THE NURSE AS SURROGATE

The role of a nurse as surrogate is central to Peplau's analysis of the nurse-patient relationship. A nurse may be a surrogate for a wife, a mother, a daughter, a physician, a priest, an educator, a police person, a friend, or all of these at different times. In these roles, a nurse is placed in a position of trust and is identified as a person who protects the client's (patient's) most fundamental interests and rights, especially while the client is helpless.

In protecting the client's interests and rights, the nurse as surrogate is an agent of reality for the patient, mediating between the patient's interests and the outside world from which the patient has been temporarily separated. In the nurse's multiple surrogate roles as parent, spouse, physician, offspring, helper, and friend, the nurse occupies a position of trust with the patient.

The nurse carries out the role of securing the patient's interests, sometimes as the eyes and ears, arms and legs of the patient. The nurse sometimes even singlehandedly embodies the role of caretaker, protector, and advocate, especially since there are occasions when no one else is in a position to fight as hard to help the patient to win the final battle of life over death. In these multiple surrogate roles, the nurse also becomes a therapist and source of personality strength during the patient's health crisis. The nurse identifies himself or herself as the human equal of the patient, as a person with fellow feelings rather than as one who imposes values and preferences paternalistically upon the patient. The surrogate never loses touch with respect for the patient's autonomy as an individual on an open, democratic, and pluralistic basis.

The surrogate role enables the nurse to compensate for a deficit in a patient's functioning as an intact and well person—for example, administering fluids to a dehydrated patient, injecting medications the client is unable to take by mouth, and changing surgical dressings on fresh incisions. These are activities the patient would normally do. These surrogate functions are vital while a patient is helpless.

The patient's deficits, however, are not only physical. They are also psychologic and interpersonal. A patient absent from family and work responsibilities suffers loss of self-esteem. The nurse's role consists in compensating for this deficit in self-esteem. The nurse can help to give meaning to a patient's loss through sickness by showing understanding and providing continuity of contact with the human community. The nurse thus mirrors, reflects, and represents the best of society from which the patient is absent. This surrogate role extends to a continuation of the patient's normal life to the extent possible. The nurse performs this surrogate role by showing care and understanding for the patient as an individual person rather than as an anonymous object.

The nurse helps form a continuing, uninterrupted two-person relation—in Martin Buber's terms, an "I-Thou" relation,[30] where both nurse and patient show equal respect for each other.

THE NURSE IN OTHER ROLES LEADING TO ADVOCACY

The nurse also helps the client to exercise patients' rights through other roles. The nurse as a resource person and health educator provides both relevant information and the help needed, either in person or in conjunction with others, for analysis and resolution of a health problem or moral issue. The nurse's expertise in technical matters associated with health is the source of that assistance to client and colleagues. As a counselor, the nurse supports the patient in the exploration of feelings, the analysis of the problem, and clarification of choices. As leader, the nurse represents the expressed desires of the patient regarding the treatment plan to other team members so as to facilitate the process of autonomy. The aim is to help the patient use all services fully in his or her own behalf. Additionally, the nurse represents the human community that has been largely interrupted by the patient's inability and helplessness.

Distinctive in Peplau's treatment, however, is that the nurse as health resource person, counselor, and leader is not paternalistic in an authoritarian sense—does not deny that the patient has rights. The patient is the reason for the nursing and health care being applied, and the patient's rights are the source and justification of the nurse's multiple roles.

THE NURSE AS ADVOCATE

The nurse who understands these multiple roles promotes, protects, and thereby advocates patients' interests and rights in an effort to make them whole and well again. Where that is not possible, the nurse makes patients as comfortable and free of pain and suffering as possible. In any event, the nurse recognizes that his or her first duty is to protect and care for the patient's health and safety. In safeguarding the patient, the nurse supports and thereby advocates the patient's interests in the restoration of the patient's health and well-being.

The role of patient advocate presupposes that, as Minnie Goodnow held at the turn of the century, "the patient comes first,"[31] that the patient defines what nursing is about, that the patient has rights, and that patients' rights depend on significant others who will protect and care for their rights when they themselves are unable to do so.

The nurse's role of patient advocate is, accordingly, the composite of a variety of nursing roles. These include the nurse as surrogate mother, surrogate physician, clinician, health educator, counselor, protector, health resource person, expert technician, leader, and friend. The nurse as patient advocate is thus the touchstone highlighting and guiding all other nursing functions.

THE IMPORTANCE OF ADVOCACY

Why is advocacy so important? Because without the advocacy and effective protection of rights, there are no rights. Rights depend on backup rights, the rights to be effectively protected in claiming one's rights. There are, we contend, no rights without the kinds of backup rights effectively protected by advocates and by a society that recognizes the role of advocates in providing relief and remedies against wrongdoing. For the role of advocates is to safeguard clients against abuse and violation of their rights.

Two arguments have been put forth against the view that to have rights entails advocacy and protection of those rights. One argument is that propounded by supporters of "natural law," who contend that to have a right is to have a right regardless of particular social circumstances in which such rights may not be honored, owing perhaps to a corrupt form of social order. In other words, persons still have their rights; only the rights are violated. Thus, slaves in ancient Greece had the right to be free, even though they were unjustly deprived of those rights. Similarly, Jews incarcerated and incinerated in Nazi gas chambers in World War II horror camps, on the natural-law view, never lost their rights to be free and the right to live. Their rights were violated. So also with a young woman who is raped. Her rights are violated, but not lost.

A second argument against the need for advocacy is one propounded by J. S. Mill. It is that "the rights and interests of every or any person are only secure from being disregarded when the person interested is himself able and habitually disposed to stand up for them."[32] On this view, we lose the rights we cannot effectively claim by ourselves. We must be our own best guardians of the rights we hold. If we do not safeguard our own rights, it is our own fault if we lose them.

ADVOCACY AS THE PROTECTION OF RIGHTS

Rights are only as strong as the ability, willingness, and resourcefulness of the people of a society jointly to protect and care for all the rights of its members. Mill's argument, while in part true (since each individual cares more for his or her rights and interests than anyone else), is partly false. The rights of anyone or of all depend on the willingness and ability of other relevant persons to bear correlative responsibilities implied by those rights. No one can protect his or her rights alone, unaided by others. This is especially true of sick and frightened patients unsure of what is happening to them and of the source of help. There are therefore no rights without advocacy of those rights by others. This applies to patients' rights as well as any others. Clearly, the nurse is in a position to advocate the patient's rights and interests.

The reasons there are no rights without advocacy, then, are that right-holders may not always be in a position to defend their rights, whereas other persons may be in such a position. Secondly, there are no rights without claims effectively made on behalf of such rights, claims sometimes made by other persons on behalf of rightholders. The right to claim is not necessarily vested in a rightholder alone. Others can and have made claims on behalf of those whose rights have been ignored or violated.

A slave, infant, or patient has rights, even if he or she cannot claim them effectively, because even though these persons are helpless to claim such rights, other people as advocates can represent the interests of a slave, child, or patient. The problem of claiming rights can be surmounted, since suitable and effective representation can and does in fact occur. If a child or patient is helpless, a parent or parent surrogate, sponsor, or advocate can step in to protect him or her. Nurses can also—and do indeed quite frequently—protect patients' rights.

MODELS OF PATIENT ADVOCACY

There seem to be three models of patient advocacy. The first, suggested by Abrams, is on the model of "civil disobedience."[33] On this model, a nurse acknowledges patient advocacy that conflicts with established authority and involves risk taking and consequences for noncompliance.

The civil-disobedience model puts the nurse on the defensive, in the position of having to show a hypothetical or shadowy court of rational authority that his or her action is the right one. The burden is on the nurse to make good this claim against the practices of established authorities. This can be hazardous to job security.

A second, related, model of patient advocacy compares the nurse to a guerrilla fighter, one who fights against the health care system.[34]

The model of nurse as patient advocate who combats established authority suffers from a similar defect to the model of nurse as civil disobedient. Both models place the enemy, opposition, or problem in the wrong place and upon the wrong set of persons. The problem is not that of the nurse. The problem is that the patient's rights are disregarded by an indifferent system in which no one advocates for the client's rights to participate actively in his or her own health care.

Instead of health-professional conflict, there is or ought to be a natural alliance between patient, physician, and nurse against ill health and disease. In this respect, health professionals derive more role guidance and support from the concept of a health team than from either the civil-disobedience or guerrilla model of client advocacy. To advocate for the client's need is to be part of and on the health team, working with others for the health of the patient. However, the nurse requires the mutual respect of other health professionals to be a member of this team, freeing the nurse from behaving like a civil disobedient or guerrilla fighter. A nurse as client advocate and a health team member is part of a third model. He or she has professional "standing." The concept of "standing" employs a term from the law given to those whose views are granted a serious hearing and consideration before a decision-making board or tribunal, without necessarily being accepted. Before such a team, group, committee, board, or tribunal, the most rational view prevails, one that can be verified as providing the best alternative for patient care. This model is one that gives standing to a nurse as a patient advocate. The appropriate use of moral and cognitive authority is preferable to a model of a nurse as a civil disobedient or urban guerrilla.

ARGUMENTS FOR AND AGAINST THE NURSE AS PATIENT ADVOCATE

There are three arguments of varying strength directed against the concept of nurse as client advocate, however. The first is that patient advocacy carries no system of institutional supports. The nurse willing to advocate a patient's rights when it matters most in situations of conflict between nurses and physicians is at risk of losing his or her job. Portraying a nurse as client advocate flies in the face of institutional political and economic realities, it is held.

A second argument is that at least some physicians regard themselves as the basic protectors of their patients' rights and resent intrusion by other health professionals into their contractual prerogatives with their patients.

A third argument, due partly but not wholly to the two foregoing arguments, is that nurses have too many other roles to spend time and resources as client advocates, and that wrongdoing, by whomever committed, is adequately corrected by persons other than nurses, such as lawyers.

Against the first argument—that patient advocacy lacks institutional supports—the nurse's role of advocacy may be interpreted as projecting a future desirable role, as patients' rights are in need of being protected; nurses have a natural alliance with their patients. Consequently, nurses are natural candidates for advocacy roles in patient care.

A rebuttal against the second argument is that physicians are not always responsible and accountable. The health care system of "checks and balances" calls for resources, skills, and abilities aimed at protecting patients' rights that are not always guaranteed or implemented by physicians. Moreover, nurses, who increasingly show evidence of higher education, quite naturally provide a form of effective advocacy in the application of increasingly complex nursing care. Evidence of high-quality nursing judgments in medical centers points to a natural advocacy role for such nurses.

Finally, there is an argument that nurses have too many important technical roles to have the time, skill, and ability to function as advocates. In response, no other group has more continuous contact with patients and families than do nurses. Therefore, nurses often have the most familiarity with patients' and families' ethical choices and are in a good position to protect those interests in serious situations.

CONCLUSION

Nurses, having a natural kinship with values of life and death and the quality of life and health care, show increasing awareness of value questions; the protection of patients' rights is a natural outcome. Patient advocacy is integral with the expanding relationships nurses have in the care of their patients. Models of nurse-patient-physician relations show that patient advocacy by nurses is essential to patients' health care rights.

REFERENCES

1. Hesse M.: Models and analogy in science. In Edwards P. (ed.), The Encyclopedia of Philosophy. New York, Macmillan, 1967, vol. 5, p. 358.
2. Black M.: Models and Metaphors. Ithaca, N.Y., Cornell University Press, 1962, p. 236.
3. Scheffler I.: Reason and Teaching. Indianapolis: Bobbs-Merrill, 1975, p. 68.
4. Szasz T.S., Hollander M.H.: The basic models of the doctor-patient relationship. A.M.A. Arch Int Med 97:585, 1956.
5. Ibid.
6. Ibid.
7. Ibid.
8. Ibid.
9. Ibid.
10. Ibid.
11. American Nurses' Association: Code for Nurses with Interpretive Statements. Kansas City, Mo., p. 4.
12. American Nurses' Association: Nursing: A Social Policy. Kansas City, Mo., 1980, p. 6.
13. Veatch R.M.: Models for ethical medicine in a revolutionary age. The Hastings Center Report 3:3, June, 1972.
14. Ibid.
15. Ibid.
16. Ibid.
17. Ibid.
18. Ibid.
19. Pelligrino E.D.: Protection of patients' rights and the doctor-patient relationship. In Thomas J.E. (ed.), Matters of Life and Death. Toronto, Samuel Stevens, 1978, p. 307.
20. Ibid.
21. Peplau H.E.: Interpersonal Relations in Nursing. New York, Putnam, 1952, p. 5.
22. Ibid., p. 9.
23. Ibid., p. 10–11.
24. Ibid., p. 12.
25. Ibid., p. 31.

26. Ibid., p. 49.
27. Ibid., p. 51-52.
28. Ibid., p. 55.
29. Ibid., p. 63.
30. Buber M.: I and Thou, 2nd ed. New York, Scribner, 1958, p. 3–34, 47–72.
31. Goodnow M. In Carnegie, E.,. The patient's bill of rights and the nurse. Nursing Clinics of North America 9:557, 1974.
32. Mill J.S.: Utilitarianism, Liberty, and Representative Government. London, Dent, 1948, p. 208.
33. Abrams N.: Moral responsibility in nursing. In Spicker S.F., Gadow S. (eds.), Nursing Images and Ideals. New York, Springer, 1980, p. 153–159.
34. Kosik S.H.: Patient advocacy or fighting the system. Am J Nursing 72(4):694, 1972.

CHAPTER 3

Moral Implications In Codes Of Nursing

Through study of this chapter, the student will be able to:

1. Examine professional codes for their moral and practical implications
2. Evaluate the functions of professional codes
3. Analyze how professional codes affect professional conduct and limit malpractice
4. Investigate how *The Code for Nurses* provides moral and professional guidelines for defining, justifying, and limiting nursing activities

INTRODUCTION

Essential characteristics of present-day professions are said to be: the development of a code of ethics guiding practice; specialized educational programs; a particular service to society; standards of education and practice; an economic and welfare program; and legal practice acts with licensing and self-government as common elements.[1] Since a code of ethics is a standard incorporated in varying degrees in all practice, education, legislation, licensing, and public participation, codes for nurses and physicians will be analyzed and evaluated in these respects. Professional codes function as a means of self-regulation, serving as guidelines for individual and collective responsibility in response to societal needs for trustworthy, competent, accountable practitioners. Professional codes are regarded as systems of rules and principles by which a profession is expected to regulate its members and demonstrate its responsibility to society.

THE *CODE FOR NURSES*

The present *Code for Nurses* functions as the basis for professional status in four ways. First, the *Code* shows society that nurses are expected to understand and accept the trust and responsibility invested in them by the public.[2] Second, the *Code* provides guidelines for professional conduct and relationships as the basis for ethical practice.[3] Third, the *Code* defines the nurse's relationship to the client as one of patient advocate, to other health professionals as a colleague, to the nursing profession as a contributor, and to society as a representative of health care for all. Fourth, the *Code* provides the means of self-regulation to the profession.[4]

Specific Provisions of the *Code for Nurses*

1. The nurse provides services with respect for human dignity and the uniqueness of the client unrestricted by considerations of social or economic status, personal attributes, or the nature of health problems.[5]

The nurse begins to fulfill this provision by accepting the client as a stranger who is given interest, respect, and courtesy. Respect for the other is unaffected by socioeconomic status, personal attributes, or the nature of the health problem. The nurse is committed to the principle of the client's right to be "fully involved in the planning and implementation"[6] of his or her own care. Each person has the moral right to decide what will be done to him or to her, together with the right to the information necessary to make those decisions, to understand the consequences, and, on that basis, to accept, terminate, or refuse treatment.[7]

The process of client self-determination may involve the nurse in the roles of resource person and technical expert. The nurse may both supply relevant information and seek the assistance of other professionals in supplementing the patient's or the nurse's own knowledge. The nurse may function as a surrogate authority figure who enables the patient to explore feelings of fear, dependency, suffering, and hopes for total recovery. As counselor and patient advocate, the nurse enlists the client in the process of problem identification, analysis, and resolution of health care needs. The collaboration is directed toward goals of recovery, of optimum function, or of dying peacefully and with dignity.[8]

A nurse who opposes the nature of the health care delivered, such as a decision to abort a fetus or to withhold treatment from a deformed and retarded infant, is justified in refusing and withdrawing from the situation as soon as other arrangements are made that provide nursing care to the patient.[9] The nursing care provided is expected to enable the patient to live with all possible physical, mental, and social comfort. It is, above all, the nursing care of the dying that "will determine to a great degree how this final human experience is lived and the peace and dignity with which death is approached."[10]

Uses of medical technology such as resuscitation measures and life-support systems pose problems to the dying patient, the patient's family, and health professionals, who must make value-laden decisions. The nurse seeks to protect values of respect for human dignity "while working with the client and others to arrive at the best decisions dictated by the circumstances."[11]

2. The nurse safeguards the client's right to privacy by judiciously protecting information of a confidential nature.[12]

The relationship between nurse and client is expected to be one of trust and mutuality. The client may share intimate, previously hidden facts unrelated to current problems on a confidential basis. However, data relevant to the client's health status needs to be shared with other members of a health care team who have common goals of client welfare. This exception may extend to a court of law, where the nurse may or may not be able to invoke the principle of privileged communication. Otherwise, the nurse is committed to the client's right of privacy on a moral basis that respects human dignity.

Information about the patient's diagnoses, treatment, and care necessary for third-party payment, peer review, and quality assurance procedures are expected to be kept confidential according to written guidelines rigidly enforced.[13] The client's consent must be obtained before the record is used for research or other purposes.[14]

3. The nurse acts to safeguard the client and the public when health care and safety are affected by incompetent, unethical, or illegal practice of any person.[15]

The role of advocate is defined in this provision as one in which "the nurse's primary commitment is to the client's care and safety."[16] As a corollary, the nurse is expected to be alert to practices by any health professional or the system itself that are "unethical," incompetent, illegal, or against the patient's best interests.[17] This requires knowledge of both state practice acts and institutional policies and procedures, as well as a clarification of the term "ethical."

The process of correction begins with the individual who may have caused harm to the patient. If necessary, institutional channels and established procedures are expected to be used for further reporting. Documentation is expected as well.

If the appropriate behavior "is not corrected within the employment setting and continues to jeopardize the client's care and safety . . . the problem should be reported to other appropriate authorities such as the practice committees of the appropriate professional organizations or the legally constituted bodies concerned with licensing. . . ."[18] Although a written grievance must be provided to regulatory bodies, every effort is made to protect the patient advocate.

An effective measure to protect clients and improve practice is the peer review. The method is based on published criteria and the procedures for making recommendations. It is intended as a method for improving health care delivery services and the safety, health, and welfare of clients.[19]

4. The nurse assumes responsibility and accountability for individual nursing judgments and actions.[20]

As an acknowledged professional, the nurse is responsible and accountable for the quality, effectiveness, and efficiency of nursing care provided. Moreover, society expects a profession to be self-regulating. However, safeguards for the patient in the form of professional examination and licensure are operative in most states. These insure minimum competencies. Recently, state regulatory bodies have been created for investigating and prosecuting professional misconduct in addition to supporting the profession's responsibility for setting standards of nursing practice.

Individual nurse responsibility is for the development and implementation of the nursing care plan and for the functions and duties of the role assumed.[21] The areas of nursing responsibility include data collection and assessment, development of the plan and of the goals to be achieved, and the evaluation of the effectiveness of the plan and of the nursing care in reaching set goals.[22]

The nurse is accountable for what is done or not done "to self, to client, to the agency of employment, and to the nursing profession."[23] Accountability includes legal responsibilities. The nurse is responsible for each act or failure to act in a given case. We would add that the nurse is accountable to society for decisions at the policy level affecting the future course of a profession, institution, or health care delivery.

Evaluation occurs at the subjective individual level and is also done by peers. The process of evaluation by self or by others implies that improvement of practice is continuous. Peer evaluation is intended as a means of self-regulation by the profession itself.[24] Through its *Standards of Nursing Practice*, updated nursing practice laws, and accreditation procedures, the American Nurses' Association demonstrates its accountability to the public.[25]

5. The nurse maintains competence in nursing.[26]

Effective nursing often makes the difference between a client's survival or death, recovery, or continued ill health. Therefore, nurses are expected to know what they are doing. Moreover, nurses are expected to maintain competence and remain currently informed of new knowledge.

Nursing care is expected to reflect knowledge of new concepts in nursing, new medications, and new techniques.

Present competence measures "include peer review criteria, outcome criteria, and the American Nurses' Association program for certification."[27] Continuing education and advanced formal education are means of keeping current with professional, scientific, and technologic advances. Scientific advances contribute to the rapidly increasing complexity of nursing service and health care delivery. The process of maintaining competence is self-initiated and self-directed with the recognition of the need for consultation with nurse specialists, educators, administrators, or leaders appropriately.

> **6.** The nurse exercises informed judgment and uses individual competence and qualifications as criteria in seeking consultation, accepting responsibilities, and delegating nursing activities to others.[28]

The practice of nursing is dynamic and increasingly complex. In primary care and in the practitioner roles in pediatrics, geriatrics, and family health, for example, new functions are performed by nurses that were formerly those of the physician. The nurse performs a physical examination and history as part of the nursing practitioner's assessment and diagnosis. Consequently, nurses are shifting nursing functions to ancillary personnel. In the process of delegation, the nurse must exercise discretion and judgment in accepting and assigning responsibilities. Consultation is freely used. The primary goal is to insure safe and effective nursing care.

A second goal is to practice within the limits of the legal practice acts for each profession. In some nursing roles, there is a need for collaborative activities to develop joint policy statements with medicine that will define differences in roles and responsibilities. Existing statements of joint policy represent expert judgment and may have standing in courts of law. A third goal is to influence constructive changes in the law.

The delivery of total health services is now beyond the capacity of any single profession. Interdisciplinary team effort in which the members share knowledge, skills, and responsibilities for total patient care nevertheless requires the nurse's recognition of limitations of competence. The nurse needs consultation from appropriate sources. These may include other nurses, physicians, or other health professionals. Distinction in role and functions that are based on education and training call for respect without disparagement of individuals having minor roles.

Personal competence, as well as education and training and policy statements, is assessed before delegating nursing functions to ancillary personnel or accepting medical functions.[29] Any nurse unsure of personnel competence has both the responsibility and, on one view, the right to refuse the assignment in question. This protects both the client and the nurse. The same right and responsibility prevail where functions are delegated that are not nursing responsibilities or that keep the nurse from providing nursing care. Similar precautions are expected to be observed in delegating functions to other members of the team who may be unqualified for the assignment.[30]

7. The nurse participates in activities that contribute to the ongoing development of the profession's body of knowledge.[31]

Systematic investigation is necessary for expanding each profession's body of knowledge. Knowledge, implying truth and beliefs based on adequate evidence, serves as the framework and beacon light of the profession's education and practice.

The American Nurses' Association has developed guidelines for nurses either conducting or involved in research. Research is expected to be conducted by qualified persons or under such persons' supervision. The study design is submitted for approval by an appropriate committee using official or professional guidelines. The purpose, the nature, the goals and the methodology of the research are evaluated in relation to guidelines for the protection of human subjects.

The subject's right of informed consent, privacy, and dignity are thereby insured. Additionally, the subject has the right to terminate participation at any time. Subjects are protected from undue risks. These principles are especially important in research consented to by parents or guardians and performed on children, the aged, and the mentally disabled. The nurse who disagrees with the research because of its problematic aspects has the right to refuse to participate or to withdraw on the basis of its adverse effects on patients.[32]

8. The nurse participates in the profession's efforts to implement and improve standards of nursing.[33]

An assumed public concern of professions is that only qualified persons will be admitted to practice. Nursing competence includes a command of skills, academic success, demonstrated responsibility, and a commitment to improve nursing practice for the benefit of others. The selection of students and evaluation of their abilities is an obligation of educators. Helping people involves more than a generous humanitarian impulse. Therefore, the American Nurses' Association has developed standards for practice, education, and service that requires the participation of each nurse for implementation.[34]

9. The nurse participates in the profession's efforts to establish and maintain conditions of employment conducive to high-quality nursing care.[35]

Nurses are now involved in the process of changing the terms and conditions of employment. This provision of the *Code* emphasizes that economic conditions of general welfare are important factors in recruiting and keeping well-qualified nurses functioning at an optimum level.

The most effective method of defining and controlling the quality of nursing care is collective bargaining. The professional state nurses' associations assist and represent nurses in negotiations with employers. One aim is to insure professionally approved standards of practice. Equally important is the support for the rights of nurses to "participate in determining the terms and conditions of employment conducive to high-quality nursing practice."[36] The appropriate channel for nurses to improve conditions of employment ethically and with dignity is through the economic and general welfare programs of the state and national nurses' associations. Increasingly, work contracts have been achieved in previously unorganized health care facilities. Old contracts were renegotiated and revised to the satisfaction of the majority of employed nurses. Some contracts were secured solely through negotiation. Others were secured only after prolonged unsuccessful negotiation and a strike in which arrangements were made to provide care for seriously ill patients in need of nursing care.

The problems of inadequate staffing and salaries will continue to detract from the professional satisfaction of dedicated nurses. A recent editorial in *The New York Times* discussed the acute shortage of nurses and pointed to the increased opportunities in other fields for women who are or could be good nurses.[37] Nevertheless, there are a million and a quarter nurses who might be responsive to improved salaries and conditions of employment in significant ways.

10. The nurse participates in the profession's effort to protect the public from misinformation and misrepresentation and to maintain the integrity of nursing.[38]

This section of the *Code* provides for individual advertising of nursing services through listings and biographies in reputable publications. The nurse may use symbols of licensure such as R.N., earned academic degrees, and symbols of professional recognition such as F.A.A.N. (Fellow of the American Academy of Nursing). No nurse is permitted to endorse, advertise, promote, or sell commercial products, since this may be mistakenly interpreted as an endorsement by the entire profession. In the course of health teaching, several "similar products or services [are expected to] be offered or described so that the client or practitioner can make an informed choice."[39] On the other hand, nurses are expected to advise patients against using products that are dangerous. Violations of these principles by other nurses are expected to be reported to the professional association, as such actions undermine public confidence in nursing.

11. The nurse collaborates with members of the health professions and other citizens in promoting community and national efforts to meet the health needs of the public.[40]

Health care as the right of all citizens is stated in this provision as endorsed by the American Nurses' Association House of Delegates in convention in 1958.[41] Planning for health services to be available and accessible to everyone requires collaboration between consumers and providers of health care at all levels. Nurses have both the right and the responsibility to help achieve quality health care for all by implementing their views through the political process and legislative action. The organization of Nurses for Political Action has been effective in directly communicating the views of nurses on key issues to legislators. The organization has both supported and endorsed political candidates favorably disposed toward nursing interests, health care services, and human welfare.

This provision of the *Code* holds that relationships with other disciplines are expected to be collaborative and supportive. By its very nature, the delivery of complex health care demands an interdisciplinary approach. Likewise, the relationship of nursing and medicine is regarded as interdependent and collaborative "around the need of the client."[42] The changing role of the nurse, particularly primary-care or specialty nurse practitioners, requires colleague relationships with physicians, with discussion of overlapping, similar, and different functions and areas of practice.[43] An editorial entitled "The Nurses' Discontent" pinpoints the importance of shared responsibility and shared authority among physicians and nurses delivering comprehensive care and the demoralization of nurses in the absence of shared decisions.

> Studies suggest that the nurses' discontent runs deeper than money or working conditions. They feel that though they perform crucial functions, they are not taken seriously. Hospital rules and traditions deny them authority to make even minor decisions. . . . Nurses have little say in how hospitals are run. Yet typically, many get to know the patients and their problems better than anyone. Some nurses' organizations promote the idea of "joint practice," to let nurses participate in decisions about patient care. They have asked that nurses be admitted to the groups that set hospital policy. But they have met with stiff resistance from [physicians] and administrators. These problems of authority deserve a careful look in considering the shortage of nurses.[44]

The challenge to nurses and nursing organizations is clearly set forth. Nurses serve all of the people. Therefore, nurses have the right to a voice in all deliberations and decisions affecting the quantity, quality, and distribution of health care and nursing services.

THE INTERNATIONAL COUNCIL FOR NURSES CODE OF ETHICS

In London in 1899 at a meeting of the International Congress of Women, a committee was formed at the International Council of Nurses. In 1905, the American nursing association, the Nurses' Associated Alumnae, with associations from Great Britain and Germany, became the charter members of the International Council of Nurses.[45] In 1928, S. Lillian Clayton, president of the American Nurses' Association, identified the principles for which the International Council stood. These were "self government of nurses in their associations, and raising ever higher the standards of education, professional ethics, and public usefulness of its members."[46] In 1948, the International Council of Nurses was officially recognized as the voice for all nongovernmental nursing by the World Health Organization. The Council is the official representative of all nursing at World Health Organization meetings.[47]

In 1950, the American Nurses' Association adopted its first complete code of ethics, used as a "model for the *Code for Nurses* adopted by the Council in 1953."[48] The *Code* was revised in 1973 to its present form.[49] It is in worldwide use. It is derived from eclectic and conflicting concepts in traditional ethics and emphasizes the nurse's responsibility and accountability.[50]

As a guideline to conduct for nurses all over the world, the *Code* recognizes that nursing practice must reflect and respect cultural and religious differences. As a result, nursing may differ in fundamental respects from one area to another. The *Code* contains the seeds of conflict if the nurse carries the laws and customs of the home area to a different one. Respect for the values of a subculture or minority group is a position that raises the dilemma of whether to respect harmful values or to work for change. For example, an African nurse may be forced to choose between psychotropic drugs and the activities of a local healer for control of the hallucinations and thought disorders of a patient with an acute schizophrenic episode.

The *Code* defines the nurse's relation to people as one in which nursing care is provided in an environment that respects individual values, spiritual beliefs, and customs. Information of a personal nature is to be held in confidence unless the nurse judges it should be shared.[51]

The nurse's responsibility for practice is one of continual learning in order to maintain competence.[52] In specific situations, the nurse sustains the highest possible standards of nursing care and uses judgment in delegating and accepting responsibilities. Personal conduct reflects credit on the profession.[53]

The nurse's relation to society is one of shared responsibility for the initiation and implementation of the health and social needs of the community.[54]

The nurse's relation with co-workers is cooperative. (The physician is not distinguished from other co-workers.) The nurse protects persons receiving care by taking appropriate action when they are endangered.

The nurse's relation to the profession is that of an active role in developing and implementing desirable standards of nursing education and practice, and in contributing to nursing knowledge. Moreover, the nurse is expected to be active in securing fair economic and social working conditions through the professional organization. Women as nurses must still struggle for equality and recognition as persons whose professional lives are separate from their personal lives. The *Code* supports the definition of a professional nurse as a person with rights and responsibilities for self, clients, co-workers, community, and profession and their nursing and health care needs. The World Health Organization recognizes the *Code* for supporting nursing education and practice. It is used as a guide to curricula development, licensing, and legislation in countries involved with shaping their health care systems to serve the people well.

THE AMERICAN MEDICAL ASSOCIATION CODE OF ETHICS

In 1980, the American Medical Association adopted a new, shorter version of its *Principles of Medical Ethics*. This version had been in the process of review since 1977. Previous revisions were in 1903, 1912, 1947, and 1957. The first code for members was adopted in 1847.[55]

Veatch cites two major problems as reasons for the 1980 revision. The first is the Federal Trade Commission's charge of illegal constraints on trade through prohibition of advertising. The new *Code* permits advertising. Similarly, the new *Code* deletes the condemnation of what were called "unscientific cults," such as chiropractic practice.[56] (The 1957 *Code* directed a physician to practice medicine on a scientific basis and to avoid association with anyone violating this principle.)[57] The second set of changes is drastic because they are based on the recognition that the "medical profession is no longer perceived as the sole guardian of the public health, and consequently the traditional paternalism of the profession is in conflict with society."[58] Consequently, the new *Code* is based on concepts of human rights for patients, colleagues, and other health professionals. The responsibility of the physician is to respect those rights and support human dignity, to engage in honest dealings, to maintain patient confidence, and to improve the community.[59] This is the very first time that the physician's responsibility is connected with the rights of patients, with colleagues, and with the rights of other health professionals ("allied professionals" in the 1957 version). The rights of patients to confidentiality are now phrased solely in terms of the constraints of law rather than, in the 1957 paternalistic version, "to protect the welfare of the patient or of the community."[60] The new position strengthens patient confidentiality, but never explicitly defines the physician-patient relationship as a contractual one based on mutual trust or other ethical principles.[61] Confidentiality, for example, could be based on the moral principle of keeping promises.[62] Honesty is another principle in the new *Code* that takes priority over the older paternalistic principle, which allowed deception on grounds of the patient's best interests. Respect for the law and responsibility for changing bad laws as physician responsibilities are made more important in the new *Code*. This can be seen as implying the physician's contract with society for improving it.[63]

The new *Code* ends with a return to earlier principles of physicians' right to choose patients, associates, and environments in which appropriate patient care services are provided. The *Code* committee concluded that these principles were primarily for the protection and benefit of patients. Furthermore, the issue of who is to decide what is in the best interests of patients is still in the firm grasp of the physician group represented by the American Medical Association. Equally clearly, the physician's freedom to choose whom to serve under what conditions is still in conflict with society's right to draft physicians for service in underserved areas or the armed forces, or to restrict them in any way.[64]

On the positive side, the new *Code* abolishes the sexist use of the pronoun "he." More important, it explicates the physician's obligations to society: exposing incompetent or fraudulent colleagues; respecting law and changing it for the benefit of patients; making relevant knowledge available; utilizing the talents of other health professionals, and contributing to improvements in the community.[65] The *Code* committee recognized that "medical ethics are . . . a specific application of the universal norms of moral behavior."[66] Moreover, the *Code* committee acknowledged that "the profession does not exist for itself, it exists for a purpose and increasingly that purpose will be defined by society."[67] In Veatch's view, the new *Code* lays the foundation for a contractual relationship, based on ethically defensible principles, between organized medicine and the society in which it practices. Unfortunately, that time has not yet arrived.

THE FUNCTIONS OF A CODE FOR NURSES

According to *Webster's Collegiate Dictionary*, a code is a "system of principles or rules (moral)."[68] A code, in the case of law, has "statutory force," with enforceable sanctions.[69] Ideally, a professional code regulates the professional conduct of its members by instituting sanctions, directly or indirectly, and thus enforcing its provisions.

The word "professional," used in these discussions of codes, is employed as a persuasive definition. That is, it is used as a value term that exhorts the reader to agree with the writer or speaker. The use of a persuasive definition is in contrast to a lexical or reportive definition that is true or false, such as that of an island as a body of land surrounded by water. The words "professional" and "unprofessional" may also be used persuasively. Ms. Jolene Tuma, R.N., for example, had her license revoked by the Idaho State Board of Nursing in August 1976 on the grounds that her conduct was "unprofessional" for advocating Laetrile and "disrupting" the patient-physician relationship. Ms. Tuma appealed to the *Code for Nurses* to support her view that she was acting professionally.[70]

A professional code may also refer to the shared values and norms to which a profession's majority commits itself. We may recall from Chapter 1 that "moral" means whatever results in good or harm. The principles of the *Code* are designed to bring about good and minimize harm or injury. On this view, there is no way to prevent moral values and principles from consideration in health care matters. Therefore, a professional code may be viewed as a set of moral principles or rules for regulating the professional conduct of its members, preferably with enforceable sanctions, and from which specific directives can be generated for the ongoing governance of its members.

The *Code for Nurses* provides moral guidelines to nursing practice in accordance with consumers' health care interests and rights. The *Code* holds nurses accountable for professionally acceptable standards of nursing care. As the *Code* has evolved, this standard of acceptable nursing care has increasingly placed the client at the center of health care. Meanwhile, both the patient and the nurse are increasingly invested with rights and responsibilities.

According to Veatch, a stark difference between codes before and after World II is the absence of "rights" language in the older versions.[71] The Nazi abuses, Veatch says, gave rise to rules governing experimentation in the Nuremberg Code (1946) and in the Declaration of Helsinki (1964 and 1975).[72] But patients' bills of rights and code reformulation using the language of rights have been a reality only since 1972.[73]

The use of rights language in codes for nurses reflects not only that patients have rights but that nurses also have a role as patient advocates. To carry out their role as client advocates, nurses have special "earned" rights and privileges, which they may invoke even against physicians if those physicians' orders are medically or scientifically contraindicated. The advent of patients' and nurses' rights implies not only a conceptual redrawing of the physician-patient relation, but also a higher set of educational and professional role requirements and responsibilities placed on nurses. One may also find the growth of the nurse's advocacy role occurring as a result of such landmark cases as *Memorial Hospital* vs. *Darling*.[74] Here, the physicians were found negligent along with the nurses in a case involving Dorrence Darling's broken leg, which turned gangrenous and had to be amputated.

By holding nurses and physicians responsible for negligence, the nurses' judgment was identified as a causal factor, one that could have made a difference in the outcome. By holding nurses responsible, the Illinois Supreme Court acknowledged the role and importance of nursing judgment. By doing so, the Court altered the physician's role from the traditional "captain of the ship" to that of a key team member along with other key team members. To hold nurses jointly responsible for negligence against Dorrence Darling, as the Illinois Court did, called for nurses to have greater treatment autonomy and the professional right to advocate clients' rights against physicians if necessary. The nurses in the *Darling* case were cited for not reporting the condition of Darling's leg cast, even if doing so meant reporting a physician's negligence—a kind of reporting that has since come to be known as "whistle-blowing."

One function of the *Code for Nurses*, then, is to upgrade the nursing profession, thus benefitting both patients and nurses, by investing nurses with rights and responsibilities. Rights enable nurses to care more effectively for clients' health care interests and rights—rights which, some nursing scholars believe, cannot be entrusted to physicians alone. But the rights of nurses are not rights *against* patients, for such rights would defeat the point of nursing and nursing advocacy. Rather, nurses' rights are rights to act *on behalf* of their clients, and such rights include nurses' rights against other health professionals, including physicians and other nurses. These rights are invokable if other health professionals fail to promote the rights and interests of patients. On this view, patients' rights come first and justify the earned rights and privileges of other health professionals, on the condition, of course, that professional rights and privileges are consistent with and compatible with patients' rights.

A second function of the *Code* is one consistent with and implied by the first function of upgrading the quality of health care. This function is to set standards to regulate the conduct of nursing practitioners, holding them accountable and morally liable for failure to live up to the standards. For the *Code* functions as an oath or promise made by the profession collectively to the public that these standards will be upheld by the individual nurse.

To regulate the conduct of nurse practitioners, the profession, by logical extension through its *Code for Nurses*, attempts to influence licensure, institutional accreditation, and curricular content.[75] The *Code for Nurses* would otherwise be an exclusively ceremonial statement without influence in the governance of nursing practitioners. Nurses would possibly pay lip service to the *Code*, but it would lack what may be termed "performative" meaning, namely that the *Code* gets things done.[76] The *Code* would have no teeth if it had no "performative force." To have "performative force," the *Code* regulates nursing practitioners by influencing the guidelines for licensure, institutional accreditation, and curricula.

CRITICISM OF THE CODE

A criticism of the *Code* and of professional codes generally is that codes reflect vested interests. These interests mask deeper conflicts between the interests of the public and the profession around what Paul Goodman used to call "pork-chop" gains in the form of higher salaries and benefits.

This criticism depends on how the *Code* is formulated, and what functions and interests it can be made to serve. The evidence is that the *Code*, while promoting the interests of the nursing profession, is clearly oriented toward serving patients' interests and rights, and placing the interests of nurses second to those of patients. This cannot always be said of the A.M.A. *Code*, since that code provides for the physician's right to choose whom to serve. The interests of patients and nurses do not collide, but rather dovetail. There are natural points of alliance between patients and nurses, partly due to both being undervalued and underserved.

CONCLUSION

The *Code* provides a floor, a moral basis for justifying nursing action, through its functions of (1) upgrading nursing by investing it with rights and responsibilities for caring for patients; (2) setting accountable moral standards for practitioners; (3) influencing licensure standards; (4) influencing educational and curricular standards of performance and conduct; and (5) appealing through its manifesto-like principles for legal incorporation and public acceptance.

Codes may have important symbolic and regulating functions for professional practices, including nursing. A symbolic function is to remind nurses and other professions of the status and importance of nursing in health care. The *Code for Nurses* carries out this role by stressing the human rights of patients and nurses to self-determination and well-being. The regulating function of the *Code* is to influence standards and practices of nursing.

REFERENCES

1. Flanagan L.: One Strong Voice. Kansas City, Mo., American Nurses' Association, 1976, p. 23.

2. American Nurses' Association: Code for Nurses with Interpretive Statements. Kansas City, Mo., The Association, 1976, p. 2.
3. Ibid., p. 1.
4. Ibid.
5. Ibid., p. 4.
6. Ibid.
7. Ibid.
8. Ibid., p. 6.
9. Ibid.
10. Ibid.
11. Ibid.
12. Ibid.
13. Ibid.
14. Ibid., p. 7.
15. Ibid., p. 8.
16. Ibid.
17. Ibid.
18. Ibid., p. 9.
19. Ibid.
20. Ibid.
21. Ibid.
22. Ibid., p. 9–10.
23. Ibid., p. 10.
24. Ibid.
25. Ibid.
26. Ibid., p. 11.
27. Ibid.
28. Ibid., p. 12.
29. Ibid., p. 13.
30. Ibid.
31. Ibid., p. 14.
32. Ibid., p. 15.
33. Ibid.
34. Ibid., p. 16.
35. Ibid.
36. Ibid.
37. Editorial, The nurses' discontent, The New York Times, August 10, 1981, p. A14.
38. American Nurses' Association: Code for Nurses, p. 10.
39. Ibid., p. 18.
40. Ibid., p. 19.
41. Flanagan: One Strong Voice, p. 629.
42. Ibid., p. 20.
43. Ibid.
44. The nurses' discontent, p. A14.
45. Ibid., p. 611.
46. Clayton S.L.: "An activity update." In Flanagan, One Strong Voice, p. 447.
47. Flanagan: One Strong Voice, p. 624.
48. Ibid., p. 602.

49. Tate B.L.: The Nurse's Dilemma. Geneva, International Council of Nurses, 1977, p. vii.
50. Ibid.
51. Ibid.
52. Ibid.
53. Ibid.
54. Ibid.
55. Veatch R.M.: Professional ethics: New principles for physicians? Hastings Center Report 10(3):16, 1980.
56. Ibid.
57. American Medical Association: Principles of Medical Ethics. Monroe, Wis., The Association, 1957.
58. Veatch: Professional ethics, p. 16.
59. American Medical Association, Principles of Medical Ethics.
60. Ibid.
61. Veatch: Professional ethics, p. 16.
62. Ibid.
63. Ibid.
64. Ibid.
65. Ibid.
66. Ibid., p. 18.
67. Ibid.
68. Webster's Collegiate Dictionary. Springfield, Mass., Merriam, 1974, p. 216.
69. Black's Law Dictionary, 14th ed. St. Paul, Minn., West, 1969, p. 323.
70. Tuma J.: Professional Misconduct. Nursing Outlook 25(9):546, 1977.
71. Veatch R.M.: Codes of medical ethics: Ethical analysis. In Reich W. (ed.), The Encyclopedia of Bioethics. New York, Macmillan, 1978, vol. 1, p. 172.
72. Ibid.
73. Ibid.
74. Charleston Community Memorial Hospital *v.* Dorrence Kenneth Darling, 33 Ill 326, 211 NE 2nd 253 1965.
75. Transcript, The Matter of Ms. Jolene Tuma. Board of Nursing, Idaho, August 24, 1976, p. 186–188, 234–235.
76. Austin J.: Performative utterances. In Austin J.L., Philosophical Papers. New York, Oxford University Press, 1970, p. 233–252.

PART TWO

Ethical Decision Making in Nursing

CHAPTER 4

Models of Morality in Everyday Nursing Practice

Through study of this chapter, the student is enabled to:

1. Clarify and rank values as the basis for moral priorities
2. Distinguish between alternative models of morality
3. Apply models appropriately to justify ethical nursing decisions

INTRODUCTION

Moral problems arise in nursing whenever and wherever there is the possibility for good or harm to someone. All health care policies and practices have consequences—some trivial, some serious, and some lifesaving. As significant members of the health care team and as patient advocates, nurses are involved in making these decisions that vitally affect the well-being of patients, families, colleagues, and other members of society.

Nursing decisions and policies, such as those expressed in the *Code for Nurses*,[1] reflect moral values, issues, and problems in everyday practice. Attempts to solve or resolve these issues are expressed through moral views or beliefs. These moral views, which concern predominant ways of looking at values, may be seen as models. A practical model provides an account designed to orient and guide activities.[2] A model of morality characterizes a perspective for viewing moral relationships. These models of morality, which reflect ways of life, overlap.

VALUE CLARIFICATION

Value clarification expresses a person's preferences, likes, and dislikes, such as one's beliefs about the importance of living, dying, God, work, truth, love, family, sex, and pleasure. Value clarification is a process that moves in three stages. It begins with an initial choice of a value from among various alternatives. Here one sifts through various alternatives and ranks them. On a second stage, one reflects on which of the chosen values are worthwhile to prize. Third, one maps a strategy of action to achieve the values one has chosen and prized. Here one decides to act on one's prized values.[3] Value clarification makes explicit a person's priorities.

A strength of value clarification is that one expresses value preferences and priorities in an honest and straightforward way. Examples are how a nurse feels about sleeping patients in the ward, the saving of seriously defective neonates, or that life is worthwhile only if a person has a functioning brain. A drawback of value clarification, however, is that the expression of one's preferences or priorities does not imply that these preferences are justifiable or that they ought to be preferred. For example, a nurse may prize quiet patients in a quiet ward, but such a value may not be good for the patients. A desire does not imply that the desire ought to be acted on. There is a well-known fallacy in moral reasoning, called the *is-ought fallacy*, which holds that what is does not automatically imply and justify what ought to be. One cannot validly infer that what one desires is therefore desirable. The value of quiet patients may be a clarified value, but it is not thereby shown to be a justifiable value. The harm that a person who drinks and then drives can do shows that chosen or prized values are not justified values. Value clarification calls for further development in the process of justification, which takes us to ethics.

ALTERNATIVE MODELS OF MORALITY

Ethics or morality has both an easy and a difficult aspect. An easy aspect is that an ethical or moral issue arises whenever good or harm results. Almost anything one does in interpersonal relations may cause good or harm. Helping a patient recover health and self-confidence is good. A smile, a frown, a grimace, eye contact or aversion, and a hand extended to another may communicate affection, friendliness, disapproval, rejection, or abuse. Doing good or harm or having them done to us occurs frequently, and these interpersonal actions affect us for better or worse. Deciding what to do for a hopelessly defective neonate or an elderly prostatectomy patient whose need for surgery is ignored results in good or harm. The difficult question is how to justify what is said to be good or harmful. Is "pulling the plug" on a 10-year-old comatose patient good or harmful, for example?

As one studies ethics, one finds no single science of moral values. One instead finds alternative models of morality and dialogue between

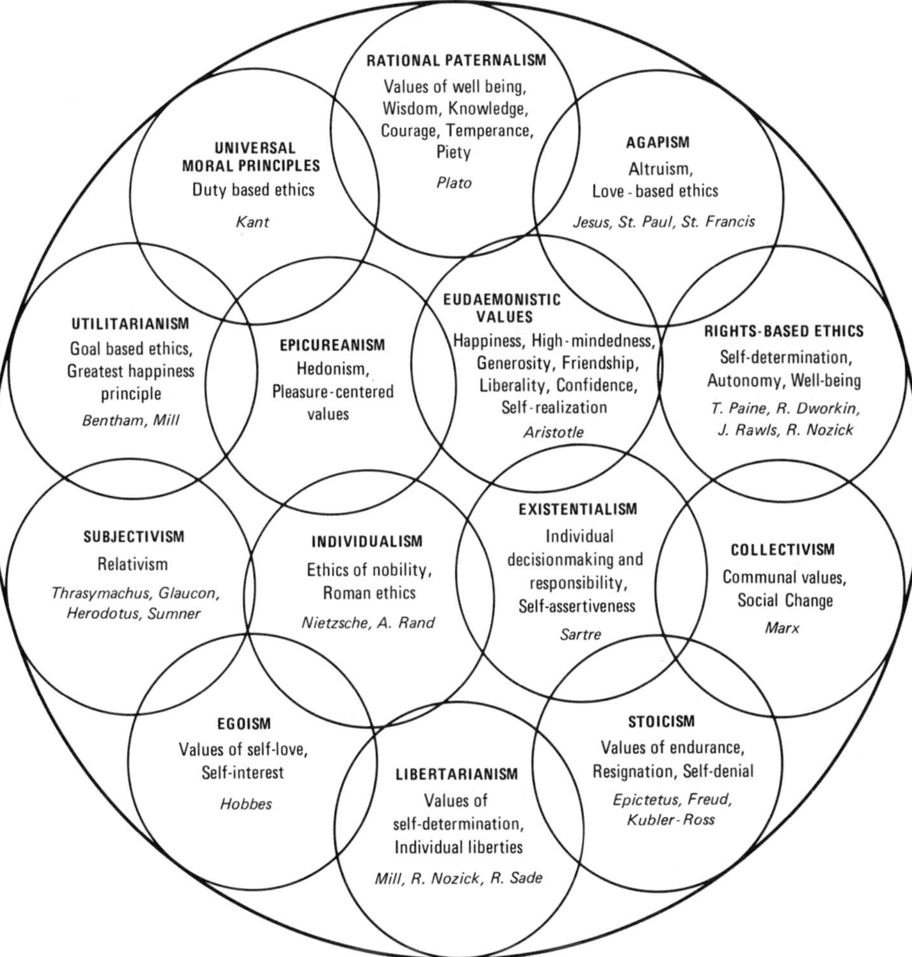

Figure 4.1. Models of morality in nursing practice.

these. Alternative models of morality orient the role of nursing in the care of patients. These models of moral values are like overlapping circles (Figure 4.1). Each model sets out its values along with an attempted justification to some decision-making aspect of nursing. St. Thomas Aquinas, for example, held that human life is a gift that is never to be taken by any human. He used principles of the Christian religion sometimes known as *Agapism* to justify his view on the sacredness of life. The principle that life is a gift is then used to "justify" a nurse's decision to save life at all cost, even the life of a hopeless infant with trisomy 18 (retardation, deafness, and various deformities) or of a comatose 10-year-old. There are other models of morality, such as the ethics developed by Nietzsche, which stresses nobility, courage, stamina, and the role of great leaders in place of equality and democracy. The point is that to do ethics means one cannot take one model of morality for granted as providing the true and final answer.[4] For, the moment one settles on such prized values as democracy and equality, there is an alternative ethical view, such as Nietzsche's or some other, which opposes democracy. Or there are the values of a 16th-century philosopher like René Descartes, or Joseph Fletcher in our time, both of whom emphasize the values of conscious life.

MORAL ISSUES AND MODELS

Paternalism vs. Libertarianism

There are 8 to 14 main models of morality that affect health care decisions. One ethical issue that affects the treatment of patients is that of Paternalism versus Libertarianism. *Paternalism* holds that the state or one's father knows best and that each individual is obligated to comply with the authority figure, be it a patient, a nurse, a physician, or the state. Brian Clark's play *Whose Life Is It Anyway*? illustrates the issue between Paternalism and Libertarianism. The physician gives Harrison, the quadriplegic, a tranquilizer against Harrison's objections. The physician also believes Harrison should be kept alive despite Harrison's wishes. *Libertarianism*, on the other hand, holds that individuals have a right to decide what happens in and to their bodies.

A famous ancient Greek philosopher, Plato (428–347 B.C.) is the major philosophical proponent of what might be called *Rational Paternalism*. Plato showed in a dialogue, the *Gorgias*, that the good in a person's own view—what that person desires—is not necessarily good. Plato cites as an example that a person may desire cream puffs at the bakery and confuse such desires with the good. (In modern life, a mother may desire to "pull the plug" on her comatose son, which may not be the wise thing to do.) Another group of philosophers against whom Plato argued in the *Republic* were the *Sophists*, such as Thrasymachus and Glaucon. The Sophists (sometimes known as Egoists, Subjectivists, or Relativists) defended the virtues of selfishness, of looking after onself first and last, and argued that "might makes right." A physician who lies when he says to the family of a patient who died "We did everything" is oriented either to a self-serving Egoist model of morality or a form of paternalism, sometimes known as "playing God."

Plato, however, argued against the sophists. Plato believed that looking after oneself first and last or doing whatever one wants if one has the power or can get away with it by stealth, pretension, or lies leads to moral and social destruction. He showed that we live only by living together. We need one another. Plato proposed a social scheme showing how people may live well together. His form of Paternalism is an appeal to knowledge, wisdom, and rationality rather than to force, tyranny, or ignorance. Plato's Rational Paternalism rules out the practice of some physicians and other health professionals who place personal wealth above a patient's health. A Libertarian rejoinder, however, is that social life without individual freedom is not worthwhile. A Platonic rejoinder is that civilized survival is more valuable than individual liberty or freedom. One issue, then, between Rational Paternalism and Libertarianism, in relation to health care and nursing, is that of freedom versus security and control.

Egoism vs. Altruism

A related issue is between *Egoism* and *Altruism*. The Egoist model is oriented to self-love. The Altruist model is oriented to the doctrine of loving others as much as oneself. Egoism and Altruism both have strengths and weaknesses. Egoism appeals to a basic drive in human nature: self-preservation. The motivation of almost all action, according to Egoism, is self-interest. Notice all the time and energy we spend caring for ourselves, combing our hair, brushing our teeth, dressing, eating, drinking, and playing. Self-interest seems to come naturally to most if not all people. A difficulty with Egoism is, as Plato pointed out, that people live together and need one another. Plato made the point that people need to have their behavior controlled in order to help and not harm themselves and others. For people to do whatever they wish—a belief expressed by the bumper sticker, "If it feels right, do it"—may be inappropriate. One might, for example, fail to respect red and green traffic lights or not answer a patient's call light because one finds that patient a chronic complainer. Another counterexample against Ethical Relativism is that in Fundamentals of Nursing courses, for example, students of nursing do not grade themselves.

The Basis of Egoism. The basis of modern Egoism is commonly identified with Thomas Hobbes (1599–1679). The main drive in human nature, says Hobbes, is self-preservation. But in a "state of nature," where people are left to themselves, there can be no society at all. In such a state, one in which people act full time on their basic motivations solely to survive, there would be a continuous "war of all against all." There would be no trade and commerce, no growth of knowledge, no arts. Rather, there would be "continual fear of danger and violent death." Human life would be "solitary, poor, nasty, brutish and short."[5] Hobbes's ingenious solution is to convert this unbearable state of nature into the nature of a state. Such a state is brought about by a *social contract*. This contract provides for individuals to agree to give up their liberty to preserve themselves in a state of nature by any means and to transfer their individual liberty and power to a sovereign whom they agree to obey. The sovereign, in exchange for everyone's obedience, assures everyone's peace and protection. This contract provides for the exchange of freedom for security. The sovereign keeps individuals obedient by developing a deputized peace force of persons to coerce and control people into continual compliance with civil laws. We are, however, never far from our basic interest in ourselves. Our reason for joining society is self-interest.

The Basis of Altruism. An important moral point of view that influences and is widely believed to justify moral choices in nursing is a love-based ethics, an ethics based on *agape* or *Agapism*. Love characterizes enduringly positive interpersonal relations, whether it be sexual love, romantic love, parental love, love for one's children, or love of country, customs, culture, and kinships. Love is the tie that binds humans together. Stories, novels, operas, poems, letters, paintings, and sonatas celebrate the force of love in human affairs. People sometimes live for and by one another's love. However, the love people feel for one another knows no greater love than the love of life, which makes all other feelings and love possible. Love is king of the positive emotions, too great and too brilliant to be extinguished or eclipsed even by its rival emotion, hate. Love is the handmaiden of peace, which makes more love possible; but it is opposed by hate, which brings about war and violence.

Perhaps it is no surprise, then, that love is the centerpiece of one of the most influential religions, namely Christianity. A contemporary philosopher, William Frankena, characterizes Agapism as holding that "there is only one basic ethical imperative—to love."[6] There are, according to Matthew 22:37-40, two commandments concerning love.

> Thou shalt love the Lord thy God with all thy heart, and with all thy soul, and with all thy mind. This is the first and great commandment, and the second is Thou shalt love thy neighbor as Thyself. On these two commandments hang all the laws and the prophets.[7]

St. Francis of Assisi (1182–1226) extends this love of God and of one's neighbor to the love of all God's living creatures, including birds. This love, and also the test of this love, is that it includes the love of lepers, love of the diseased and dying, love of the poor, love of all living things as God's "creations."[8]

Agapistic or love-based ethics enjoins each person to love others as much as oneself. Such an ethics sometimes calls on people to do extraordinary deeds on behalf of their fellow human beings, which people are not always capable of or interested in doing.

According to Jesus, when someone smites us, we are asked to turn the other cheek. When there is not enough bread and fish, we are taught to share what there is. On this view, we individually gain by giving of ourselves to others. There are two kingdoms, the earth and a higher, eternal kingdom. We live in this kingdom for a short time, but we live in the other one forever.

The ethics of love applied to nursing and health care means that nurses show love, trust, and kindness for their patients. The word "care" is implied by the term "love." Care seems to be a pivotal part of nursing, essential to its calling. An important advantage of a love-based ethics is that love is at or very near the core of all positive emotions, or, to shift the metaphor slightly, love is the fuel and driving force of all worthwhile human feelings.

Three difficulties exist, however. One is that the force of love seems to derive, as does romantic and sexual love, from desire, and, as such, needs no command or imperative. It is surprising, then, to see love characterized as a commandment in the Scriptures, and to see love characterized by W. Frankena as an imperative. If love, so to speak, flows from the heart, it needs no commandment either from an ancient or recent source.

A second and possibly more insuperable three-part difficulty is that love, as another saying goes, may be blind. It is not always discriminating. One needs a basis for deciding in a pinch to whom to extend love. As one of Bruno Bettelheim's books puts it, *Love Is Not Enough*. There is a need for wisdom, reason, and moral priorities. A second, related part of this difficulty is that there are too many beings to love, and choices need to be made as to who is worthy of love. Third—and this may explain the need to issue a commandment to love—while romantic and sexual love may come "naturally," the love of lepers, the poor, the diseased, trees, and other beings may not be a love that comes so easily. We are limited not only as to who the recipients of love may be, but also as to whom we are capable of and interested in loving. In either case, to borrow an economic metaphor, the demand for love exceeds the supply. There is just not enough to go around.

There is, finally, this rejoinder to the Agapist from the ancient Greek philosopher Aristotle (384–322 B.C.). One cannot be happy, according to Aristotle, without being healthy, reasonably wealthy, and goodlooking. The point is that one cannot identify happiness or love exclusively with the otherworldly.[9]

Majority Rule vs. Absolute Moral Principles

Another moral issue is majority rule versus appeal to absolute moral principles. This issue is sometimes expressed as an appeal to the "greatest happiness of the greatest number."[10]

Utilitarianism. Classical Utilitarianism was developed by Jeremy Bentham (1748–1826) and John Stuart Mill (1806–1873). Bentham was the first to develop a "hedonistic calculus." He notes that, no matter what moral philosophers and moralists say, we are all governed by two masters: pain and pleasure. The point about ethics is to minimize the first and maximize the second as much as possible. This is now called cost/benefit analysis, which some people would define as cost/risk/benefit ratio. One may ask about any desire: What does it cost? What is the risk? What is the benefit? To Bentham, the basis for judging any pain and pleasure, the principle of utility, depends on seven criteria. They are "(1) its intensity; (2) its duration; (3) its certainty or uncertainty; (4) its propinquity or remoteness; (5) its fecundity . . . or the chance it has of being followed by 'similar' sensations; (6) its purity" as a pleasure of being followed by more pleasure rather than pain, and "(7) its extent . . . the number of persons to whom it extends (or . . . who are affected by it."[11]

An example of Utilitarian ethics applied to everyday nursing is the nurse's decision to give pain medication. This depends on the medication's predicted effect of diminishing or eliminating the intensity of pain considered in relation to its side effects, such as the slowing of respiration. Similarly, a person taking a drink of alcohol does so to get a pleasure of some intensity. Intensity also figures in the most intimate human experience—namely, sexual intimacy leading to and including sexual intercourse. Richard Wasserstrom, a contemporary philosopher, argues that the high degree of intensity in sexual intercourse is a basis for marital exclusivity in our present culture. According to Wasserstrom,

> It is obvious that one of the more powerful desires is the desire for sexual gratification. . . . Once we experience sexual intercourse ourselves—and in particular once we experience orgasm, we discover that it is among the most intensive, short term pleasures of the body.[12]

A second criterion, duration, is also of concern to everyone. "How long will this pleasure last?" is a common question. Vacationers and honeymooners alike are known to dread the end of their bliss in some Paradise Island for return to the drudgery and dreariness, drabness, boredom, and monotony of their lives and work. Conversely, how long a patient has to continue a particularly painful treatment again speaks to the relevance of duration in judging pleasures and pains.

Bentham's third criterion, certainty or uncertainty, is an important consideration in health care. Even the most innocuous, routine treatment such as an aspirin tablet or a tonsillectomy has the element of risk in it. For some patients, either of these beneficial therapies ends in death. Considerations of sureness and risk are relevant in evaluating which pleasures and pain to live by. A fourth criterion, propinquity or remoteness, concerns the nearness or distance of an intended pleasure or pain. Patients farthest away from the nursing station are apt to get the least attention. An example of fecundity or fruitfulness that applies to nursing is continuous patient care, preferably by similar personnel, as basic for a patient's healing process.

Purity refers to unmixed feelings. An excess of alcohol may, for example, be followed by a painful sensation. The aim of nursing is one of relieving suffering and promoting health. Nursing is impure when mixed with business dealings with the patient. Finally, extent, to Bentham, concerns the numbers of people affected by a consideration of pain and pleasure. Nurses with six to eight acutely ill patients in their charge will have to distribute their nursing services to a greater extent than if assigned to half that number.

An advantage of Bentham's classical Utilitarianism is that it puts us in touch with feelings of pleasure and pain. A strength of the utility principle is that, in questions of resource allocation, it appeals to the principle of *sufferability*, one that includes the capacity of all sentient beings to suffer. The principle of resource allocation is based on the Utilitarian and also democratic maxim framed by Bentham, "Everybody is to count for one, nobody for more than one."[13] This means that the pleasure-pain calculus considers that "the equal pains or pleasures, satisfactions or dissatisfactions . . . are given the same weight, whether they be Brahmins or Untouchables, Jews or Christians, black or white."[14] The idea that each counts for one is basic to the principle of social equality. In nursing, the equality principle means that nurses are to treat all patients with equal consideration.

A difficulty of Bentham's Utilitarianism is that it leaves too little room for moral values other than pain and pleasure. Other important values are freedom of the will, duty, love, respect for the individual, truthfulness, or even saving an individual's life if doing so collides with the application of the pleasure-pain calculus.

John Stuart Mill attempts to remedy Bentham's difficulties. According to Mill, an action is right if it conforms to "the greatest-happiness principle."[15] This ethics is called "goal based" because it renounces *a priori* or absolute preconceptions of how best to provide the good that is defined by the greatest-happiness principle. Rather, the Utilitarian ethics follows inductive methods of trial and error, currently called "cost/benefit analysis," with the avowed aim to help the maximum number of persons to flourish. To Mill, "actions are right in proportion as they tend to promote happiness, wrong as they tend to produce the reverse of happiness."[16] To Bentham's criteria, Mill adds quality of pleasure or pain, a quality appropriate for human beings. He adds this further requirement: "Utilitarianism requires" a person "to be strictly impartial as a disinterested and benevolent spectator. . . . In the golden rule of Jesus of Nazareth, we read the complete spirit of the ethics of utility. 'To do as you would be done by' and 'to love your neighbor as yourself' constitutes the ideal perfection of Utilitarian morality."[17]

Mill offers a proof for the principle of utility:

> The only proof capable of being given that an object is visible is that people actually see it. The only proof that a sound is audible is that

> people hear it. . . . In like manner, I apprehend the sole evidence it is possible to produce that anything is desirable is that people do actually desire it.[18]

In this passage, Mill commits the is-ought fallacy by inferring that what is desired is therefore desirable. That is like saying that, because Hospital X policymakers desire nurses to work a double shift on occasion, such a policy is therefore desirable and ought to be put into practice.

An advantage of Mill's greatest-happiness principle is that it takes the consequences of our actions seriously, a point which no opponent of Utilitarianism can ignore.

Although Mill's Utilitarianism has these strengths, there are several difficulties. Although Mill invokes the ethics of Jesus, Utilitarianism is concerned with aggregate happiness, doing good for the greatest number, which is not equivalent to caring for and loving everyone. A few examples may show the difference between the ethics of Jesus and Mill's Utilitarianism. If a tank with 10 soldiers and an innocent hostage tied visibly to its front is firing at you and 60 friends and neighbors, more lives are to be saved by destroying the tank and all its occupants, including the innocent hostage. Therefore, doing so is not wrong on Utilitarian grounds. But such an action is morally wrong, according to the ethics of Jesus. Similarly, in triage health care problems in which some lives can be saved, Utilitarian ethics emphasizes help to the greatest number. In the face of limited resources, an application of Utilitarianianism calls for the subordination of some people, such as the terminally ill, to the care of the majority of persons. However, to pick an analogous problem, if 85 percent of the population of a hypothetical society live well at the expense of 15 percent who live miserably, Utilitarianism seems to have no constraint against such a policy. Some would argue that such a practice is morally wrong. A difficulty of Utilitarianism is that appeal to majority happiness overlooks the value of the individual who, although in a minority, may deserve help. The health care needs of mentally ill, retarded, aged, and other vulnerable patients, for example, may call for taxes the majority opposes.

Utilitarianism has not answered these and other difficulties, as what to do about sacrificing some individuals for the good of the majority. One response is that there are situations in wartime or in disasters in which there is no way other than to consider the well-being and health of the majority while sacrificing individuals. The use of triage—of sorting out the wounded into those who will survive without help, those who will die anyway, and those who can most benefit from help—is an example of the application of Utilitarian principles. A prominent example of concern for the majority's happiness is the military draft, which places a number of persons, usually young men, at risk in defense of the large majority of citizens. Another example of Utilitarian ethics is the distribution of scarce resources in response to majority happiness. Still another example in health care is the risk nurses and physicians take when they are exposed to patients with contagious diseases. An objection to Utilitarianism arises, however: Any such policies, which subordinate certain individuals or groups of individuals, can never be just.

Universal Moral Principles. Utilitarian ethics is opposed by the equal and uncompromising application of fixed principles, regardless of changing circumstances. If one chooses not to treat a neonate with trisomy 18, giving the only available respirator to a neonate with only a slight respiratory difficulty instead, one appeals to a Utilitarian principle: Maximize benefit, minimize harm.

Opposed to Utilitarianism is the idea of *principled morality* or *deontologic ethics*, whose major proponent was the great philosopher Immanuel Kant (1724–1804). Kant held that an act is good if everyone ought, for rational reasons and in similar circumstances, to act in the same way without exception. The basis for doing this is that it is rational, universal, free, and uncoerced.[19] This is called the *categorical imperative* or *universalizability principle*, and it tells us to act always on that principle on which everyone in the same situation ought to act. One is to act from the point of view of a rational impartial spectator, which alone is a worthy moral position. Kant cites five examples of categorical imperatives relevant to nursing ethics: (1) Suicide or taking any life is wrong, because if everyone who felt like it committed suicide or killed someone else, the human race would soon be extinct. (2) Always keep promises. To break a promise, if generalized, says in effect that promises are not morally important. But they are; moral and social life could not occur without promises. (3) Never squander your talents. You owe it to the human race to develop to the optimum. (4) Always help those in need. Everyone at some time or other needs the help of others. (5) Always tell the truth. To be rational and moral requires one to be truthful, regardless of consequences to oneself.

On the basis of the categorical imperative and these examples of always preserving everyone's life, keeping promises, developing one's talents, helping others in distress, and never lying, Kant formulates a substantive principle, which is to act so that one treats oneself or any other person always as an "end" and never as a means only.[20] Kant's principle is a welcome antidote to the wanton disregard of patients, family members, and health professionals in relation to hard cases in everyday nursing.

Paul Freund cites an example from World War II showing how the "greatest-happiness" criterion or majority rule prevailed over uncompromising principles. A choice between allocating scarce supplies of penicillin to wounded soldiers in Africa or to soldiers with gonorrhea had to be made. The principled action would have been to give the penicillin to the wounded. But the decision was to give it to those "wounded in brothels."[21] This decision exposes a moral difficulty of Utilitarianism by appealing to Kantian moral principles, which show no doubt as to who gets scarce penicillin, namely those who are wounded in battle. If, however, one appeals to some version of triage or to the greatest benefit of the greatest number, the appeal to some form of Utilitarianism seems to provide the morally preferable decision. To Ethical Relativists, it depends on one's expected moral outcome.

However, there is a price one pays in sacrificing moral principles. A war, a sports contest, a business deal may be won; a hospital emergency may be solved, all by ignoring a Kantian moral imperative to keep a promise, tell the truth, or treat each patient as an end and not as a means only. A price to all concerned is that the moral quality of everyone's life will decline.

There is no room in Kant's categorical imperative for special privileges, irrational acts, or coerced acts. The universalizability principle states the right act regardless of anyone's or everyone's inclination, impulse, convenience, or even of the majority welfare. To act morally is to do what is rational, universal, and desirable for the whole human race, independent of anyone's pleasure, and without regard for the consequences.

There is an important difference between the categorical imperative and the famous Golden Rule, which superficially resembles the categorical imperative. The Golden Rule directs that we treat others as we would like to be treated. The categorical imperative says instead to treat oneself and all others as everyone including oneself ought to be treated—freely, rationally, and impartially. If, for example, one enjoys smoking or drinking excessively, then on Golden Rule grounds one may justifiably impose cigarettes and alcohol on others. The categorical imperative rules out such conduct.

There are difficulties, however, with appeal to Kantian principles. One difficulty is that their application is sometimes impractical. Worse, the unswerving application of rigid principles can have disastrous consequences. Moreover, disregarding consequences of actions is a contradiction of what it means to do ethics. Even Kant's principles lead to consequences that are in principle good rather than evil—which explains why people should consider Kant's principles carefully. Even if one acknowledges the essential rationality of Kant's principles, this does not mean one follows every example of his to its inevitable conclusion. To lie to an evildoer such as a Nazi is not necessarily wrong.

Contemporary Moral Views. Kant influenced four contemporary moral philosophers who have had an impact on nursing ethics.

To John Rawls, the idea of justice as fairness occupies center stage in ethics. Justice is uncompromising. To understand justice as fairness, we are to imagine that we all have a "veil of ignorance."[22] This means to imagine that we do not know our biological, social, and economic place in the world. We do not know whether we will be born smart, stupid, average, beautiful, ugly, male, female, healthy or unhealthy, white or black, rich or poor. On this basis, according to Rawls, we would choose two principles. One is that we would all have equal political liberties. The second principle is that economic inequalities would be constrained by three provisions. These provisions are that inequalities are justified only if (1) they contribute to the advantage of all, (2) if they help the least advantaged, and (3) if they contribute to "the fair equality of opportunity."[23] There are certain difficulties in implementing Rawlsian priorities regarding the role of need and merit in health care, even on a just basis. However, appeal to justice as fairness uncompromisingly rules out certain socially profitable practices such as slavery, segregation, abuse, and disrespect, regardless of what advantages there are for such practices. Rawls' aim is to equalize access to the primary goods of life, such as power, money, and good health.

In response to Rawls' work, Nozick makes the point that only "individuals have rights,"[24] rather than states or corporations. Anything but a minimal state infringes on individuals' rights. Support for public assistance and health care, as examples, imposes "forced labor" on taxpayers. A minimum obligation to any individual means that if one sees a little boy drowning in a puddle of water, one has no obligation to save the child. Such a position seems counterintuitive. However, Nozick shows, perhaps by exaggeration, that there are limits to one's obligations.

A closely allied Libertarian is Sade, who argues that health care is not a right or privilege, but a "purchasable commodity"[25] on the open market.

Finally, Dworkin argues that the function of states is to protect individual rights. To Dworkin, individual rights are "political trumps held by individuals,"[26] which no state may take away. However, the emphasis in the concept of rights Dworkin defends identifies rights with the idea of equality rather than liberty. To Dworkin, individual rights are held equally. To Dworkin, people do not have a right to equal shares or equal treatment in the distribution of health care resources, but a right to equal consideration and to treatment as equals. One can recognize that the rights both to liberty and to equality are important to patients and nurses alike.

Finally, a recent, important, and influential philosophical-psychological contribution to nursing ethics is the work of Lawrence Kohlberg. He proposes to refute Relativism and Subjectivism by identifying three levels and six stages of moral growth and development. Level 1 is Preconventional. Stage 1 in Level 1 is oriented by fear of punishment and obedience to authority. Stage 2 is instrumental and relativistic. "You scratch my back and I'll scratch yours." The second level is the Conventional Level, with Stages 3 and 4. Stage 3 is marked by "nice-guy, nice-girl" behavior, approved by the peer group. Stage 4 consists in conforming to "law and order." Level 3 consists in Postconventional, autonomous, principled behavior. Here, Stage 5 is a "social contract, constitutional-legal orientation." Finally, Stage 6 consists of a "universal-ethical principled" orientation.[27]

Kohlberg's emphasis is not on conscience, as consciences differ. Kohlberg's appeal is rather to universal principles, like saving life, preventing harm, and truth-telling. Human beings grow morally in these ways and through these six stages, according to Kohlberg.

There are merits in Kohlberg's stages of moral development. One advantage is that Kohlberg provides a good argument against Subjectivism and Relativism. A second strength of Kohlberg's analysis is that it suggests parallels between intellectual and moral development.[28] The brighter one is, the more apt one is to be moral.

There are, however, several difficulties with Kohlberg's analysis. First, an account of how one develops morally, even if true, does not imply or justify how one ought to behave or develop. The is-ought fallacy is committed here. Second, one may arrive at the right moral decision of preventing harm by a conventional or even preconventional, Egoist move. Even Kohlberg's example of stealing a cancer-curing drug for one's wife appeals to self-preservation, a Hobbesian value, at the Preconventional or Egoist stage. Egoism is not always morally wrong. The Egoist action might in some cases be the right thing to do. Third, there are no proofs that the moral hierarchical method, in which one arrives at universal moral principles, is the valid and sound view in all cases. Fourth, if the way one developed morally could not be altered by a moral agent, then one could not be said to have a free will with which to make moral decisions. But if one could do nothing to alter ones moral behavior, there would be no point in telling anyone what optimal, desirable moral development would be. Kohlberg's stages of moral development would be like describing the growth of a tadpole into a frog.

If, however, Kohlberg intended his six stages as a proposal as to how individuals ought to develop morally, in which free will is assumed, then people would have a choice. Where people make choices, good as well as bad may result. If there is a choice as to how to develop morally, then we would have no sure way of knowing how moral development ought necessarily to proceed. Followers of Nietzsche, Thrasymachus, Existentialists, and others who give their moral reasons for denying the moral desirability of the sixth stage have not been shown that their position is morally wrong in all cases. One may prefer truth-telling and doing away with the use of placebos. Yet, there are reasons involving the prevention of harm, that could justify lying and giving placebos, in some instances. To reiterate, Kohlberg has not been able to show that stages of hierarchical moral development from the lowest, Egoism and obedience, to the highest stage of acting on universal principles is the way to become increasingly moral. If Kohlberg were successful, he would show that ethics has a true and valid answer. This, however, has not been shown.

Individualism vs. Collectivism

A further example of a moral issue is that of Individualism versus Collectivism. The first emphasizes individual liberty, individual self-determination, initiative, self-reliance, and self-realization. To an Individualist, social institutions are the sum total of individual efforts and actions. One form Individualism takes is Existentialism, which holds individuals responsible for their actions and inactions equally. If a nurse fails to put the guard rails of a bed up, for example, resulting in an 80-year-old patient's falling out of bed, breaking his hip, getting pneumonia, and dying, the nurse is responsible for killing the patient.

A major Existentialist, Jean Paul Sartre, holds individuals responsible because "we are," he says, "all condemned to be free."[29] One can only be held responsible for one's acts if one is free to choose. To Sartre, one is free. Therefore, one has to choose, and to choose is to be responsible.

Collectivism, on the other hand, holds society as a whole responsible for human problems, including widespread starvation, lack of drinking water, and the lack of health care in many parts of the world.

One form of Collectivism is Marxism, originating with Karl Marx (1818–1883). To Marx, individuals are not free; only groups of individuals with power are free in capitalist societies. Those with power are free to exploit others, turning the majority into wage slaves. This form of Collectivism calls for total social change rather than the piecemeal social program proposed by Bentham and by Existentialists.

There are strengths and weaknesses in each of these models. Individualism, especially Existentialism, emphasizes attractive qualities associated with individual liberty, individual initiative, hard work, and rewards for individual merit. However, individuals can amass power and abuse others. Out of such abuse comes the appeal of Collectivism. This doctrine promises to do for individuals what they cannot possibly do alone, namely, organize to form better rules for achieving social and economic justice. Appeal to collectivities, sometimes identified as corporate bodies, can also provide for more widespread needs and wants than is possible by appeal to Individualism. Collectivities and sometimes corporate organization provide security from the basic human wants. They sometimes do so, however, at great cost to individual liberty and to individual self-development.

Values in Conflict

People also want irreconcilable moral values in health care. They want the prevention of harm,[30] but they also want the minimum of suffering, along with freedom of choice, as illustrated by Jehovah's Witnesses' refusal to accept blood transfusions. People want a long life, pleasure, and affluence. They want both to eat and reduce. People want meaningful democractic participation, fair and equal treatment, and speedy and impartial application of justice. They also want their own way, and some people think justice is on their side. One cannot have all these values.

These alternative moral models show that ethics is not a science with verifiable answers. For there is for some issues no rational way to resolve divergencies and conflicts. Nor can one beat someone else's position down by some definition of what is "ethical" or "unethical," found in a professional code, such as the *Code for Nurses*. Against the idea that there is objectivity in ethics, there are divergencies in moral views, along with tragedy and stalemate. As I. Berlin, a contemporary philosopher, points out, if two patients need one kidney dialysis machine, for the one excluded there is tragedy. For Barney Clark's mechanical-heart operation, there were thousands of applicants who have since died.

Four Aspects of Ethics

To clarify what ethics is, we may consider four senses of ethics.

Formal Aspect. One sense of ethics is formal, expressed through a professional code. The *Code for Nurses*, for example, refers to "unethical behavior." Also ethics derived from religion with a creed, code, and cult implies moral rules, such as the Ten Commandments, on the basis of a religious doctrine.

Conventional or Sociological. A second sense of morality is a conventional or sociological sense, in which one elicits moral conduct from an empirical study of one's culture or customs. Nurses in the 1920s stood up when a physician entered a room and "obeyed" medical orders without question.

Philosophical Models of Morality. A third sense of morality occurs if one identifies ethics with some philosophical model and shows the interplay and dialogue between such models. In that sense, ethics is more like an art than a formal or factual science.

Everyday Intuitions. According to a fourth sense of ethics, one may use ethics in its everyday intuitive role. In this sense, ethics may be revealed through a figure in literature, such as Platon Karataef, a wise peasant in Tolstoy's *War and Peace*, or through Huck in *Huckleberry Finn*. This is the everyday common sense of the person in the street who expresses moral views.

An attempt to provide an ethical justification makes reference to all four senses. A model of morality usually emphasizes one or more but not all of these senses. Thus, ethics has objective aspects, as well as subjective and relativistic ones. A mistake some people make in doing ethics in nursing or any other field is to regard ethics as exclusively formal, scientific, philosophic, or a matter of everyday intuitions. Ethics is a composite of all four.

Paradigm Case Arguments

All is not futile. There is a passageway between the unacceptable alternatives of objectivity and subjectivity in ethics. A promising lead consists of refuting paradigms or standard examples.[31] Paradigms or standard examples are partway between subjectivity and objectivity. In metaphysics, F.H. Bradley once argued that "Time does not exist." Another philosopher, G.E. Moore, then offered this refuting paradigm with the example, "I had breakfast before lunch." A paradigm in ethics is the same Moore's classic refutation of Mill, who held that whatever is desired is therefore desirable. Moore cited examples of bad desires to refute Mill's argument.

PARADIGM ARGUMENTS IN HEALTH CARE: A FIVE-PRONGED ARGUMENT FOR RIGHTS

To turn to an example of how the paradigm case argument may work in health care and nursing ethics, the view was held not so long ago that patients and nurses have no rights. To refute this, appeal is made to standard examples of rights in health care, examples that show how rights function.

Tuskeegee

The ignoble Tuskeegee experiment showed as decisively as any refuting argument can that, if there are any morally justified values at all, they include human rights of patients, subjects, and health professionals to informed consent. From 1932 to 1972 a 40-year experiment was performed to study the difference between those syphilis patients who were treated with penicillin and those who were not.[32] A public health nurse helped persuade over 300 black men with syphilis to forgo the penicillin treatment, even though it had already been tested and was available.[33] According to Elizabeth Carnegie, a nurse, "experiments performed on human subjects by professionals ... violate" the rights of subjects if done without informed consent.[34]

As this experiment was exposed to public scrutiny, its immorality became obvious. The Tuskeegee experiment was a horrendous evil, a moral outrage, a gross violation of justice.[35] The Tuskeegee example is also a paradigm or standard example against the thesis that the nurse does not need to know anything, that a nurse just takes orders and keeps quiet. The exposure of the Tuskeegee experiment shows that there is no place for ignorant nursing. Nursing based on ignorance is a contradiction. Ignorance includes the moral ignorance of those who unthinkingly cooperate with an evil experiment. A nurse to be effective needs to have a high degree of knowledge, including the knowledge needed to help make justifiable moral decisions, which is possible in clear cases of this kind. As a paradigm case argument or standard example, the exposure of the Tuskeegee experiment is an instance that refutes the contention that patients and subjects have no rights, such as the right to informed consent.

Nazi Experiments

A second prong in favor of informed consent of patients and subjects as a right was the monstrous evil of certain Nazi medical experiments. Dehumanized Nazi experiments "related to sterilization techniques, cold water survival, decompression and heteroplastic transplantation."[36] In addition, the Nazi genocide program, entitled "Euthanasia," which consisted in "techniques of efficient killing," eliminated "thousands of patients with chronic disease or mental illness."[37] According to one writer, a group of Nazi physicians, called "doctors of infamy," under Hitler's chief physician, Karl Brandt, carried out the selection and killing of patients "deemed physically or mentally unfit, with injections of barbiturates, phenol, and in most cases through carbon monoxide gas, the lethal component of exhaust gases from motor vehicles."[38] As a result of Nazi medical atrocities, the Nuremberg Code, an international guideline, emerged after the Nuremberg doctors' trial. Among "its principal points are that informed consent must be obtained from all subjects."[39] Both of these paradigms or standard examples count as refuting arguments against the view that there are no rights for participants in health care, such as patients, subjects, and nurses. The infamous abuses of human rights contributed to what some people call Nuremberg morality; this is made explicit and incorporated in the 1975 Declaration of Helsinki (see Appendix).

The Women's Rights Movement

A third prong in favor of the right to informed consent is the women's rights movement and, in particular, J. Thomson's important article, "In Defense of Abortion." Whatever the merits or weaknesses of Thomson's argument on abortion, her view of moral rights as a form of self-defense against abuse contributed strongly to antisexist morality. She emphasized a vital principle in the ethics of health care and in social life that applies to nurses in particular. The principle Thomson enunciated is that to have rights at all is to have rights in and to one's body.[40]

Nurses' Rights

In nursing, Claire Fagin and her teacher Hildegard Peplau refuted the idea that patients and nurses have no rights by arguing that nurses have a right to refuse to administer electroconvulsive therapy (ECT).[41] Another refutation in nursing is the argument against the "master-of the-ship" doctrine that the physician knows best. In *Charleston Memorial Hospital* vs. *K. Darling*, physicians were held responsible for neglecting the patient. One nurse was also charged with neglecting to report her observations, which could have saved the 18-year-old Darling's leg. After 14 days in a poorly prepared cast, Darling's leg turned gangrenous and had to be amputated.[42] The *Darling* case showed that responsibility is not confined to a physician or the hospital alone. It is also attributed to nurses. With responsibility, training, and ability come decision-making rights or privileges to decide within rules, such as those enjoyed by auto drivers or professional practitioners. One writer calls these "discretionary rights."

Karen Ann Quinlan

A fifth and last prong is presented by the case of Karen Ann Quinlan, in which the person affected is unable to make a decision. One then tests the next best idea to informed consent—namely, proxy consent. Sometimes a nurse has to act on behalf of a patient or subject who is comatose or otherwise defenseless. Here, one can use a retrospective or subjunctive analysis,[43] and ask what that person would want if that person were in a rational frame of mind.

RIGHTS AS A FORM OF MORAL STANDING

Although one may not think too well of some recent abuses or excesses of rights assertions, the paradigm examples cited show the role and justification of human rights. Rights as rallying symbols, cries, and slogans are generated by detecting and exposing violations of justice. To have rights is to have a form of moral standing. When you have rights, like your right to a paycheck, you know where you stand and where others stand. Your right to your paycheck means it is yours and your employers, if they have not paid you, owe it to you. The attempt to take your paycheck away from you is a gross violation of justice.[44] To have rights worth having is to have a just entitlement to a sphere of protected freedom of choice and action.

THE MEANING AND IMPORTANCE OF RIGHTS

There are five conditions that help define rights of importance. The first is that to have a right is to be free to exercise it or not as one chooses, without being blamed or punished for exercising or not exercising one's right. Thus, my right to vote means I may vote, I have permission to vote, and I may rightfully demand or claim that right; but I am not required to vote, and no penalty or harm should come to me if I choose not to. Similarly, a patient's right to treatment means a patient may demand or claim the right to treatment but is not required to undergo it if he or she so chooses.

A second condition of any right of importance is that others have duties to facilitate one's exercise of rights in appropriate ways. The poll watchers and police have a duty to protect my right to vote if I exercise that right. Similarly, a patient's right to treatment means relevant health professionals have corresponding duties to assure and protect that patient's right.

A third condition of any right is that one's right accords with rationally defensible principles of justice. Such principles generally coincide with equality, impartiality, and fairness. They also reconcile conflicting claims of need and merit in a fair proportion. Rights based on justice rule against legal and institutional rights that have no basis in justice. If Barney Clark, the mechanical-heart recipient, for example, had been the richest person in need of this operation, giving him the first heart for that reason would have been unfair or unjust.

A fourth condition is that a right of importance is enforceable. Other relevant persons are both to recognize and effectively protect a person in the exercise of his or her rights. According to L. Becker, a philosopher, enforceability means that "if I have a right to your help . . . and you refuse, some sort of arm twisting is in order."[45] Enforceable rights are specific and special. In nursing the enforceability provision means that in a hospital that honors a bill of rights, provision is made for mechanisms called "whistle-blowing" for reporting violations of patients' rights. Patient-care and ethics committees may also provide for implementation of human rights in the health care setting.

A fifth and related condition is that if a right is violated, set aside, or overridden in favor of some other right or value, the person whose right was violated or set aside is given compensation. The concept of rights violations implies that something is owed to the victim.[46] Rights thus imply freedom, duties, and justice. These conditions, in turn, imply enforceability and compensations for violations or infringements. These conditions show how seriously a society takes rights and therefore how important such rights are.

The Transcendence of Human Rights

Resulting human rights are moral rights of a very important kind, shared equally by all persons. These human rights are the union of two kinds of rights: self-determination rights and rights to well-being. One can critically evaluate legal and institutional rights by reference to human rights. The importance of rights is the conceptual link they provide between being a rightholder and being a person. To deny patients and nurses their status as rightholders, with all the conditions implied, in effect denies their status as persons.

Rights and Moral Standing

To have moral standing means that persons are entitled to be recognized and heard, and to have their views considered fairly and equally. Rights to protected freedom and care serve as a basis for claims and actions. To have moral standing is to be respected.[47] It is also to act responsibly by respecting the rights of others, and thus working within the rules for achieving and maintaining everyone's moral standing. A right as a form of standing is a social achievement, not a self-evident characteristic found in human nature; nor is a form of standing an inalienable birthright. There are no rights against wildlife or against events in nature, like snow, rain, typhoons, or lightning. Rights are for people, and the duties rights imply are imposed upon and accepted by people.

The Justification of Rights

The justification of rights consists in showing, through standard examples, why a world with rights is morally preferable to one without rights. Rights enable people to do things, like vote, pray, go to school or go to a hospital, receive social security, and do things to enjoy life. Rights are like red and green traffic lights, showing where people stand. A view of rights that regards rights as a form of moral standing, as entrenched and seriously held social values, places rights partway between moral objectivity and subjectivity; as being in some respects objective and in other respects subjective. Rights, after all, result from interests and desires. Yet rights are also a composite of other values, like freedom, love, restraints, duties, and justice. Beyond that, rights break down in the recognition that tragedy and stalemate, too, are aspects of the ethical life of human beings that no formalization or objectivity can overcome.

CONCLUSION

Rights, with all their infirmities, are still better than a world without rights or a world with too few rights reserved for owners of power, goods, and people. A world with equal rights, including patients, subjects, and health professionals, elevates everyone's moral standing. As truth is to the realm of facts and descriptions, rights are to social institutions. Human ideas and institutions without truth and rights are empty.[48]

REFERENCES

1. American Nurses' Association: Code for Nurses with Interpretive Statements. Kansas City, Mo., The Association, 1976.
2. Scheffler I.: "Philosophical models of teaching." In Scheffler I. (ed.), Reason and Teaching. Indianapolis, Bobbs-Merrill, 1975, p. 67.
3. Steele S.M., Harmon V.M.: Values Clarification in Nursing, 2nd ed. New York, Appleton-Century-Crofts, 1983, p. 13–14.
4. Rachels J.: Can ethics provide answers? In Caplan A., Callahan D. (eds.), Ethics for Hard Times. New York, Plenum, 1981, p. 1–30.
5. Hobbes T.: The leviathan. In Jones W.T. et al. (eds.), Approaches to Ethics, 3rd ed. New York, McGraw-Hill, 1977, p. 182.
6. Frankena W.: Ethics, 2nd ed. Englewood Cliffs, N.J., Prentice-Hall, 1973, p. 56–59.
7. Ibid., p. 56.
8. Jones W.T.: A History of Western Philosophy, 2nd ed. New York, Harcourt Brace, 1969, vol. II, p. 149–152.
9. Aristotle: Nicomachean Ethics, Martin Ostwald, tr. Indianapolis, Bobbs-Merrill, 1962, p. 21–22.
10. Mill J.S.: Utilitarianism. New York, Liberal Arts, 1957, p. 10.
11. Bentham J.: Morals and legislation. In Jones W.T. et al. (eds.), Approaches to Ethics, 3rd ed. New York, McGraw-Hill, 1972, p. 260.
12. Wasserstrom R.: Is adultery immoral? In Arthur J. (ed.), Morality and Moral Controversies. Englewood Cliffs, N.J., Prentice-Hall, 1981, p. 118–119.
13. Hart H.L.A.: Between utility and rights. In Rylen A. (ed.), The Idea of Freedom: Essays in Honor of Isaiah Berlin. New York, Oxford University Press, 1979, p. 79.
14. Ibid.
15. Mill: Utilitarianism, p. 6.
16. Ibid., p. 10.
17. Ibid., p. 22.
18. Ibid., p. 44.
19. Kant I.: Fundamental Principles of the Metaphysics of Morals. New York, Liberal Arts, p. 38.
20. Ibid., p. 46.
21. Ramsey P.: The Patient as Person. New Haven, Yale University Press, 1971, p. 257–258.
22. Rawls J.: A Theory of Justice. Cambridge, Mass., Harvard University Press, 1971, p. 136–142.
23. Ibid., p. 302.
24. Nozick R.: Anarchy, State and Utopia. New York, Basic Books, 1974, p. xi.
25. Sade R.: Medical care as a right: A refutation. N Engl J Med 285:1288, 1971.
26. Dworkin R.: Taking Rights Seriously. Cambridge, Mass., Harvard University Press, 1978, p. xi.
27. Kohlberg L.: Stages of moral development as a basis for moral development. In Moral Interdisciplinary Approaches. Paramus, N.J., Newman, 1971, p. 86–88.
28. Olson R.G.: A Short Introduction to Ethics. New York, Random House, 1978, p. 105.

29. Warnock M.: Existentialist Ethics. London, Macmillan, 1967, p. 39-49.
30. Hutt P.: Five moral imperatives of government regulation. Hastings Center Report 10(1):29-31, 1980.
31. Macklin R.: Return to the Best Interests of the Child. In Gaylin W., Macklin R. (eds.), Who Speaks for the Child. New York, Plenum, 1982, p. 294-295.
32. Marshal C.L., Marshal C.P.: Poverty and health: The United States. In Reich W. (ed.), Encyclopedia of Bioethics. New York, Macmillan, 1978, vol. 3, p. 1320.
33. Carnegie E.: The Patient's Bill of Rights and the nurse. In Nicholls M., Wessels V. (eds.), Nursing Standards and Nursing Process. Wakefield, Mass., Contemporary Publishing, 1977, p. 69.
34. Ibid.
35. Cranston M.: What Are Human Rights? New York, Taplinger, 1973, p. 68.
36. Vastyan E.: Medicine and war. In Encyclopedia of Bioethics, p. 1696.
37. Gruman G.J.: Death and dying: Euthanasia and sustaining life: Historical perspectives. In Encyclopedia of Bioethics, vol. 1, p. 267.
38. Redlich F.C.: Medical ethics under national socialism. In Encyclopedia of Bioethics, vol. 3, p. 1016.
39. Ibid., p. 1018.
40. Thomson J.: In defense of abortion. In Feinberg J. (ed.), The Problem of Abortion. Belmont, Calif., Wadsworth, 1973, p. 128.
41. Fagin C.: Nurses' rights. Am J Nursing 75(1):82, 1975.
42. Charleston Community Memorial Hospital v. Dorrence Kenneth Darling, 33 Ill. 326, 211 NE 2nd 253, 1965.
43. Bandman B. and E.: The nurse's role in an interest based view of patients' rights. In Spicker S., Gadow S. (eds.), Nursing: Images and Ideals. New York, Springer, 1980, p. 137-145.
44. Cranston, M.: What Are Human Rights? New York, Taplinger, 1973, p. 68.
45. Becker L.: Individual rights. In Regan T., Van DeVeer D. (eds.), And Justice for All. Totowa, N.J., Roman and Littlefield, 1982, p. 203.
46. Ibid.
47. Singer P.: The concept of moral standing. In Caplan A., Callahan D. (eds.) Ethics for Hard Times. New York, Plenum, 1981, p. 31-36, 40-41.
48. Rawls J.: A Theory of Justice. Cambridge, Mass., Harvard University Press, 1971, p. 3.

CHAPTER 5

Ethical Decision Making in Nursing: Values and Guidelines

Through study of this chapter, the student will be able to:

1. Apply the principles of self-determination, well-being, and equity as an integral part of the nursing process
2. Assess the patient's capacity, voluntariness, and ability to communicate for effective participation in shared decision making
3. Develop the nursing role as leader, technician, teacher, counselor, and surrogate in facilitating the patient's participation in shared decisions
4. Utilize nursing guidelines and strategies in supporting the client's full participation in shared decisions on the basis of identified goals, values, and rational life plans

INTRODUCTION

Ethical principles apply throughout health care and nursing practice. To give or to withhold care to a dying patient is a moral decision; so is activity focused on facilitating patients' participation in making health care decisions. Client choices may be justified by the principle of self-determination. Other decisions may be justified by the principle of patients' best interests. Individuals, goals, values, and circumstances vary. Ethics is not a science with true or false answers. Ethical decisions cannot be reached "simply by following handy formulas. No matter how carefully one issue has been resolved, the solution cannot be applied in cookbook fashion to another problem. Rather each issue . . . must be examined in the context of its particular circumstances."[1]

The rapid evolution of high technology in health care has brought about better health, an increased quality and length of life, and "new sources of hope for the ill."[2] A change brought on by the "technological revolution"[3] is the wide range of available choices within health care. The question has moved from that of acceptance or rejection of a single intervention for a specific condition to the more complex question of which intervention to choose. Since each of these options carries different estimates of success, different side effects, and different degrees of intrusiveness, the implications for the patient's way of life are profound. The role of the health care professional is being redefined. The ends and the limits of health care are widely questioned. Consumer expectations are changing. Generally, patients expect to maintain control and be responsible for decisions involving their lives and health in the light of the values and goals they hold dear.

The ideal of shared, pluralistic, and reasonable decision making in health care is the model examined in this chapter. The proposed guidelines provide a basis for nurses to engage in justifiable ethical reasoning (see Figure 5-1).

VALUES RELATED TO HEALTH CARE DECISIONS

Values and Principles Underlying the Decision-Making Process

Human beings hold many values simultaneously and without conflict. In times of illness and stress, certain values come to the forefront and take priority. Values of special significance to the decision process will be discussed here and in more detail throughout this work.

The Principle of Self-Determination. Patient self-determination is an important value to be respected and enhanced by nurses and other participants in health care decisions. The American Nurses' Association, in its *Code for Nurses*, supports the self-determination of clients as a moral right.[4] Although the doctrine of informed consent has distinct legal implications, "it is essentially an ethical imperative . . . rooted in the fundamental recognition . . . that adults are entitled to accept or reject health care interventions on the basis of their own personal values and in furtherance of their own personal goals."[5]

> The right to control one's body and one's treatment and the emphasis given to self-determination, privacy, freedom, autonomy, the emphasis on not being deceived, and being given complete and truthful information, all point to an important aspect of a rights-based view, namely the role of an individual patient's will in individual decision making.[6]

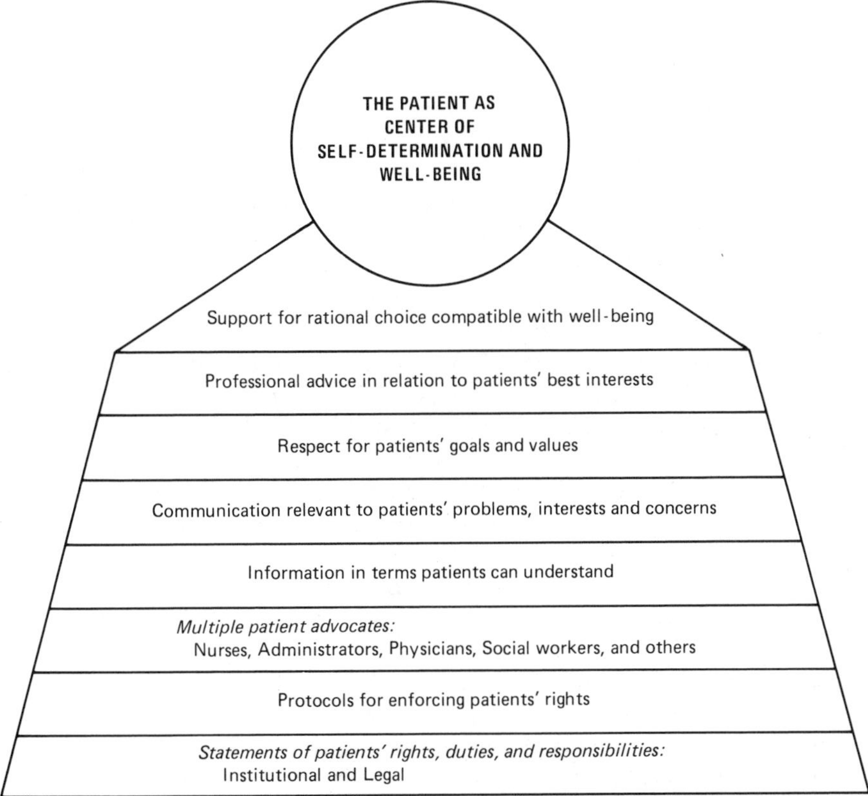

Figure 5.1. Forces that foster patient participation and well-being in health care decisions.

This statement takes the position that respect for persons necessarily supports "self-determination as a shield . . . valued for the freedom from outside control it is intended to provide. It manifests the wish to be an instrument of one's own and 'not of other men's acts of will' . . . As a sword, self-determination manifests the value that Western culture places on each person to be a creator—'a subject, not an object.'"[7] This position recognizes that persons define their values and assume responsibility for their particular life-style and health practices.

The Principle of Well-Being. Serving the patient's well-being through improving health is another justifying reason or warrant for nursing and all other health care.[8] "The nursing profession exists to give assistance to those persons needing nursing care."[9] The obligation to promote patients' well-being is assumed to be the operational principle of the health care system by consumers and care providers alike. Well-being is further supported by the principle of beneficence, which says that one ought to prevent harm and promote the good.[10] The nurse sees the nursing role as that of friend rather than as servant to the patient.

In practical affairs, conditions such as diabetes, fractures, and infections may be treated in several ways. Most health consumers accept the decision of the professional in the expectation that the patient's well-being is served by the recommendation of the nurse or physician. However, issues such as amniocentesis and termination of aggressive treatment in cancer patients with metastases for whom treatment is ineffective are value choices rather than purely technical or clinical questions.[11] The patient makes this choice on the basis of furthering his or her well-being. A still different way of serving well-being is achieved by supporting the patient's preference for one intervention over another that is recommended. For example, a patient with a slipped disc can be treated medically, orthopedically, or surgically. Previous episodes of prolonged bed rest for this specific patient were so depressing that the patient prefers the greater risk of surgery.[12] A professional baseball pitcher may prefer continuous cortisone for his inflamed elbow rather than move to the outfield.[13]

Evaluating the patient's choices in terms of well-being emphasizes nursing and provider commitment to principles of promoting the good and avoiding harm by limiting the alternatives. Patients cannot demand whatever they wish. The choice is "among medically accepted and available options, all of which . . . have some possibility of promoting the patient's welfare, including always the option of no further medical interventions, even when that would not be viewed as preferable by the health care providers."[14]

Clearly, the definition of well-being is a broader concept than self-determination alone. The concept of well-being takes the patient's best interests into account in relation to the patient's self-determined goals and values. This process requires dialogue between practitioners and patients in which the patients' views, goals, and values are related to the available treatment options. Thus, the principle of self-determination expands to include the contribution of relevant practitioners concerned with the patient's well-being in the process of shared decision making. Self-determination and well-being may therefore be regarded as compatible values.

The compatibility of self-determination and well-being takes the form of shared decision making. Shared decision making recognizes the professional's expertise along with patients' evaluations of their options, the consequences of each option, and relevance to their well-being. Shared decision making also permits consideration of the well-being, goals, and values of family members. Constraints arise against permitting a patient to exhaust family resources when little or no patient benefit is likely.

The Principle of Equity. The ideal that people be treated "fairly and equally with all concerned"[15] has implications for the consumer and provider of health care. A traditional approach "is the Aristotelian principle of formal justice that like cases be treated alike."[16] This principle is applicable in the practice of government support of all dialysis treatments for everyone with end-stage renal disease. Arbitrariness is in principle eliminated. The principle of treating like cases alike also implies that differences are treated differently.

To treat patients fairly may be to treat them differently, since their needs differ. There are, however, practical difficulties in applying both parts of this principle. Nursing resources are especially difficult to distribute fairly. Even patients with identical surgery and expected outcomes in the intensive care unit have different physical responses, emotional reactions, and interactional needs. Rarely is the nursing service adequate to meet all the patient care needs defined by responsible nurses. Nevertheless, a major value of nursing practitioners is to promote the well-being of their patients. Nurses do this by respecting their patients' rights and treatment options. In this way, patients are treated fairly as equal participants in making shared health care decisions.

Values Expressed in Patient-Professional Models of Relationship

The paternalistic model is one of patient trust of and dependency on the physician's moral sensibilities and technical competence. This model conflicts with the model of patient self-determination, in which patients retain all control of their own health and medical care. The paternalistic model and the self-determination model represent the extremes of the patient-professional relationship.

Either model is an inadequate reflection of the complexity and scope of current health care delivery. Shared decision making more adequately reflects the values of the patient's self-determination and the concern of care providers for the patient's best interests.

Values Expressed in Nurse-Patient Relationships

The role of the nurse in shared decision making rests on important premises of this work. The first premise is that every competent adult has the right to decide what will be done with his or her person, that is, to accept, terminate, or refuse treatment.[17] The second premise is that the patient's care, safety, and well-being are the nurse's primary commitment. This view places the patient in the center of professional scrutiny and activity with full patient involvement, understanding, and agreement. The third major premise of this work is that the present and increasing complexity of health care requires an interdisciplinary approach to patient care situations. An important function of the nurse is to promote collaboration on behalf of the patient among professionals involved in that person's care.

NURSING GOALS, REALITIES, AND STRATEGIES OF DECISION MAKING

Nursing Goals

The goal of the decision-making process in nursing is to "advance the ability of patients to maintain control of and be responsible for decisions regarding their lives and their health."[18]

Situational Realities: Patient Status

To be an effective participant in the decision process, three factors are essential.[19] First, the patient possesses the capacity to participate. Second, the decision is voluntary. Third, the patient acquires access to essential information relevant to the health problem and to related life goals, plans, and values.

The capacity to participate effectively depends on the "mental, emotional, and legal" ability to do so.[20] The "decisionmaking capacity is specific to a particular decision and depends . . . on the person's actual functioning in situations in which a decision about health care is to be made."[21] Obviously, infants, young children, comatose persons, and severely mentally disabled persons are incapacitated. They require separate consideration. In borderline cases, careful assessment of the patient's comprehension and reasoning by nurses in contact with the patient in various situations and times of day and night is a major contribution to the evaluation process. Thus, nurses are in the best position to evaluate the effects of psychotropic drugs on the patient. Through observation, nurses can identify gaps in patients' information and supply the missing knowledge. Eventually, the patient's capacity or incapacity to make a decision regarding treatment must be established and resolution secured.

Determination of the patient's capacity to make a decision relates to the individual's abilities, the demands of the decision task, and the probable consequences of the choice. The President's Commission views the capacity to make decisions as requiring:

1. Possession of a set of values and goals
2. The ability to communicate and to understand information
3. The ability to reason and to deliberate about one's choice.[22]

A framework of goals and values is necessary for the patient to decide what is good or bad for him or her. The ability to seek, receive, and give information with understanding requires language and conceptual skills sufficient to grasp the task at hand. Life experience is useful for appreciating the significance of alternative medical interventions and life-styles.[23] The capacity to reason and to deliberate enables the patient to evaluate the effect of alternative decisions on his or her goals and plans.[24] This capacity includes the ability to weigh probabilities and possibilities in terms of present and future consequences to the self.

The President's Commission suggests criteria for assessment of the patient's capacity to make a particular decision regarding treatment. These criteria are:

1. The ability to understand relevant facts and values
2. The ability to weigh a decision within a framework of values and goals
3. The ability to reason and deliberate about this information
4. The ability to give reasons for the decision, in light of the facts, the alternatives, and the impact of the decision on the patient's own goals and values.[25]

If a patient possesses these abilities and yet makes a decision in direct conflict with the goals and values self-selected, that individual may be lacking relevant facts. The patient may be proceeding on inadequate information and mistaken assumptions. In this case, the nurse and other care providers are obliged "to work with the patient toward a fuller and more accurate understanding of the facts and a sound reasoning process."[26] If a patient's decision is in conflict with the patient's own well-being and the consequences are serious, the issue of the patient's capacity needs further scrutiny. If the consequences of a patient's decision to well-being are minor, less scrutiny is required. A patient may have the capacity to refuse aspirin for a headache, but not amputation of a gangrenous leg.[27] This position rejects the idea that the patient who expresses a preference regarding a treatment necessarily possesses the capacity to make that determination. An "expressed preference" does not rule out a serious deficiency in the patient's reasoning capacity that works against the patient's future well-being.[28] Equally wrong are judgments of capacity based on the content of a decision that health professionals view as "wrong, irrational, or otherwise incompatible with the evaluator's view of what is best for the patient."[29] Such a standard denies the values of self-determination. The use of this standard manipulates the decision-making process by taking it away from the patient without consideration of his or her values and goals.

In everyday practice, it is only those patients who disagree with a health professional's recommendation who are scrutinized regarding their decision-making capacity. If the patient agrees with the decision, and the family does too, the patient's capacity remains unquestioned. Patients' refusal of treatment detrimental to well-being gives grounds for questioning the patient's decision-making capacity. The patient's refusal is the beginning—rather than the end—of dialogue with the patient around the problem situation. If the patient both fully understands the situation and demonstrates sound reasoning ability, the patient's decision to refuse treatment is final and is to be respected.[30]

The second necessary condition for informed consent is that the patient's final choice is voluntary, free from coercion and manipulation. The principle of voluntariness is both a legal and a moral imperative that respects the self-determination of the patient.

Serious illness is coercive of patient and health professional alike, since there are often no options or unsatisfactory options available. The limits are real and beyond human control. Thus, voluntariness is often partial in specific cases. Limited voluntariness in patients who are acutely or seriously ill and dependent on professional expertise for guidance is clearly evident. These patients are particularly susceptible to subtle, or even overt, manipulations of their wills and, consequently, compromise of their voluntariness. A great deal of routine nursing and health care falls into the category of forced treatment, since it is given without the informed consent of patients. Patients are expected to turn, cough, breathe deeply, get out of bed, and urinate, for example, on the nurse's command. Routine laboratory and diagnostic tests are usually ordered and performed without the patient's consent on the assumption that the patient's admission to a hospital is in itself a consenting act.

Forced treatments include interventions given without patients' consent or even against their objections. Mandatory vaccination, chlorinating the public's drinking water, and sedating violent mental patients are examples of forced treatment performed to serve the public good.

A coerced decision results when a patient is threatened with undesirable consequences unless he or she agrees to the intervention. Psychiatric patients may be threatened with discharge unless they agree to electroconvulsive therapy as the "only hope for lifting depression after drugs fail." Patients who refuse treatment such as getting out of bed when the nurse is ready to do it may receive threats of the nurse's being too busy or unavailable later on. The greater the disparity in power and status between the patient, the nurse, and the physician, the greater the potential for the abuse or neglect of voluntariness among "captive" patient populations such as those in nursing homes and mental institutions. Sometimes the family coerces a patient to accept an unwanted intervention with little hope of benefit. Conversely, the family may either directly or subtly manipulate a patient into refusing expensive treatment with potential benefit.

Manipulation of the patient to secure agreement to an intervention is easily accomplished with clients who completely trust and depend upon their physicians and nurses for decisions. Such patients regard themselves as ignorant. They grant health professionals expertise and adherence to the moral principle of serving the patient's well-being.

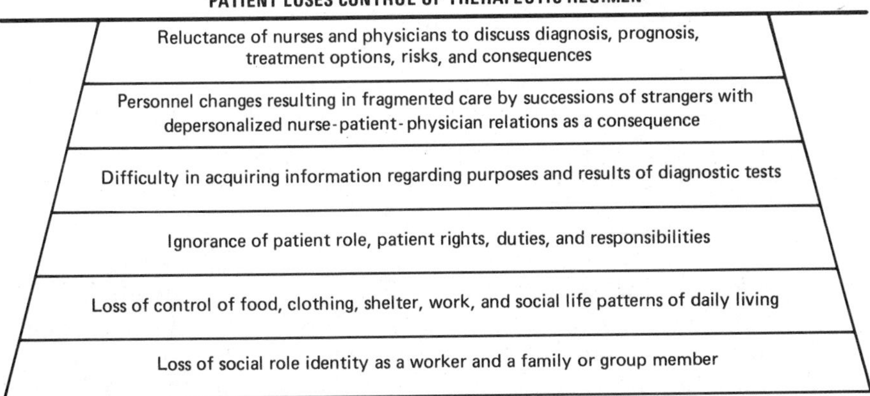

Figure 5.2. Constraints on the patient's participation in health care decisions.

Therefore, it is easy "to package and present the facts in a way that leaves the patient no real choice. Such conduct, capitalizing on disparities in knowledge, position, and influence, is manipulative in character and impairs the voluntariness of the patient's choice."[31]

There are many forms of manipulation. Information can be withheld or distorted. The patient is not informed of alternatives. Risks or possible complications of the recommended treatment are overlooked or minimized. The manner of presenting information strongly influences the patient's perception and response to it. The facial expression, the tone of voice, the relative physical position of the informant and the informed (the informer standing and looking down at the patient), and other aspects of a presentation selectively slant the message toward a particular direction. Information can be presented in so general and positive a way that risks or alternatives are minimized "without altering the content. And it can be framed in a way that affects the listener—for example, 'this procedure succeeds most of the time' versus 'this procedure has a 40 percent failure rate.'"[32] (See Figure 5-2.)

A third aspect of patient participation in health care decisions is open, continuous communication between professionals and patient related to "the facts, values, doubts, and alternatives on which decisions must ultimately be based."[33] The objective is to establish a dialogue so as to enhance the self-determination and well-being of the patient.[34] A recitation of facts and risks couched in technical jargon followed by the signing of a standardized consent form may satisfy legal requirements but hardly fulfills the ethical imperative of respecting a person's self-determination.

The President's Commission views the core substantive issues to be discussed by patient and professional as:

1. The patient's current medical status, including its likely course if no improvement is pursued
2. The intervention(s) that might improve the prognosis, including a description of the procedures involved, a characterization of the likelihood and effect of associated risks and benefits, and the likely course with and without therapy
3. A professional opinion, usually, as to the best alternative.[35]

The patient's current medical status is recognized as the physician's responsibility in the American Hospital Association's statement of *A Patient's Bill of Rights*, adopted in 1973. The statement affirms the patient's right to know his or her diagnosis, treatment, and prognosis.

The privilege of a medical diagnosis is reserved by law for licensed physicians. Some states, of which New York is one, use the word "diagnosing" in the nurse practice act. A nursing diagnosis is distinguished from a medical diagnosis as "that identification of and discrimination between physical and psychosocial signs and symptoms essential to effective execution and management of the nursing regimen."[36] Thus, the nurse's role consists of supporting the patient's right to know his or her medical status, and clearly identifying and sharing the patient's psychosocial response to that knowledge so that nursing care restorative of well-being can be provided.

Those medical and nursing interventions that a nurse performs are appropriately discussed with a patient as part of health teaching and health counseling. These functions are explicitly stated in the New York State Nurse Practice Act (as one example of laws in states that use this concept), which defines professional nursing as "diagnosing and treating human responses to actual or potential health problems, through such services as case finding, health teaching, health counseling, and provision of care supportive to or restorative of life and well-being. . . ."[37] In the opinion of Jane Greenlaw, R.N., J.D.:

> As long as you make it clear that you're giving your opinion as a nurse, and speaking only from your own experience and knowledge, you can feel free to answer questions about the patient's course of treatment. You can relate your experience in caring for other patients undergoing the same treatment and answer questions about alternative treatments.[38]

On this view, the nurse can discuss medications, temperatures, blood pressures, wound care, and any other nursing or medical interventions that the nurse performs "supportive to or restorative of life and well-being."[39] The nurse can facilitate the patient's discussion of values and goals in relation to the nursing care plan and goals.

Holder and Lewis, a lawyer and philosopher, view "the negotiations necessary to obtain the patient's informed consent as the responsibility of the person who will perform the procedure. . . . The physician may delegate the discussion to another but retains the legal responsibility to make sure the patient understands."[40] The nurse's legal responsibility for a preoperative consent form consists of witnessing the patient's signature as the act of that person. The nurse's moral responsibility is to support the patient's right to understand the purposes and significance of the proposed intervention. If the patient's knowledge is seriously deficient, the nurse's duty is to inform the responsible person so that the proposed surgery or diagnostic procedure is performed on the basis of a fully informed consent in relation to the patient's own values and goals.

Ironically, minor surgery, for which written consent is routinely secured, may be far less risky than many drugs that nurses give without question to themselves or to patients. In interventions of this kind, nurses have an unusual opportunity to teach the patient regarding drugs and their effects. Drugs are both lifesaving and life-threatening, as when unexpected reactions and interactions occur. This is health teaching directed towards the patient's understanding of the specific intervention used, the benefits, the side effects, and risks. This function supports the patient's self-determination and well-being.

A third substantive issue is the professional's opinion of the best choice. In cases of surgery or a serious diagnosis, the professional is usually but not always the physician. The only justification for any intervention is the benefit to the patient. "The decision . . . has two components: whether to treat and how to treat."[41] The decision belongs to the patient. In studies conducted by the President's Commission, the findings showed that little or no discussion of treatment options occurred between physicians and patients in hospital settings. Physicians generally made the decisions and proceeded to treat without patient participation.[42]

Most treatment refusals studied were related to lack of information regarding the purpose, nature, and risks of diagnostic and therapeutic measures ordered. "Conflicting information given to patients by different health care professionals"[43] was another source of treatment refusal. This is a predictable occurrence in hospitals where patient care is provided by many different people and communication among these people is not direct. The result is that patients are insecure about who is in charge, who has the qualifications, and who is to be trusted. In situations where the authority structure is clear, where professional roles of nurses and physicians are clarified, and where the lines of communication are open and direct, the nurse and physician can relate to the patient as colleagues equally concerned with the patient's participation in shared decisions. Professional collaboration is essential for enhancing patients' participation in decisions and for coordinating activities toward this goal. The element of uncertainty can never be eliminated in patient discussions. Instead, it is given its due in relation to the probabilities of success based on empirical data.

Patients who are acutely ill, distressed, and in pain are constrained in their ability to understand, accept, and use the information communicated to them. The physicians and nurses are usually strangers. The language may be technical. The hospital setting may be frightening. If all the health professionals involved with each patient are clear about what is to be communicated regarding the physician's treatment recommendation, the discussion can proceed and enlarge as the patient's state of readiness and receptivity improve. Time is required.

Written and audiovisual materials discussing specific interventions are useful in nonemergency situations. Some physicians require patients to write their own consent forms for elective surgery as a test of their understanding and as the basis for further patient participation in the decision process. The inclusion of families can be significant in the patient's understanding of the physician's or nurse's treatment recommendation.

Nursing Strategies for Facilitating Patient Participation in Health Care Decisions

The aim of the nursing strategies used in this context is to facilitate relationships between patients, nurses, physicians, professionals, and families "characterized by mutual participation and respect and by shared decisionmaking."[44] The patient's history, diagnosis, illness, and relationship with the physician may be the determining factor in the patient's decision processes. However, health care in hospitals has become increasingly technological; nurses are now the mainstay of intensive care units where they directly apply complex technologies. Physicians representing many subspecialties may be involved in phases of the patient's care. An important nursing function is to coordinate the medical, technical, and nursing activities on behalf of the patient's well-being into a meaningful process that the patient and family can utilize in the shared decision process. This function is stated in nursing laws and codes as patient education, health teaching, and health counseling.[45] The process of communicating essential information to the patient may be carried out independently as part of the nursing care. The patient's response is shared with other health professionals and family as discussion and deliberation around the patient's well-being ebbs and flows when needs and concerns change. In everyday practice situations, nurses "typically have a central role in the process of providing patients with information."[46] Nurses are increasingly viewed by the public and by themselves as patient advocates. In this role, nurses help patients gain better health and more control of their participation in health care.

Another way for nurses to facilitate patients' informed participation in health care decisions is to function effectively as interdisciplinary team members working with others to solve patients' problems. The client benefits from the improved communication and easier access among professionals whose focus as a team is on the whole patient rather than on a limited aspect. A team that functions effectively can better manage interdependent problems and integrate services.[47]

Questions of what person or persons or discipline will serve as primary communicator arises when people from many disciplines work with each patient. A related question is how to communicate consistent messages to the patient and family. A further question relates to the communication of the team concept to the patient and to the family.[48] One measure of effective communication is the consistency of messages from health professionals to client, and the accuracy of the client's information.[49] This is in contrast to settings where there is little communication among professionals. This results in the patient's receiving separate, different, and sometimes conflicting messages from individual professionals.

Formal interdisciplinary team meetings are the ideal. Meetings are held regularly with a focus on client problems and management issues. Problems are usually aired and settled by the group, which uses negotiation and conflict resolution processes. Meetings enable nurses to communicate patient concerns in a systematic fashion to an interdisciplinary group in which the problem can be analyzed and the nurse's perceptions, inferences, hypotheses, and recommendations confirmed or disconfirmed by a group whose focus is the patient's well-being. The nurse is recognized as a colleague in a vital professional role. The principle of feedback is utilized in all interactions. The nurse's contribution to patient care is formalized, recognized, and placed in the context of total care to the patient and family.

Patient care is not always formally organized along team lines. Some health care is conducted informally among professionals discussing a patient problem or need. In hierarchical settings, communication tends to be from the top down. These are barriers to the patient's participation in health care decisions. This presents a challenge for effective nursing support of patients' rights to self-determination.

Specific ways of developing strategies to facilitate the patient's self-determination, well-being, and participation in shared health care decisions are suggested here. They are offered as guidelines to clarify thinking and data collection related to ethical problems. This is not a scientific method that will lead to conclusions based on empirical testing. Stalemates and tragedies will remain moral realities, despite the best efforts of the best-intentioned health care professionals.

GUIDELINES FOR SHARED DECISION MAKING

Definition of the Problem

The process of defining the problem begins with the collection of pertinent data. The patient's understanding of the health care situation and what is perceived as problematic is a useful beginning.

> Mrs. L, an 84-year-old competent woman, is hospitalized for bowel obstruction. A malignancy of the lower bowel with metastases is diagnosed and abdominal surgery with a colostomy recommended. The nurse finds the patient weeping, and seeks the cause of the distress. With the nurse's assistance, the patient reveals that she has been scheduled for major surgery that she does not want.

The nurse collects further data regarding:

1. The extent to which the patient understands the information given her regarding her diagnosis, prognosis, proposed treatment, risks, and the alternatives. Gaps or distortions in the information need to be rectified. Family or significant others can be included in these discussions of diagnosis, prognosis, treatment, risks, and alternatives with the physician, surgeon, or the nurse, alone or together as is most appropriate.

> Mrs. L understands that she has cancer and that an opening will be made in her abdomen for her fecal wastes to come out.

2. The nurse seeks clarification from the patient, family, and significant others regarding the problematic nature of the recommended treatment. The nurse gently inquires regarding factors relevant to the patient's life goals, plans, and values. Religious and psychosocial factors are sometimes significant factors in patient discussions as well.

> Mrs. L responds that although she has two "good" daughters, both have husbands, children, and full-time, responsible jobs for economic reasons. Neither could care for her. Therefore, she lives alone and with occasional help for shopping and cleaning, she is independent. Mrs. L is now a widow after 62 years of married life and is proud of her ability to maintain herself without being burdensome to anyone. She is religious and unafraid of death. She said of her husband's terminal illness, "He was no use to anyone and in great pain; therefore, his suffering had to end." She fears the surgery but fears the loss of her independence and the prospect of a long lingering death in a nursing home even more. She is determined to refuse the surgery as prolonging the dying process. "I have to die sometime, and I've had a good long life" is her summarizing statement of values. The daughters see the situation as a dilemma. They want their mother to live with as much comfort and as long as possible. Neither can afford to care full time for their mother. The daughters respect her self-determination but value her well-being more.

3. Nurses, physicians, patient and family continue the discussion of the meaning of the diagnosis; the prognosis; the available options, one of which is no treatment, and the consequences of each in the light of the patient's goals and values (see Figure 5-3). Communication includes providing the patient with information regarding home care and nursing assistance, Medicare and Medicaid financial aid, and the possibili-

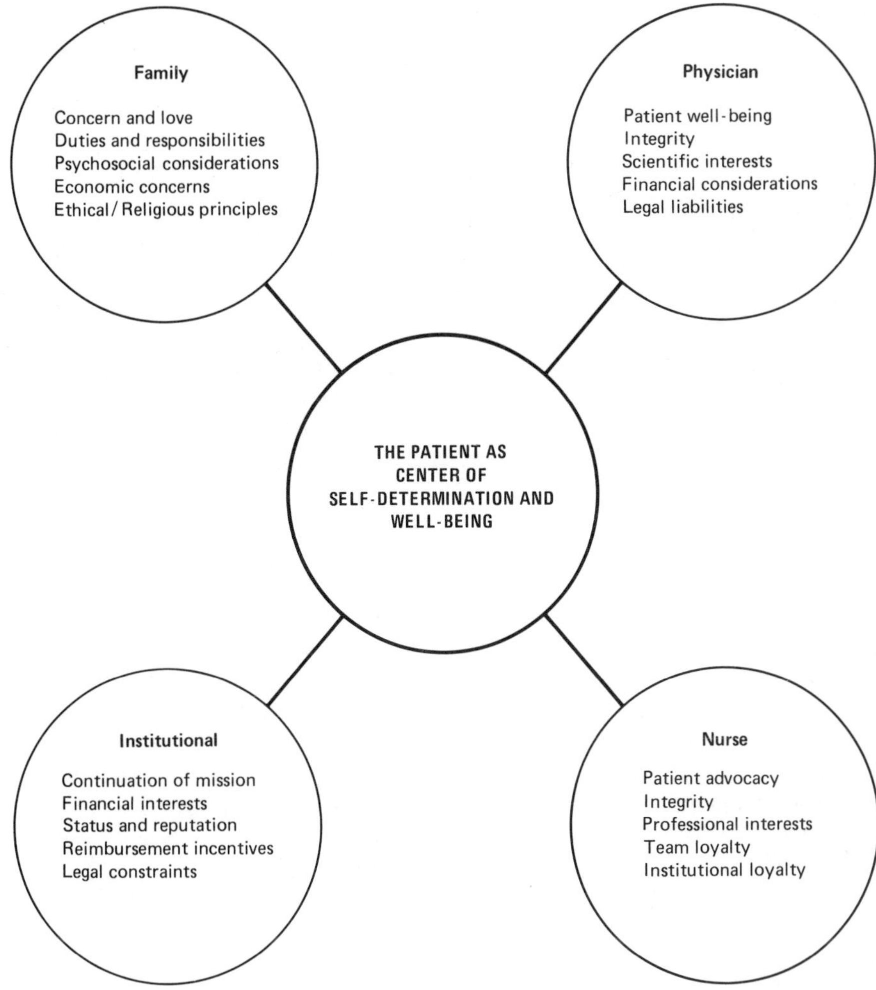

Figure 5.3. Values that impact on patients' participation.

ties of returning home after surgery. The dialogue between patient and nurse is aimed toward identifying those aspects of the situation that are problematic to the patient and those values that have priority.

Identification of the Ethical Problem

When patient, nurse, physicians, family, and significant others are satisfied that the relevant facts have been fully considered, the ethical problem appears to be the patient's self-determination right to refuse treatment in conflict with the professional recommendation of surgery most consistent with the patient's well-being. Moreover, the patient's situation has the elements of a dilemma. Neither the decision to treat nor the decision not to treat will truly benefit the patient. The known outcomes of surgery will be a colostomy and an indeterminate life span. In Mrs. L's case, the quality-of-life dimension is largely a subjective factor related to the mutuality and reciprocity of her relations with her daughters, grandchildren, and friends. If Mrs. L is to be treated as an end and not solely as a means in accordance with the Kantian principle, does her survival override the uncertain quality of her life following surgery? The cost/benefit considerations are the cost of the surgery and the necessary postoperative care in relation to Mrs. L's advanced age. The surgery may relieve the bowel obstruction but will not affect the course of the cancer, which has already matastasized.

Priority might well be given in this case to Mrs. L's right to self-determination. She has a right to accept, refuse, or terminate treatment on the basis of her understanding and use of essential information regarding diagnosis, prognosis, treatment, risks, and alternatives.

> Mrs. L. says she does not want the surgery but wants to go home.

Factors that Facilitate or Impede the Patient's Participation in Shared Decision Making

The patient's right to refuse treatment is ordinarily acknowledged as his or her choice on the basis of knowledge of the options and consequences. Factors that facilitate the patient's participation in the decision to accept or reject surgery are numerous in this example. The nurse supports the patient's right to self-determination unless support carries serious destructive consequences. In that case, the nurse will support the patient's well-being or best interests.

Mrs. L's daughters are deeply concerned and want what is best for their mother, including her return to her home. The physicians concerned spend time discussing the options, benefits, risks, and consequences of each choice, including that of no treatment. The patient's fears of pain, dependence, and a prolonged process of dying are seriously considered in relation to family and community resources. The benefit/risk ratio to the patient of the extensive surgery originally planned is weighed and a medical decision made to provide the patient with a colostomy—palliative surgery—instead. This decision is recommended to the patient as one that will relieve her immediate bowel obstruction and give her a longer time to live with incapacities that can be controlled.

> Mrs. L's daughters and nurses believe this recommendation to be a reasonable compromise. They believe that they have resources to cope with the pain and the dying process when it occurs.

The constraints in the situation are due to the patient's inexperience and intense fear of hospitalization, surgery, and dependence. She fears pain and death less than surgery and dependence. She humorously says,

"When the Lord says, 'Bingo,' you have to go." She has difficulty grasping the mechanics of the bowel obstruction and the function of the colostomy.

> The nurse carefully explains the procedure, draws pictures, and arranges a visit from a patient with a colostomy. The presence and spread of the cancer and the palliative nature of the surgery are not hidden or misrepresented.

The Decision-Making Process

After a considerable expenditure of time and effort with patient and family discussing options, risks, and consequences in relation to the patient's goals and values, the need for surgery becomes urgent. The patient is asked to consent to surgery with the right to refuse without withdrawal of care. The principle of the patient's right to self-determination is fully supported in the more inclusive context of her well-being.

> Mrs. L. agrees to the palliative surgery.

The Implementation of the Principle

The limited surgery will be performed. Mrs. L will be taught to care for her colostomy. Discharge plans will include health teaching and provision of her nursing needs by community health nurses. Housekeeping assistance will be provided by home health aids.

> Mrs. L will be followed in the oncology clinic until she needs referral to a skilled nursing facility or hospice for terminal care.

Summary

The nurse-patient decision-making process includes the following steps:

1. The nurse and patient develop a dialogue in which they interact about the patient's health concerns and problems and in which the nurse helps frame a therapeutic setting showing concern.
2. The nurse makes data evident to the patient.
3. The nurse presents proposed alternatives and consequences of the patient's health problems in discussion with the patient and in conjunction with physicians and relevant others.
4. The dialogue between patient and nurse includes discussion of the implementation of treatment alternatives with consideration of costs, risks, and benefits.
5. Finally, the nurse encourages the patient to come to the best possible resolution and accommodation to the patient's health care situation.

In all five steps, the nurse shows respect for the patient's right to self-determination and well-being.

INCAPACITY TO MAKE DECISIONS

The terms *incompetence* and *incapacity* are roughly synonymous. Decision-making capacities are an important requirement for exercising self-determination rights. Infants, small children, the comatose, the severely retarded, and seriously disturbed persons are identified as clearly lacking decision-making capacities. One problem, however, is to determine appropriate criteria for deciding hard cases on the border of incapacity. Examples are patients who are mildly retarded, young children and adolescents, and those who become increasingly senile.

The reason for having a clear boundary is that a competent patient may forgo, refuse, or terminate treatment, whereas incompetent persons' "wishes may be overridden in order to protect their lives and well being."[50] When persons are considered incompetent, other interested persons exercise decision-making capacities on behalf of the incompetent. A father, knowing his 10-year-old has cancer in the leg, may consent to surgical amputation of his son's leg while actively seeking the child's assent to the procedure as life-saving. A person judged competent (and this is a legal and minimal indicator of capacity) is one who is put in a position to exercise and enjoy self-determination rights.

According to a conflicting view, the emphasis is not on a patient's self-determination, but on the patient's best interest or well-being. On this view, as expressed by Kant, "the ability to be self-determining" involves the ability to be self-legislating." To be self-determining means one "is able both to formulate purposes, plans, and policies . . . and to carry out these decisions, plans or policies without undue reliance on the help of others."[51] However, to be a person or moral agent, on this view, implies the ability also "to adopt rules" that a person "holds to be binding on himself" or herself and on "all rational beings."[52] The capacity to be self-determining, on this view, depends on a person having a "rational will."[53]

On the basis of these two views, there are two standards to deal with those who lack a decision-making capacity. These standards are "substitute judgment" and "best interests." The standard of substitute judgment "requires that the surrogate (the person who stands in for the incapacitated person) attempt to replicate faithfully the decision that the incapacitated person would make if he or she were able to make a choice."[54] There are constraints imposed on the surrogate, namely "the same limitations that society legitimately imposes on patients who are capable of deciding for themselves."[55] There are, additionally, "reasonableness" requirements concerning certain risky procedures, for example; a substitute decision maker may not make these decisions on behalf of an incapacitated person.[56] On the other hand, "decision making guided by the best interest standard requires a surrogate to do what, from an objective standpoint, appears to promote a patient's good without reference to the patient's actual or supposed preferences."[57]

The substitute-judgment standard is intended to be faithful to the tradition that honors individual self-determination. The best-interest standard, on the other hand, is intended to carry out the patient's rational interests, those the patient would choose if that person were rational. For example, an incapacitated Jehovah's Witness known to refuse blood transfusions will be treated differently by each standard. If the standard of substitute judgment is used, a Jehovah's Witness may die from lack of blood. With the best-interest standard, the Jehovah's Witness patient may be given a transfusion and saved.

The nurse's role as advocate and watchdog is to protect the patient's best interests and impose rational restraints against legally and morally impermissible health care interventions. But which of these standards to use is sometimes an intractable dilemma. If priority is given to a patient's well-being over self-determination, expressed in substitute judgment, then the best-interest standard is invoked. In emergency situations, the best-interest standard is usually applied. The further away the health care members are from a patient's circumstances, the more apt these health care members are to invoke the best-interest standard. A difficulty with the best-interest standard, however, is that appeal to this standard may mask an ambiguity—the patient's best interest or the best interests of other people in society. These two standards do not always coincide. Nevertheless, the best-interest standard may present a rational form of the Golden Rule. This cannot always be said of the substitute-judgment standard.

The substitute-judgment and best-interest standards may be regarded as bipolarities. Justifiable health care decision making takes appropriate account of both. One guideline for ethical decision making is to respect and develop the grounds for self-determination wherever possible. This value is at the core and foreground of personhood, and one's best interests are at the periphery and background, marking the boundary between a person's life and death. Well-being depends on self-determination and the fulfillment of one's best interests. When these conflict, as they do for Jehovah's Witnesses, the best-interest standard prevails.

Two concentric circles may portray the relation between self-determination and one's best interests, with rational self-determination at the core of a person's being. This value is sometimes called *independence* or *autonomy*. When independence fails or is inoperative, as it is in infancy and in a comatose state, the best-interest standard comes into play.

CONCLUSION

Choice is an important value for every person. Nursing strategies for facilitating patients' choices enhance the values of personhood, especially at critical times in a person's life, when he or she is ill, incapacitated, dying, or vulnerable due to age, mental disability, or socioeconomic status. A nurse often knows what to do and how to do it, and who can best do that which is needed for maximizing the patient's well-being. At times, the nurses' priority on behalf of the patient's best interests may conflict with the patient's choices. This may present an ethical problem without a true or final answer. In ethics, one cannot ask for more. As Aristotle long ago pointed out, one cannot expect the same precision in ethics as in mathematics or science.

REFERENCES

1. President's Commission for the Study of Ethical Problems in Medicine and Biomedical and Behavioral Research: Summing Up. Washington, D.C., U.S. Government Printing Office, 1983, p. 72.
2. President's Commission for the Study of Ethical Problems in Medicine and Biomedical and Behavioral Research: Making Health Care Decisions. Washington, D.C., U.S. Government Printing Office, 1982, p. 33.
3. Ibid.
4. American Nurses' Association: Code for Nurses with Interpretive Statements. Kansas City, Mo., The Association, 1976, p. 4.
5. President's Commission: Making Health Care Decisions, p. 2.
6. Bandman B. and E.: The nurse's role in an interest-based view of patients' rights. In Spicker S.F., Gadow S. (eds.), Nursing Images and Ideals. New York, Springer, 1980, p. 129.
7. President's Commission: Making Health Care Decisions, p. 45–6.
8. President's Commission: Summing Up, p. 67.
9. American Nurses' Association: Code for Nurses, p. 15.
10. Frankena W.K.: Ethics, 2nd ed. Englewood Cliffs, N.J., Prentice-Hall, 1973, p. 47.
11. President's Commission: Making Health Care Decisions, p. 42.
12. Ibid., p. 43.
13. Ibid.
14. Ibid., p. 44.
15. Webster's New Collegiate Dictionary. Springfield, Mass., Merriam, 1974, p. 386.
16. President's Commission: Summing Up, p. 70.
17. American Nurses' Association: Code for Nurses, p. 4.
18. President's Commission: Making Health Care Decisions, p. 16.
19. Ibid., p. 55.
20. Ibid.
21. Ibid.
22. Ibid., p. 57.
23. Ibid., p. 58.
24. Ibid., p. 59.
25. Ibid., p. 60.
26. Ibid.

27. Ibid.
28. Ibid., p. 61.
29. Ibid.
30. Ibid., p. 62.
31. Ibid., p. 66.
32. Ibid.
33. Ibid., p. 69.
34. Ibid.
35. Ibid., 74.
36. Nurse Practice Act, Title VIII, Article 139, New York State Education Law, 1972.
37. Ibid.
38. Greenlaw J.L.: When patients' questions put you on the spot. RN 46(3):79, 1983.
39. Nurse Practice Act, New York State Education Law, 1972.
40. Holder A.R., Lewis J.W.: Informed consent and the nurse. Nursing Law and Ethics 2(2):1, 1981.
41. President's Commission: Making Health Care Decisions, p. 76.
42. Ibid., p. 80.
43. Ibid.
44. Ibid., p. 36.
45. Nurse Practice Act, New York State Education Law.
46. President's Commission: Making Health Care Decisions, pp. 147–48.
47. Bradley J.C., Edinberg M.A.: Communication in the Nursing Context. New York, Appleton-Century-Crofts, 1982, p. 278.
48. Ibid., p. 278–279.
49. Ibid., p. 279.
50. President's Commission for the Study of Ethical Problems in Medicine and Biomedical and Behavioral Research: Deciding to Forego Life-Sustaining Treatment. Washington, D.C., U.S. Government Printing Office, 1983, p. 124.
51. Houlgate L.D.: The Child and the State: A Normative Theory of Juvenile Rights. Baltimore, The Johns Hopkins University Press, 1980, p. 50.
52. Ibid.
53. Ibid.
54. President's Commission: Making Health Care Decisions, p. 178.
55. Ibid.
56. Ibid.
57. Ibid., p. 179.

CHAPTER 6

Ethical Decision Making in Nursing: Critical Reasoning

Through study of this chapter, the student will be able to:

1. Convert implicit assumptions into explicit assumptions or inferences
2. Apply inferences in practical or ethical decision making according to the suggested schema
3. Discriminate between deductive and inductive reasoning and arguments
4. Identify common fallacies of reasoning used in reaching unsound conclusions
5. Utilize syllogistic reasoning for testing and evaluating inferences in everyday nursing practice
6. Justify clinical and ethical nursing decisions through the use of warrants

INTRODUCTION

Nurses will be in a better position to protect both their rights and the rights of patients to self-determination and well-being through skill in the use of critical reasoning.

Critical reasoning provides ways of evaluating the inferences people make in everyday living. In this chapter, standards of logic will be applied to nursing with a view to minimizing pitfalls in reasoning and in reaching justifiable ethical decisions.

INFERENCES IN CLINICAL AND MORAL DECISIONS IN NURSING

The Nature of Inference

We make inferences almost every moment of our conscious lives in both practical and professional pursuits. An inference is defined as "the act of passing from one proposition, statement, or judgment considered as true to another whose truth is believed to follow from that of the former."[1] If I see a man in pajamas walking down a hospital corridor, I infer that the man is a patient.

Inferences Distinguished from Assumptions

Inferences are distinguishable from assumptions. To make an inference is to accept one statement or thought on the basis of another. Assumptions are statements that we either take for granted, suppose, or state tentatively. Assumptions are made explicit or ignored. One can afford to ignore some assumptions, but not others; and it takes an alert, thoughtful, and well-trained person to know the difference. A well-trained and/or alert practitioner can convert hidden assumptions into explicit assumptions or inferences. A health professional, for example, might assume that the cause of Ms. S's being pale is that she has anemia, without, however, making this into an explicit assumption or inference. When patients go to a physician or nurse, they correctly or incorrectly assume that what the physician says is true. They have neither the training, experience, nor knowledge to test all the assumptions that occur or are presupposed in treatment decisions.

The Evaluation of Inferences

Two metaphors used to characterizing inferences are "bridges" and "railroad tracks."[2] This means that any move made in a train (as with a train of thought) from one place to another calls for rails, which limit where the train (or train of thought) can go. The train or inference may go to the wrong place, but it can only move on rails. The rails are analogous to the rules of logic that govern inferences. These rules are designed to prevent inferences from being mistaken and for keeping one's thoughts on the tracks. One way to appreciate the role of inference in ethical decision making is to note not only one analogy—that of inferring to riding on the railroad—but also the analogy of inferring to related metaphors, such as departing, acting, passing from one place to another, arriving, and achieving (passing from the data, arriving at a conclusion and achieving a result). One need not embrace the railway or bridge-crossing metaphor to accept the role of standards for making rational inferences, with standards being analogous to railroads or bridges. Our concern is to evaluate inferences as valid, sound, cogent, invalid, unsound, true, false, irrelevant, or insignificant.

One can also study the outcome of those inferences in the form of conclusions and rationally assess the relation between the premises and conclusions of inferences. An inference may be correct or faulty. It may be stunning, revealing, surprising, illuminating, or none of these. To function in nursing is to make countless inferences. By applying canons of reasoning, one can make increasingly effective inferences, including those in nursing ethics.

Theoretical and Practical Inferences

Inferences form the basis of clinical and ethical decision making. "If Ms. S has A,B,C,D (chest pain, severe cough, sputum, elevated temperature), then she has pneumonia" is an example of a theoretical or clinical inference, which may or may not be correct. The belief of some health enthusiasts that if they practice good health habits, such as jogging, then they will have good health is an example of a practical inference. The conclusion of a practical inference enjoins one to act in a certain way.[3]

Ethical Inferences

To form an ethical inference, one inserts an ethically justifiable principle or goal in place of a practical goal, such as keeping one's weight within normal limits, which is practical. For example, the principle of preventing harm may count as a morally justifying reason for taking the patient's pulse before giving a patient digitalis, since the pulse may be below the safety line. Or, if a nurse aims to relieve a patient's pain (based on the moral principle to minimize suffering), and morphine is a way to relieve pain, then the nurse will infer that she is to give the patient morphine.[4] We make inferences in practical or ethical decision making, as when we judge an act to be practically or morally right or wrong, good or bad. For example, Ms. A, the nurse, finds Mr. L, a cardiac patient, smoking. Believing that smoking is harmful, Nurse A tells Mr. L, the patient, "You ought not to smoke." Schematically,

2. Principle: Cardiac patients ought not to harm themselves.
1. $Data_1$: Smoking is harmful to cardiac patients.
   $Data_2$: *Mr. L is a cardiac patient.*
3. Decision: Therefore, Mr. L ought not to smoke.

An Inference Scheme

Inferences are schematized as follows:

Data + (Generalizations, hypotheses, assumptions, if-then statements)
→ Conclusion

The premises and conclusion of an inference may be either theoretical or practical.

The Testing of Inferences

Accurate theoretical or clinical inferences also count as reasons for making ethically justifiable health care decisions. The strength of the data determines the strength of the conclusion. In studying ethical inferences, one can also study the relation between the premises and the conclusion to determine if the conclusion is warranted[5] or justified. To evaluate inferences in this way calls for canons of logical reasoning.

CANONS OF REASONING

Good decision making in nursing calls for the application of logic to nursing problems through an awareness of common pitfalls in the reasoning process.

Deductive and Inductive Reasoning

Reasoning consists of two aspects, (1) making an inference or drawing a conclusion and (2) doing so on the basis of premises or reasons. For example, Nurse A is taller than Nurse B, and Nurse B is taller than Nurse C. Therefore, Nurse A is taller than Nurse C. One can see that if the premises are true, the conclusion has to be true. This is a deductive argument. To assert the premises and then deny the conclusion commits a contradiction. When the conclusion follows necessarily, we have a deductive argument.

If we use a patient situation, "Patient A has chest pain, a cough, sputum, elevated temperature, and a positive X-ray," one can infer inductively that A has pneumonia. An inductive argument is one whose conclusion may not be true even when the premises are true. In an inductive argument, the conclusion is not necessarily implied by the premises. The premises could be true, but other yet unknown premises could affect the conclusion and show that the conclusion is false. Thus, the patient, Mr. A, may have a malignancy in the lung or tuberculosis. Any reasoning within a closed system of rules or symbols, such as baseball, arithmetic, geometry, algebra, or chess, makes use of deduction, in which the conclusion follows necessarily from the premises. For example, if there are 180 beds in Hospital H and 165 are filled, assuming that 1 patient occupies each bed, one can conclude that there are 15 empty beds, and that this reasoning is certain. This is deductive.

In actuality, most reasoning (or argumentation) is inductive. In such reasoning, the conclusion may be likely or probable but is not conclusive. Let's consider this example, "'Ninety-three percent of a random sample of American newborns weigh more than 5.5 pounds.' Baby Jones is a (full-term) newborn American. Therefore, Jones weighs more than 5.5 lbs."[6] Here, the conclusion, while not certain, is highly probable. On the other hand, if one said that all newborns are babies and Jones is a newborn, we could conclude for certain that Jones is a baby. Although this argument is trivial, the argument is valid and, in addition, the premises and conclusion are true.

Soundness and Validity

If one says,

> Premise: All health professionals are nonsmokers.
> Premise: *All nurses are health professionals.*
> Conclusion: Therefore, all nurses are nonsmokers,

the conclusion validly follows from the premises. For if the premises are true, the conclusion is likewise true. But when we look at the substantive data of this argument, we see that the first premise, namely that "all health professionals are nonsmokers," is false; and although the second premise, that all nurses are health professionals, is true, the conclusion we know to be false. The reason this argument or form of reasoning is valid is that, if the premises were true, the conclusion would be true. In fact, this argument is unsound. It has one false premise and a false conclusion. An argument cannot be sound if either premise or the conclusion is false.

Formal or deductive logic deals with classes, independent of actual circumstances or data about the members of those classes. Induction, on the other hand, consists in drawing conclusions on the basis of actual evidence. Thus, one has to investigate whether all health professionals are nonsmokers. Since the facts are collected in an inductive argument, the above premise is false; and from any false premise one can never arrive at a true conclusion. Hence the argument is unsound. One could also establish the unsoundness of the argument by observing that there are some nurses who are smokers. Thus, deductive reasoning deals with the forms into which facts fit and inductive reasoning deals with the facts collected from observations, data, experimental evidence, and verification.

One makes nursing decisions either deductively or inductively. Deductive reasoning provides certain conclusions, and inductive reasoning results in probable conclusions. These rules apply to ethical decision making as well. For example, Nurse A knows that Carolyn, aged 23, has leukemia and that her mother will sue the hospital if anyone tells her this. Nurse A believes that all patients have a right to know the truth about their conditions if they ask, and health professionals have an obligation to tell. Therefore, the statement, "If Carolyn wants to know her diagnosis, she has a right to be told," follows conclusively. But if Nurse B believes that Carolyn's mother has a right to have her wishes respected on the grounds of Carolyn's best interests, or if Nurse B believes that Carolyn's mother, a wealthy benefactor, may effectively jeopardize hospital research programs, then Nurse B may weigh or evaluate this decision inductively. One can infer deductively or inductively. One pitfall of reasoning is to regard inductive inferences as if they were deductively certain.

FALLACIES: SOME PITFALLS OF REASONING

Some arguments are irrelevant rather than invalid or unsound. In such arguments, the conclusion does not follow either.

Appeal to Force

One irrelevant argument used is appeal to force to cause the acceptance of a conclusion. If Carolyn's mother threatens to sue the hospital if Nurse A tells Carolyn the truth about her condition, that threat is not relevant. If, however, Carolyn's mother tells the nurse that Carolyn's last days would be unhappy if she knew she were dying, such a reason may be inaccurate, but relevant to the issue of truth-telling. If Dr. R. orders a drug dose that is clearly wrong, and Nurse A questions Dr. R., who says, "I'll see that you're fired if you question me," Dr. R is appealing to force to cause Nurse A to accept his or her decision. When a rational frame of reference is assumed, appeal to force is relevant only if it is shown to provide evidence for the conclusion. When a nurse says, "I have to give you this injection," the appeal to force is relevant if there is evidence that the penicillin injection is a necessary condition of the decision or conclusion. When a mother yanks a child away from an oncoming car, the use of force is relevant to the decision, which is to save the child's life.

Abuse of the Person

Another pitfall of reasoning occurs if one substitutes abuse of a person for relevant reasons for a decision. The abuse fallacy occurs in one of four forms. The first is *personal abuse*. Here the individual is criticized on grounds that have nothing to do with a conclusion or decision. If, for example, Nurse A wishes to resuscitate 5-year-old Sandy, who is dying of a brain tumor, Nurse B's argument, "You're just afraid of dying yourself," is no argument. Or if Dr. K tells a patient who refuses an x-ray, "You're just paranoid," that health professional is committing a personal-abuse fallacy. There may be good reasons for not resuscitating Sandy or for an x-ray, but they do not include irrelevant personal abuse.

A second form of abuse is *circumstantial abuse*. Here, in place of an argument, one chides a person for believing or doing X on the grounds of membership in a group that habitually does X. If, for example, Nurse A resuscitates Sandy, and Nurse B says, "You're a Catholic," this may be true but irrelevant to the reasons Nurse A may have for resuscitating the child. Or if Nurse C says that what Dr. L did was magnificent, and Nurse

D says, "Oh, you both work at Hospital H," Nurse D's statement is circumstantial abuse. It is not relevant to whether Dr. L did or did not do a good job.

A third version of abuse is known as "*You're another.*" If Nurse A finds Dr. S using drugs, and Dr. S retorts, "I've seen you use them," Dr. S's statement may be true, but irrelevant to the issue of Dr. S's drug use. A version of the "you're another" (*tu quoque*) abuse fallacy is used in ethics in the principle that "two wrongs don't make a right."

A fourth and last version of the abuse fallacy is known as the *genetic fallacy*. Instead of accepting or refuting evidence on relevant grounds, one abuses a person by casting doubt on the person's origins. A health professional, for example, tells a patient, "The reason that you're a drug addict is that your parents were of lowly origin. Considering where you came from, no wonder you're an addict."

There is, however, a difference between the genetic fallacy and the *genetic method*. The latter is useful in medicine and the life sciences. A nurse's examination makes use of the medical history of a patient, and history is relevant and useful for diagnosis. The genetic fallacy occurs if one uses someone's origins exclusively for drawing a conclusion for invariably abusive purposes.

Appeal to Ignorance

This fallacy appeals to ignorance as a form of evidence. For example, long before smoking became implicated in lung cancer and heart trouble, cigarette-company proponents said that there was no proof that smoking caused cancer. This created the impression or implied the conclusion that smoking did not cause cancer. The absence of complete proof for a conclusion, such as that smoking is a causal factor of cancer, does not mean that the evidence can be discounted. The appeal-to-ignorance fallacy is committed by shifting the burden of proof for a conclusion to the other side and demanding complete proof for the opposite conclusion. Since complete proof is often impossible, the implication is that the opposite conclusion is true. If a patient enters the hospital emergency room complaining of a chest pain and, on the basis of EKG and other tests, the health professionals find nothing wrong, the fallacy of the appeal to ignorance consists in saying, "We couldn't find anything wrong. Therefore, there is nothing wrong." The health professionals in this situation may not know of some other cause of a chest pain, such as esophageal disease. The absence of evidence for a proposition does not establish the truth of the opposite conclusion.

Appeal to Populace

Appeal to the populace, a further pitfall in making inferences, consists in arguing that everyone else does something. Therefore, it must be good. For example, an operating-room supervisor says that all her colleagues are using antiseptic X for cold sterilization, therefore it must be good. Popularity does not prove quality.

Appeal to Authority

A frequently used fallacy or irrelevant reasoning occuring in health care is the *appeal to authority*. The appeal to irrelevant authority is that of a person with established authority in one field who tries to qualify as an expert in another field in which he or she is insufficiently prepared. For example, a psychiatric nurse of many years is generally not an expert in surgical nursing. Therefore, that person's opinion on surgery is less than expert. Similarly, Nurse A commits the fallacy of appealing to authority if she recommends Dr. H, an eminent cardiologist, as an expert moral philosopher, economist, or political scientist.

Appeal to Pity

Another fallacy consists in the irrelevant *appeal to pity* to bring about the acceptance of a conclusion. For example, a drug addict on a detoxification unit appeals to Nurse A for morphine to relieve his or her distressing withdrawal symptoms, such as vomiting, convulsions, twitches, and severe abdominal pain, on the grounds that he or she is a drug addict.

False Cause

The fallacy of *false cause* occurs when a speaker assumes that because two events have occurred in temporal sequence, the first is the cause of the second. Nurse A, for example, sees a patient, Ms. L, who had Laetrile followed by a cancer remission. Nurse A incorrectly concludes that Laetrile causes cancer remissions. Beating the drum and claiming that the rainfall is related commits false cause, for example. People who believe that walking under ladders causes bad luck, as one example of superstition, also commit the fallacy of false cause.

Hasty Generalization

Another fallacy, identified as an inductive fallacy, consists in making a universal statement on the basis of a limited sample. The example of one bad-smelling old patient cannot be generalized to the conclusion that all old patients smell badly. Sexist, racist, religious, or ethnic stereotyping also generalizes about people of a particular sex, race, sect, or ethnic group on the basis of a small sample. If Nurse Jones treats Ms. Smith, a South American patient whom she sees smoking a cigar, and then infers that all South American women smoke cigars, she is committing the fallacy of *hasty generalization*.

There are two further versions of hasty generalization or induction. One is the *slippery-slope fallacy*, which assumes that if one exception to a rule is allowed, the person granted the exception will ask for others in succession. This leads to an uncontrollable set of events with unwanted results. In courting behavior, some females in some cultures are cautioned by their parents not to let males "go too far." A kiss is said to lead to other sexual behavior, leading to an uncontrollable chain reaction with unwanted consequences, such as a pregnancy, VD, or AIDS. Therefore, one is told not to allow the first kiss.

One antiabortion argument is that if abortion is morally and legally permissible, thus allowing the murder of a fetus, it will be followed by infanticide and then by the killing of children, the mentally ill, and the nonproductive old. In time, killing will become morally permissible. Another example of the slippery-slope fallacy consists in arguing that if euthanasia is allowed for one individual or group, there will be no way to stop the moral and legal permissibility of killing any unwanted person. Some hospital authorities who oppose collective bargaining for nurses similarly argue that if one permits nurses to make salary demands, the hospital will shortly go bankrupt.

A second version of the fallacy of hasty generalization or induction is *slothful induction*. This fallacy consists in the refusal to allow any evidence to be considered that refutes one's conclusion. This fallacy is sometimes identified as holding *a priori* assumptions,[7] the method of tenacity,[8] or the use of self-sealers.[9] By whatever name, these expressions of slothful induction are all ways of insulating oneself against criticism. For example, the new staff nurse wants to discuss a forthcoming surgical case involving the amputation of a frightened patient's left leg. The head nurse says, "Here at Hospital R, only the surgeon talks directly to the patient about forthcoming surgery. That's the policy. No one questions that policy."

The dogmatic refusal to question the ways of a group is dramatically illustrated in efforts to burn people at the stake for believing that the earth was not flat or that the earth is not the center of the universe. Dogmatists and book burners have refused to allow others to believe that *Homo sapiens* could evolve from other animals, that sex could be a driving force in human nature, or that injecting a person with a disease could provide an immunity. Part of the education of the human race consists in exposing and confronting dogmas and the refusal to question wherever it occurs. An important freedom and an antidote to slothful induction is the right to inquire, no matter where the inquiry leads. A nurse or physician who refuses to question a particular treatment or diagnosis just because it was made by a specialist in that disease is committing the fallacy of slothful induction.

Accident

The fallacy of *accident*, the converse of hasty generalization, consists in the indiscriminate application of a rule to every situation without regard to "accidental" variations or altered circumstances.[10] For example, a nurse believes in the Kantian imperative of always telling the truth. Her patient says, "If I have cancer of the breast with metastases, I will kill myself. I have no intention of dragging on for years in pain and in misery the way my mother did." This nurse then tells this patient that she has cancer of the breast with metastases, without counseling and preparing the patient for the bad news. If a physician orders an adult dose of Thorazine for all patients without questioning the variations of dosage due to the person's body weight, age, and degree of disturbance, the physician is committing the fallacy of accident.

Complex Question

The *complex-question* fallacy consists of asking a question whose answer depends on the affirmative answer to a prior question. The question, "When did you stop beating your wife?" presupposes the answers to two prior questions. The first question is, "Do you have a wife?" The second question is, "Did you ever beat your wife?" If the person addressed was and is a bachelor, then the question does not arise. A health care example is the question to patients, "Do you want to take your insulin and have this surgery and live, or not take your insulin, not have this surgery, and die?" Similarly, the question, "Are you part of the problem or part of the solution?" is a complex question, sometimes known as the fallacy of *exclusive alternation* or *black-or-white thinking*. If one is presented with two alternatives, that does not mean they are mutually exclusive or that there are not other alternatives. One who supposes that there are only two alternatives is said to commit the fallacy of black-or-white thinking. For example, a patient need not be a Christian or Jew. The patient may be a Hindu or Muslim, or Buddhist or Zoroastrian or Humanist. Similarly, if one says there are two alternative treatments for some cancers, chemotherapy and Laetrile, one commits the black-or-white fallacy. There may be other alternatives, or one of these may not be a real alternative.

A head nurse who asks Nurse A, "Why didn't you give Ms. R [the patient] digitalis yesterday at 6 P.M.?" commits the complex-question fallacy if either Nurse A was not on duty at that time or Ms. R died before the time referred to in the question.

Is-Ought Fallacy

The *is-ought fallacy* consists in arguing that because X (some custom or practice, decision or policy) is the case, therefore it follows that X ought to be the case. For example, if someone says, "Nurses are physicians' handmaidens: therefore, nurses ought to be subordinate to physicians," commits the is-ought fallacy. Similarly, the statement, "Nurses give direct care to clients. Therefore, nurses ought to stay at the bedside," also commits the is-ought fallacy. Another example of the is-ought fallacy is that nurses get low salaries. Therefore, nurses ought to get low salaries. A physician's or nursing supervisor's desire to have her or his orders followed does not by itself imply that such orders ought to be followed. Just because some pre-Nuremberg medical experimenters conducted research without consent of subjects does not imply that doing so was or is morally right. The fact that nurses work overtime does not imply that they ought to do so.

A particularly subtle use of the is-ought fallacy arises when health care decisions are regarded as value free. To regard choices among medical or nursing alternatives as value free means that patients' and health professionals' values are denied. The implication is that health professionals decide exclusively what treatment to use without patient input. There are values in all sorts of health care decisions, such as the respect and worth accorded the nursing role in a hospital, or the way an injection is given. Values are embedded in decisions regarding the equipment a hospital purchases and maintains. Values are expressed or denied in the controls of health care, including educational standards of nurses and medical practitioners.

The relation of values to facts is, as the President's Commission reports, a dynamic interaction, not a static separation of facts and values. Smoking cigarettes, for example, is a cause of lung and heart disease. This is a fact, but it also has value implications of what a society and individuals in it ought to do. To avoid the is-ought fallacy, a further premise to the effect that lung disease and heart disease are undesirable is needed.

There are other well-documented fallacies in logic books, but these pitfalls of reasoning are some that may constrain effective ethical decision making in nurse-patient relations. As a general rule, an argument is valid only if what is stated in the conclusion contains no more than is implicitly or explicitly contained in the premises. An important point about logical decision making is that the further one departs in one's conclusion from the premises, the less likely the argument is to be rational.

WARRANTS FOR CLINICAL AND ETHICAL DECISION MAKING

Syllogistic Reasoning

As a general rule, the syllogism is the key to the rational organization of thought.[11] Whether in traditional or modern logic, the syllogism is a powerful logical scheme for inserting the data and conclusions of one's everyday inferences, and of subsequently testing and evaluating those inferences. A syllogism takes the form: If A, then B, and if B, then C. Therefore, if A, then C. An example of a logical syllogism is the following:

If nurses ought to tell their patients the truth when their patients ask, and Nurse A is taking care of Carolyn, who has *leukemia and who asks what she has,*
Then, Nurse A ought to tell Carolyn the truth that she has leukemia.

Or if:

Cancer is bad, and
Smoking is a cause of cancer,
Then, smoking is bad.

Schematized, one has:

C is B
S is C
———
S is B

Inference Schemes

For our purposes, syllogistic and other inferences can be evaluated as valid or invalid, sound or unsound, relevant or irrelevant. There are warrants for drawing conclusions, sometimes called *inference tickets* or *inference licenses*.[12] These warrants entitle one to move rationally from the premises to the conclusion of an argument or inference. In this connection, the philosopher Wittgenstein remarked, "'An inner process' stands in need of outer criteria."[13] The criteria for the inner process are warrants. The inner process may be something unknown or undecided or some unknown condition inside one's body, such as an undiagnosed disease or syndrome of unknown parameters. One needs suitable warrants, entitlements, grounds, or backing for valid, sound, ethical decision making. An inference scheme might look like this:

Data and Warrant→ Conclusion.[14]

For example, the datum, "Mary was born in Nebraska of American parents," together with the warrant, "People born in the United States of United States parents are United States citizens," entitles one to conclude correctly that Mary is a United States citizen. The inference scheme provides a way to picture the setting for clinical and ethical decision making. The scheme consists of relevant health care data and reasons for the practical or ethical decision as to what to do in a given nursing situation. The data may be that Mr. L smokes, and that Mr. L has lung cancer. The warrant may be that smoking is a cause of cancer. If this is a moral inference, one includes the statement that smoking is bad and ought to stop. The conclusion is that Mr. L ought to stop smoking.

Warrants

Warrants are needed to justify clinical and ethical health care and nursing decisions, assuming that one wishes to make rational decisions. In this connection, the President's Commission gives this example of a warrant: "Promotion of patient well being provides the primary warrant for health care."[15]

In emphasizing the patient's well-being, the President's Commission presumably considers other values, like the patient's desire or even the patient's self-determination, as less of a warrant for deciding what to do for the patient than the patient's well-being. Whether the Commission's statement is justified or consistent is another matter. Here, our concern is with the use of warrants in bioethical decision making. A warrant is a justification or reason for a bioethical decision in nursing.

Warrants for inferences or decisions, such as whether to resuscitate Sandy, a 5-year-old brain-tumor patient, or not, are sometimes referred to as *inference warrants, inference licenses, inference tickets*, or as *rights to infer.*[16] A license (of a certain kind) is a warrant granting those who hold it the right to practice their profession appropriately.

Warrants and Rights

Similarly, a right warrants or justifies a nursing decision. In Brian Clark's play, *Whose Life Is It Anyway*?, Harrison, the competent quadriplegic, has a right to decide what happens in and to his body. His right to decide warrants and justifies his decision over his body as paramount.

Rights function as warrants, entitlements, standards, and principles, and give reasons for ethical decisions in nursing. A nurse's intellectual right to believe in an intervention by a drug or other treatment calls for relevant criteria to justify that belief. The criteria are independent of the strength of a nurse's belief or conviction. A nurse's recommendation for Laetrile, for example, depends on the strength of the evidence for its use rather than on the depth of a nurse's convictions.

An important basis for deciding when an intellectual warrant applies consists in testing the appropriateness of analogies. In making inferences, especially inductive inferences, we draw comparisons, using metaphors, such as that life is a gift or that we own our bodies or our children. We test analogies by examining whether counterexamples undermine the use of analogy. An argument can show, for example, that one does not own one's children or one's patients. One refutation consists in showing that one's so-called patients are one's clients, for example. Another argument might show that children grow up to be independent of parents and are therefore not owned by them. The method of testing analogies consists in examining principles against hard, everyday cases and in appropriately qualifying principles in the face of refuting instances.

Value Arguments and Their Breakdown

We noted that in a valid, deductive argument, the conclusion is certain. In an inductive argument, however, the conclusion is likely or probable. In a value inference, the values one person or group of persons favors may collide with the values held by another person or group of persons. In such an event, there may be a moral stalemate. This is illustrated in the value of conserving all life in collision with the Jehovah's Witness's right to refuse lifesaving blood transfusions.

In addition to moral stalemates, there are unresolvable moral dilemmas, some of which result in human tragedy. One illustration is the scarcity of health care resources. Thousands of eligible patients applied for the artificial heart to save their lives. Only one person, Barney Clark, was chosen to receive it, since only one artificial heart was available. This example shows that in ethics there is a feature that is not always rationally resolvable, namely, tragedy.

The Role of Paradigms in Ethical Decision Making

A promising lead in the search for rational guidelines to decision making consists in appealing to paradigm case arguments or standard examples, sometimes identified as the method of counterexamples. If someone says, "All life is a gift," one refutes this statement by citing a patient in dire pain for whom life is an unbearable burden.

CONCLUSION

Ethical decision making has rational aids from various resources, some provided for by advances in science. Concerning moral issues, we are in much the position with which Otto Neurath, a sociologist, characterized the human dilemma of matching problems with solutions. He pointed out that we are like people having to repair our sailboat in the middle of the ocean.[17] We have talents and resources, such as canons of critical reasoning; but we also have obstacles, and some moral dilemmas about who lives and dies and how. Not all of these are neatly solvable.

REFERENCES

1. Webster's New Collegiate Dictionary. Springfield, Mass., Merriam, 1974, p. 590.
2. Ryle G.: If, So, and Because. In Black M. (ed.), Philosophical Analysis. Ithaca, N.Y., Cornell University Press, 1950, p. 329–331.
3. Anscombe G. E. M.: On practical reasoning. In Raz J. (ed.), Practical Reasoning. Oxford, Oxford University Press, 1978, p. 34.

4. Kenny A. J. P.: Practical reasoning and rational appetite. In Practical Reasoning, p. 63.
5. Ryle G.: If, So, and Because, p. 329–331.
6. Gordon M.: Nursing Diagnosis Process and Application. New York, McGraw-Hill, 1982, p. 14.
7. Hospers J.: An Introduction to Philosophical Analysis, 2nd ed. Englewood Cliffs, N.J., Prentice-Hall, 1967, p. 186.
8. Peirce C.: The fixation of belief. In Klemke E. D., Kline A. D., Hollinger R. (eds.) Philosophy: The Basic Issues. New York, St. Martin's, 1982, p. 38.
9. Fogelin R. J.: Understanding Argument, 2nd ed. Englewood Cliffs, N.J., Prentice-Hall, 1967, p. 186.
10. Copi I.: Introduction to Logic, 6th ed., New York, Macmillan, 1982, p. 106–7.
11. Ibid., p. 210.
12. Ryle G.: If, So, and Because, p. 329–338.
13. Wittgenstein L.: Philosophical Investigations. Oxford: Oxford University Press, 1952, p. 153.
14. Toulmin S., Rieke R., Janik A.: An Introduction to Reasoning. New York, Macmillan, 1979, p. 77.
15. President's Commission for the Study of Ethical Problems in Medicine and Biomedical and Behavioral Research: Making Health Care Decisions. Washington, D.C., U.S. Government Printing Office, 1982, p. 44.
16. Feinberg J.: Social Philosophy. Englewood Cliffs, N.J., Prentice-Hall, 1973, p. 55.
17. Neurath O.: Foundation of the Social Sciences, International Encyclopedia of Unified Sciences. Chicago, The University of Chicago Press, 1944, vol. 2 (1), p. 47.

PART THREE

Nursing Ethics Through the Life Span

CHAPTER 7

Nursing Ethics in the Procreative Family

Through study of this chapter, the student is enabled to:

1. Understand the functions, values, and dynamics of traditional and nontraditional families
2. Distinguish between ownership, partnership, and club-membership models of family relations
3. Facilitate the family's participation in shared decision making in the clinical and ethical aspects of family planning, sterilization, and artificial and in vitro fertilization and implantation
4. Develop the role of the nurse in genetic couseling based on facilitating the family's evaluation of its goals, values, and rational life plans

INTRODUCTION

A new family that brings out the best in each member is usually and desirably motivated by love, including sexual love. The morally idealized family of a young male and a young female coming together out of love and respect for each other is aptly dramatized through the visual, literary, and musical arts, in love stories such as *Romeo and Juliet*, in operas such as *La Bohème*, and novels such as Sinclair Lewis's *Arrowsmith*. Love as a mode of family interaction may also be depicted in sculpture, as in *The Family of Man*, in which a man and a woman with a child between them embrace. Touching, reaching out, kissing, and embracing are expressions of love that bring people, usually of the opposite sex, to want to share the rest of their lives in fun, joy, and happiness. For love is the essential ingredient that binds new two-person families together. This love of two people is ordinarily and desirably transmitted to offspring.

The family is commonly regarded as the source and justification of almost all values. To a recently born child, the family is the substance and boundary of its universe. The family gives stability and sustenance to a child's first experiences, once aptly termed by William James as "a booming, buzzing confusion." The family thus converts the child's initial confusion into an orderly ongoing system. The family is the young child's universe. The child's value relations depend on the love and quality of care of its parents and significant others who share in the parenting.

The first role of the nurse is to strengthen the positive love, and to affirm and sustain creative family-life values. The nurse's second task is to help the troubled family achieve the strength and stability of a family that supports each member's worth in the process of growth and development.

FAMILY FUNCTIONS AND VALUES

The American family is changing its values, leadership, size, membership, roles, and functions. Despite change, it remains the basic social unit, the source of human capacities for relatedness and caring for another. Today's family systems are experiencing value conflicts as new life-styles are considered and tested. New configurations emerge as single parents, stepparents, parent and live-in friend, surrogate parents, and lesbian or male homosexual parents form a family in conjunction with one or more children.

Burgess's widely quoted definition of the family reflects its changing character. He defines the family as

> . . . a group united by marriage, blood, or adoption, residing in a single household, communicating with each other in their respective roles, and maintaining a common culture. . . . The family is in transition from a traditional family system controlled by mores, public opinion, and law to a companionship family system based on mutual affection, intimate communication, and mutual acceptance of division of labor and procedures of decision-making.[1]

Mutuality of interests, values, and goals is seen as the basis for becoming partners in a relationship. Increasingly, the goal of individuals starting families is that of happiness and self-actualization through affectionate ties with others. The pursuit of individual goals within a family can sometimes conflict with family Utilitarian goals of the greatest good for the greatest number, which sacrifice the interest of the minority to those of the majority. Kant's ethics of duty can be a powerful force in parental behavior and decision making through the use of a principle that calls for right action without exception.

Some of the functions of the family flow out of its definition. Burgess et al. see the family as most valued because it provides emotional support through reciprocal expressions of love and caring acts. Our culture places a high value on the factor of love and choice of mate. Burgess sees the family's second function to be its commitment to the provision of an environment in which its members share experiences, activities, and companionship. The third function Burgess defines as the care and rearing of children. Lastly, the family is one of society's primary agencies for transmitting the culture from one generation to the next.[2] As the primary unit of society, the family is the center of authority and decisions regarding the procreation of children, the provision of comprehensive care regarding their health and education, and all of the necessary supports to life and well-being.

THREE MODELS OF FAMILY AND MARRIAGE

Ownership Model

One model of marriage and family, regarded as the traditional model by some, is the model of ownership. Here, one member, usually but not always the male spouse, has the unshakable conviction that he is the boss, one who owns every member of the family in a master-slave, dominance-submission relationship. This model finds natural appeal within human nature in the conviction learned early in life that if one owns anything, one owns one's body.[3] Moreover, in the early, formative years of an infant's life, parents may act wisely by following the Ownership Model, which implies close responsibility and care. One does, after all, speak of "Mrs. Jones's children" in a way that clearly communicates a possessive relationship. To own something is to protect and cherish it. For that reason, the association of ownership with one's body and one's life provides a naturally persuasive case for a woman's rights regarding abortion.

In a family oriented to the Ownership Model, we find a morally "strong role differentiation," to adapt a concept from a recent work by A. Goldman. Such moral role differentiation entitles one person to have special powers, privileges, and exceptions from the moral rules that apply to other family members.[4] The family sovereign may, for example, be given the best food at the table, the best chair in the home, and the most attention, and may never be expected to help with the dishes, the lawn mower, or the vacuum cleaner. The family sovereign may also go anywhere, such as the neighborhood bar or to a distant city or country, and may do anything, including extramarital sexual relations. Other family members must obey the sovereign. The Ownership Model invests authority and the source of all family duties in a single individual and requires unquestioning obedience to the will of the master.

One may distinguish two kinds of ownership. On the benign ownership view, the master rules, with most decisions beneficial to the master as well as to other family members who obey. On this view, the family sovereign makes reasonably good decisions most of the time, is efficient, consistent, and accountable for the general well-being of all family members. But such a sovereign nevertheless exercises sole decision making with unquestioning authority. If that sovereign is incapacitated unexpectedly, absent, or dead, one effect of such a sudden change is to turn a family from order into chaos. For in this kind of family pattern, other family members are unprepared to step in and make everyday family decisions.

A second version of the Ownership Model is a malignant sovereign who shows no responsibility for the good of other members of the family. Such a family sovereign is likely to squander family resources at the local bar or on frequent and expensive outings and to act impulsively and without regard to obligations to other family members. Such a sovereign is truly a tyrant.

In a recent article, M. Robbins and T. Schacht discuss the role of the nurse in family hierarchies. Although "we cannot observe hierarchies directly," they write, "we can infer them from our observations of the sequence and direction of behavior. For instance, who talks first? Last? Longest? Who talks to whom? When? Where? About what? If one family member consistently approaches the staff about the patient's health care, may we hypothesize that he or she holds an upper position in the family and has the task of being an "expert" on the patient's status?"[5]

Although Robbins and Schacht are concerned that a "nurse's attempt to communicate with family members may meet with resistance if the communication inadvertently violates the family communication hierarchy,"[6] our concern is with the nurse's value role in relation to the values of the family. We think, additionally, that a value-oriented nurse may, for example, question the practices of any fixed hierarchical pattern, one implied by the Ownership Model. According to J. Quint Benoliel, although a nurse's primary responsibility is to a patient, a family is regarded as the patient's "support system." On the assumption of holistic nursing—treating the whole patient—a nurse who treats a patient is also treating a family.[7]

The Ownership Model may also provide a perspective for perceiving nurse-patient-family relationships. The nurse or other health care team members may view patients as subordinate within the health care hierarchy. Nurses and physicians may regard themselves as sovereign beings who in effect "own" their patients, which means that their patients in effect have no right to question them.

Partnership Model

A second model, one more compatible with rights talk and its principles of justice and fairness in a family, is a Partnership Model. According to the Partnership Model, everyone in the family feels that he or she has an investment in achieving wise, benevolent, just, fair, and compassionate decision making. The slogan "all for one and one for all" prompts the members of this family model to cohere. They each stand to gain by committing themselves to the good of the family. All are beneficiaries, and all share the burdens as nearly equally as possible. In a family oriented to a Partnership Model, there is a weak or even no moral role differentiation between family members, due to their different social roles. On this view, the husband who on the Ownership Model never wipes the dishes, does laundry and cleaning, or cares for the children, may well be expected to do so on the basis of a fair and equitable distribution of family chores.

A Partnership Model entails a rights-based view, one with a full complement of self-determination rights and subsistence rights accorded to each family member or held in trust.[8] In a Partnership-oriented family, the rights of family members are approximately equal.

Two types of Partnership Models may be distinguished. In one kind of partnership, there is a senior partner and a junior partner or several junior partners. Even George Orwell's *Animal Farm* sardonically points out that "some animals are more equal than others." So, too, in some families in which partnership is the practice, there nevertheless is a recognition that one member is the senior partner. Perhaps this seniority is due to age, experience with life problems, an edge in wisdom, financial or physical power within a family, charm, or charisma. But the consequence of such a "senior partnership" may be slippage back to the Ownership Model.

For this seniority version of the Partnership Model, a problem arises that is similar to the use of the "team" analogy in health care. On a sports team, there is generally a captain and even a coach, who gives the orders which other team members follow. In a sense, a political democracy is a partnership. However, anyone versed in *realpolitik* is aware that despite James Madison's noble sentiments to the effect that the people in a democracy are the governors and rulers, in practice, only one person or at most a small number of persons make all the important decisions. Thus, the seniority version of the Partnership Model dominates families and nurse-client-physician-family relations.

A second version of the Partnership Model is that of virtual equality of all family members in decision making. This may be more of an ideal type, one with fewer examples than the seniority version. If rights are taken seriously in nurse-family relationships, then the principle "each member counts equally" is respected. The value placed on partnership in the family may be extended to perceiving the nurse as a partner in the therapeutic process. J. Quint Benoliel writes that

> . . . a nurse-family relationship that promotes partnership as the central means for seeking solutions and resolutions is an essential component

> of delivery of nursing care in such a manner that the integrity of each person is preserved.[9]

An advantage of the Partnership Model is that shared decision making, whenever feasible, distributes burdens and benefits, liberties and duties on a roughly equal basis. A Partnership Model provides for open and for self-correcting decision-making procedures in a family. This is in contrast to a single decision maker in the Ownership Model. John Stuart Mill's eloquent reason for freedom of expression readily applies to the Partnership Model of family life. Mill gives the reason for providing the freedom to dissent as an opportunity to substitute truth for error.[10] To paraphrase Mill, a single decision maker under an Ownership Model is robbed of the chance to correct mistakes that comes with the alternative decision makers found in the Partnership Model. Benoliel puts the case for nurse-family partnership well. She writes, "Partnerships with families require an openness to the possibility that there are many different ways of sharing power within groups."[11] A Partnership Model also develops strong bonds and existentially felt commitments to the good of the family.

A drawback of this model, however, is that a Partnership Model-oriented family, sensing few or no bonds or commitments outside the family, may develop insularity and aloofness to persons outside the family. The slogan "One for all and all for one" may exclude others and also result in pitting a family against society. The close-knit family is akin to a close-knit profession whose members may show indifference and callousness to those outside the profession. Likewise, the close-knit family may regard others with suspicion, alienation, and hostility and erect "high fences" or barriers to keep the family in and strangers out.

A result of such family insulation is the development of a dubious notion that the ethics of intimates in the family is all there is and that there are no ethics that applies to strangers.[12] A related difficulty is that a family with strong partnership involvements may suffocate individuals and prevent them from developing separately. Partnerships have their price, and one of the most costly may be the chains all of the members unwittingly wear.

Some further issues arise for nursing in the relationship with families—issues such as: Can the nurse be regarded as a full partner and not as an intruder if the nurse voices views that are unpopular to a family? If the nurse's religious, political, and philosophic views affect his or her beliefs on abortion, sterilization, mental illness, euthanasia, and experimentation, and these are in collision with the views held by a family, what significance is to be placed on the nurse's values and what on the family's values?

Club Membership Model

In response to the difficulties of both Ownership and Partnership models, a third model is the Club Membership Model. On this view, the relation of family members is like that of members in a club, who can come and go as they please, use the facilities and locker rooms, play the sports they like, take a shower, and leave when they wish. The members have only to abide by rules involving relations to other members, the use of the facilities, prompt payment of dues, and respect for the property and propriety of fellow members.

In a Club Membership Model, where each person does "his or her own thing," there is weak moral role differentiation among the members, with scope for relativism and moral anarchy. The Club Membership Model endorses liberty or self-determination rights but no subsistence rights. Special privileges and powers conferred by the club override moral considerations to outsiders. The Club Membership Model of a family is one of loose affiliation of its members. Alliances between members may be formed, but without deep and abiding alliances to the club. Moreover, the Club Membership Model tolerates indifference to the lives and quality of lives of its members as well as to persons outside the family.

The Club Membership Model is like a professional association, a social institution, or a miniature society. Citizenship is in a society, writ small, but a society nonetheless. Here, personal bonds are loose, with scope for individual self-development and a minimum of Paternalism. The Club Membership Model is also like some family communes, in which the affiliation is loose, roles diffuse, boundaries highly permeable, and the membership continually changing. In this respect, Club Membership is at the other end of the spectrum of behavior controls exerted by the Ownership Model. The Club Membership Model also has advantages and drawbacks. To its credit, it emphasizes individual liberties and noninterference. But to its discredit, there are too few rules to guide its members to care for one another.

Relations Among These Models

Only in the Partnership Model are family members liable to develop autonomous relationships of mutual respect and self-respect. For these reasons, although all three models provide points to consider, one that is maximally rights-based and one that therefore seems morally preferable to the others is the Partnership Model. This model provides a full complement of self-determination and well-being rights. What counts most in this model is the members' caring for themselves and one another. However, the defects that such a model provides, such as neglect of outsiders and suffocating relations within the partnership, call for appropriate consideration of each of the other models as well.

FAMILY DYNAMICS AND VALUES

Whatever its composition, the family is an interacting, interdependent unit operating by rules and expectations, values, and relations of intimacy. Relations are permeated by feelings of affiliation, loyalty, caring, and pride or conflicting feelings of hate, shame, and rejection. Family experiences are the source of adolescent and adult values, which are usually modified or extended but sometimes rejected in adult life. The most basic values, such as respect for human worth, honesty, and truth-telling, have their roots in family experiences. Stephen Toulmin, a philosopher, distinguishes the ethics of intimates from the ethics of strangers.[13] He argues that the ethics of strangers does not take adequate account of individual circumstances and needs. To strike a balance, Toulmin suggests that we look to Leo Tolstoy, the 19th-century Russian author of *War and Peace, The Death of Ivan Ilich,* and *Anna Karenina.* Tolstoy held that morality was only possible among intimate relations, as in families, between lovers, parents and children, and neighbors. As Tolstoy saw it, ethics is for those people within a person's walking distance. The moral universe stops when one takes a train, for the people one sees there are casual and commercial contacts, not close relations. Moral relations become less significant as one relates to acquaintances and strangers.

Abuse

Although love and consideration among family members is the desirable feeling, other feelings, such as indifference, hostility, impatience, and verbal and physical abuse, do occur. Awareness of abuse may help expose, confront, and minimize abuse and contribute to its replacement by positive love-generating feelings. Family members reflect social, psychological, and economic realities, which may reveal conflicts between spouses early in marriage. Some newlyweds are known to feel disenchantment shortly after their first sexual or social relationships and see faults in the other person that grow to intolerable proportions. Such disenchantment may well lead to abuse and even a habitual pattern of abuse between husband and wife, lovers, partners, or companions. Such couples live together but they cannot stand each other. At worst, they abuse each other. Abuse is also evident in developing family relationships and may become the basic pattern of interaction between husband and wife.

Patterns of abuse make the nursing of such family members difficult. In the Ownership Model, there may be less overt abuse, since the issue of who rules the family is settled. But in either the Partnership or Club Membership model, there may be enough role ambiguity for one- or two-way abuse patterns to set in and become the dominant motif of family interaction.

Identifying abuse and knowing what counts as abuse is important in deciding what to do about it as distinct from some lesser wrong. For abuse is a serious harm or offense. The occurrence of abuse justifies interference with the abuser's right to freedom. Abuse may be direct or indirect, active or passive, intentional or unintentional. Abuse involves violation of another's rights.

The following scenario illustrates a husband's physical abuse of his wife. Jones, 28, an unemployed cement mixer, goes to the neighborhood bar and spends the family's meager resources on gin and tonic. At 2 A.M. he comes home to his anxious wife, who asks where he was all evening. He says, "None of your business," and falls into bed with his clothes on. She moves away. He gets angry and wants sex. She does not. He attempts to rape her. She screams. He hits her. A nursing role in such a situation, according to the Governor's Task Force on Domestic Violence, is to provide the following help:

1. Give the woman a safe space.
2. Help restore her sense of control.
3. Help restore her sense of dignity and confidence.
4. Help restore her sense of security.
5. Ask the woman questions appropriately.[14]

The nurse's role is to support a victim of violence by letting her know what social, legal, and nursing services and remedies are available and what options are open to her. By keeping careful records, nursing agencies can join other social agencies in advocating the victim's interests and preventing recurrence of physical abuse. The nurse's role in developing awareness, recognition, exposure, and confrontation of abuse is designed to minimize and to eliminate it. For abuse, the serious violation of a person's human rights, is the antithesis of decent human behavior. Nurses as nurturers have both a right and a duty to safeguard people, especially the powerless, against abuse.

Divorce

Although divorce is a legal event, the process of separation is fraught with moral problems for both spouses and children. Their lives, once intimate and cohesive, are separated, disorganized, and rearranged in new and unfamiliar patterns. Divorce is an increasing phenomenon in American life. There were a little over 2 million marriages in 1976. In the same year, over a million, or nearly half that number, were divorced. An average of at least one child was involved in each divorce.[15]

Divorce does not end the feelings and ties of spouses with children. It simply puts distance between them and enables them to use the children as pawns to continue the conflict if they so choose. Divorce is the death of a marriage, which by its nature places every family member at risk. The process of family rearrangement is slow, involving the ethical, emotional, psychological, physical, social, and economic dimensions of family life over a period of years. The impact of divorce is heavy on each member, but perhaps heaviest on young children whose foundation of security is in the "omnipotence" and "omniscience" of the parents.[16] The predictability of their world is shattered, and each child carries a load of self-blame and guilt. Children worry about what they did wrong and what they can do to reunite their parents. The child is deeply attached to both parents, and when one parent ostensibly abandons the child, the fear of abandonment by the other parent is usually strong. The family system, however disrupted by marital discord, represents survival to the children affected. Older children of school age and adolescents may be more verbal in expressing their rage and frustration at what they perceive as parental failure, but even they often regress, fail in schoolwork, and engage in antisocial activities in the effort to reunite their parents around their problems.

Levels of vulnerability differ among children, yet all can benefit by adherence to ethical principles governing relations. The process of separation and divorce need not be made any more traumatic than necessary by respecting the rights of every family member to a truthful explanation of reasons for the divorce. Children are powerless, and their rights particularly need to be respected. Children are entitled to the truth in terms they can understand. If the parents are divorcing because of one partner's alcoholism, crime, mental illness, or desertion, the children need to know this so that they will not fill in the vacuum with self-destructive mythology. If the parents are separating because one prefers another, or because of incompatibility, this too needs to be said without blame. In this way, the child is not forced to choose between "the good parent" and "the bad parent." The parents must exert themselves to the utmost to avoid adversarial, visitation, and custodial battles involving children. This causes considerable conflict and ambivalence, with possibly permanent damaging effects. Each parent's right to continue relationships with a child needs to be respected and facilitated by the other parent. Parents need to consider the ethical principles of rights and fairness in their relations to each other so that one parent, usually the mother, does not carry an undue share of the physical, psychological, and financial burden of child care. If both parents adhere to Kantian ethical principles of placing their parental duty to their children above considerations of individual comfort and convenience, it is quite possible for parents to unite around such issues as truth-telling and promise-keeping with their children. If the ethical principle of love as concern for the welfare of each family member is paramount, even though parents are divorced, it is possible to change the effects of divorce from crisis proportions to an event with "potential for growth and enhanced maturity"[17] of all concerned. The nurse can facilitate that process through exercise of her role as moral agent reinforcing ethical principles of duty, rights, and fairness.

THE NURSE'S ROLE IN FAMILY ETHICAL ISSUES

What can the nurse do to help a troubled family or parent to decide what ought to be done, in the light of their own value preferences and life situation, about a health problem? The nurse can use a problem-solving method, beginning with an assessment of the facts and a clear definition of the problem by the nurse and parents together. A next step may be for the parents to identify their ethical principles and value choice in relation to the problem and the alternatives. The nurse can facilitate the process by raising questions to clarify understanding of all the options.

Family decisions are of several kinds. Decisions can be made unilaterally by one parent who assumes the authority for the whole family, as in the Ownership Model. Or decisions can be made by majority vote or by consensus, in which discussion continues until there is commitment to the decision, as in the Partnership Model. In some families, there is an absence of deliberation and decision processes so that external events and forces shape the decision, as in the Club Membership Model. The authoritarian family values the duty and responsibility of one or both parents as the main factor in decisions. The family seeking consensus of its members values sharing responsibility and commitment to group decisions.

The nurse can serve as a catalytic agent to the family, identifying the need for decision in the problematic situation by means this family considers right for them. He or she can encourage open discussion of the problem with respect for the rights of all concerned.

ETHICAL ISSUES IN FAMILY PLANNING AND STERILIZATION

For some couples, the number of children conceived and brought to term presents no problems. Such parents regard "life as a gift" to be respected and preserved, and the use of contraceptives unnatural. For them, abortion is both tragic and unthinkable. To other couples, the omission of contraceptives with consequences of an unwanted pregnancy are tragic and unthinkable. Other couples decide that for personal and social reasons of overpopulation, they will not have any children. Such individuals may be sterilized.

Those who morally oppose contraception must contend with the inescapable fact of individual, family, and group inability to meet the nutritional, health, housing, clothing, and educational needs of its members.

One argument holds that to bear a child who must then suffer poverty, hunger, disease, and neglect of their human capacities, because there are more mouths to feed than there is food, is cruel and unjust. A new trend of voluntary sterilization is emerging in the United States, with an estimated 3 million American couples using either vasectomy or tubal ligation. Voluntary efforts here and abroad are insufficient, however. Policy proposals recommend that American aid to emerging countries should be tied to population control. The counterargument is that food and aid should be given solely on the basis of human need. Thus, the ethical controversy continues regarding individual liberty to produce as many children as desired and the duty of parents, and ultimately society, to provide children with the necessities of life, including health care.

Critics of population control say that separating nurture from procreation creates a dualism that downgrades the body as an inseparable element in all human events. A counterargument is that nurture is a significant human commitment to the welfare of another. In contrast, procreation is biological and without commitment to the care of the life generated. Thus, the supporters of family planning say that nurture is ultimatedly the more significant act.

ETHICAL ISSUES IN ARTIFICIAL INSEMINATION

The ethical arguments for and against artificial insemination are related to the differing definitions of the meaning of marriage, parenthood, and the family system and to the rightness or wrongness of reproductive interventions. The Roman Catholic position views artificial inseminations by either donor or husband for reasons of sterility or of fallopian tube closure as morally wrong. The reason given for this position is that the act

> . . . violates the marriage covenant wherein exclusive, nontransferable, inalienable rights to each other's bodies and generative acts are exchanged by spouses.[18]

The ethical arguments in favor of artificial insemination are based on a definition of marriage of mutuality and happiness. In Joseph Fletcher's conception, "marriage is not a physical monopoly."[19] Agreement to an anonymous donor by husband and wife is necessary for informed consent to the donation. Donation of sperm by the husband to the wife is free of problems to supporters of artificial insemination. The issues become more involved, however, when an anonymous ovum is needed to implant in the wife's uterus, or a uterus is needed in which to implant the wife's ovum to carry the fetus to term for a couple unable to have its own child. Granted, these are futuristic events, but they have a high probability of actuality in the near future.

The argument supporting artificial insemination by donor or by husband is that the human acts of sexual intimacy and procreation are different and separate. The main argument is that parenthood is not primarily a matter of biology but instead a broadly human function of commitment to the care and rearing of a child.

ETHICAL ISSUES OF IN VITRO FERTILIZATION AND IMPLANTATION

Similar ethical arguments are used either to justify or denounce in vitro fertilization of the mother's ovum by the father's sperm in a glass dish in the laboratory, followed by implantation of the embryo in the mother's body. Critics of the act say it is unnatural and undermines the marriage covenant of sexual love for procreation. It treats the procreative dimension of sexuality "as a mere biological function and defines parenthood in terms of nurturing life, not generating life."[20] Utilitarian advocates of the procedure point to the happiness achieved by the couple finally able to bear their own child. Others point to the great benefits to genetics and obstetrics coming from this research, which will be of benefit to future generations.

In vitro fertilization experimentation raises ethical issues in policy formation. Should this costly research, which ultimately benefits a few, be financed by scarce public funds needed for the benefit of the many? Is a child conceived in this manner subject to public curiosity, stigma, and rejection as a subhuman being? Other ethical complications are raised, such as the use of either or both a donor sperm, egg, or uterus, with part or all of these arrangements outside the marriage. What if the surrogate mother, who carries a fetus fathered either by her own husband or the male partner of the contracting couple through artificial insemination, desires to keep the child at birth, or the baby turns out to be deformed or retarded and is rejected by both the genetic and the contracting parents? The identity of the infant may be in question as well as the identity of the real parents. Who is morally responsible and accountable for this baby, the woman who offers her uterus for hire, the genetic mother and father, or the contracting couple who pay a large sum to a particular woman?

The nurse's role is to identify her or his own attitudes clearly so as to differentiate them from the values of the prospective parents and the pregnant woman. This may require consultation and deliberation with colleagues until the nurse is clear on basic ethical values regarding life. If the nurse disapproves of artificial insemination, in vitro fertilization and implantation, or surrogate motherhood, then the nurse had best withdraw at the beginning of the procedure, since such decisions are legal and clearly the right of consenting adults implementing the principle of moral self-determination.

ETHICAL ISSUES IN GENETIC COUNSELING

An example of genetic counseling is the case of a young Ashkenazi Jewish couple of Orthodox beliefs who marry with the intent of having children. The nephew of one of the spouses is born with Tay-Sachs disease, an inherited disease characterized by mental and physical retardation, blindness, convulsions, and death within the early years of life. It is 100 times more prevalent in Jewish children and especially in Ashkenazi Jews. There is a genetic test for the presence of an essential enzyme. If the mother is pregnant, amniocentesis will reveal the presence of the required enzyme. If the enzyme is absent, the child will be born with Tay-Sachs disease.[21] The alternative is abortion. The question arises as to whether parents, nurses, physicians, relatives, friends, society, a nation, or world organizations have the right or the duty to plan future generations? A related question is whether couples at risk, such as this one, simply bear children at will. Planning in this context means securing the available genetic tests premaritally, prenatally through amniocentesis if the parents are in a vulnerable group, or postnatally, as is done routinely for PKU (phenylketonuria) on newborns in some states. At issue is whether this should be a voluntary choice for individuals or whether the state should intervene with mandatory screening, as is now done for PKU on all newborns in New York State. Phenylketonuria (PKU) is a recessive heriditary disease caused by the body's inability to oxidize an amino acid for lack of an enzyme. If it is not promptly detected and treated with proper diet, brain damage and severe retardation occurs. If promptly treated, the infant suffers no damage.[22]

The success of the PKU screening program on infants carries ethical implications for other vulnerable groups, its supporters maintain. We have seen that Ashkenazi Jews have a higher than average incidence of Tay-Sachs disease. African and Mediterranean groups have a higher incidence of the hereditary disease of sickle-cell anemia. Once this gene had an adaptive value in resisting malaria. The ethical issues extend beyond the domain of the individual's right to privacy. The issue is that of the state's right to interfere with its citizens before they reproduce children with hereditary diseases who become dependent for treatment and care. The care of these children aggravates the problem of allocating scarce resources.

A further controversial ethical issue is that of eugenics or the improvement of the genetic pool through genetic engineering. The possibilities of genetic selection and modification are becoming a reality through basic research. The science of genetics promises to revolutionize our lives through challenge to our presuppositions about the duties owed to the ill and infirm coming from new data about disease and inheritance.[23]

The help nurses may offer clients is both moral and scientific. Every individual bears the impact of genetic transmission in his or her physical characteristics. Fortunately, undesirable genes, such as those for Huntington's chorea, retinoblastoma, Tay-Sachs disease, phenylketonuria, Down's syndrome, and sickle-cell anemia, as examples, are relatively rare in the general population. Yet some people, such as the couple in the example given, have a high familial probability of carrying the gene for disease. Genetic screening is a simple, effective way of determining their transmission status regarding Tay-Sachs disease. Genes are the way we project ourselves into the future through our children and their children. The ethical issue is the parents' liberty right to produce children without regard for genetic consequences. The counterargument to reproductive freedom is the parents' duties to the potentially afflicted child, other family members, and to society for the emotional, social, and financial cost of treatment and care.

Prospective parents from vulnerable groups may experience considerable difficulty in even considering themselves as other than young, healthy parents competent to deliver a perfectly normal child. Public education through mass media and community organizations such as schools, churches, synagogues, and television is an effective means of alerting vulnerable groups to the existence of genetic disease. The nurse has opportunities to counsel prospective parents in pediatric and obstetric clinics, and school health, public health, and occupational health programs regarding the availability of genetic screening. A painful way for parents to learn of the possibility of familial genetic traits is through the experience of a relative, such as the diagnosis of Tay-Sachs in a sibling's child. The tragic reality of a very young child's rapid deterioration and death has a crushing impact.

As tragic as the circumstances surrounding the Tay-Sachs child are to the parents, perhaps the traits for sickle-cell anemia present more difficult decisions. There may be

> . . . no evidence to show that health disabilities are associated with carrying a sickle cell gene, except under extraordinary environmental conditions. The gene for hemoglobin S, even when present in a double dose . . . is remarkable for its variability of expression, and decisions about eugenic interventions to reduce its frequency are fraught with difficulty.[24]

This poses ethical problems for the black or Mediterranean couple regarding screening of a prospective spouse so as to avoid transmitting a double dose of a disease that may be benign, debilitating, or lethal. It also involves the issue of truth-telling to a prospective mate if one has the trait, with the possibility of ending the relationship. There is also the question of the availability of life insurance or job security if the truth is told. For a short time, New York State required non-Caucasian, non-Indian, non-Oriental individuals to take a blood test for the sickle-cell trait before issue of a marriage license. This caused public outrage on the basis of its discriminatory effect on blacks. The effect was to stigmatize them, causing peril to their employment, health insurance, and loss of privacy. This law was repealed as ineffective in reducing the frequency of persons in the sickle-cell gene pool.[25]

The case of retinoblastoma is even more complex and requires policy decisions. Retinoblastoma is a malignant glioma of the retina of the eye occurring in young children and showing a hereditary pattern.[26]

> It used to occur in no more than 1 in 30,000 people. It now occurs in England in as many as 1 in every 18,000 births. This exponential increase took place roughly between 1930 and 1960 and [is] almost entirely the result of physicians' being able to detect the tumor, treat it, and allow the individuals to survive and go on to reproduce.... Between 60 to 90 percent of the individuals actually manifest the tumor, ... get it in both eyes and would be blinded or die except for new developments in surgery and radiation therapy. Now 70 percent are saved from blindness and at least four out of five survive.[27]

Thus, the disease is costly to treat, requiring highly specialized eye surgery and treatment, is genetically transmitted, and leads to blindness in some cases. Since this is a dominant gene, it will be passed on by the survivors to ever-increasing numbers of offspring, who will in turn require costly treatment and care. The ethical issue then becomes the right of individuals at risk to pass on retinoblastoma to half their offspring, who must then be treated at public expense, versus the right of the state to refuse treatment on the basis of scarce resources and priorities of prevention. Private insurance carriers may also refuse the risk because of its unfairness to other policyholders who bear the burden of cost.

The argument then extends to preferential treatment of retinoblastoma cases, who tend to have above average intelligence. In reality, most states practice preferential treatment. Patients receiving kidney dialysis three times weekly, for example, cost the state very much more than a chronically mentally ill or retarded person living in either a custodial public institution or substandard community facility.

The state has several possible policy options in regard to retinoblastoma that might be applicable to other vulnerable groups or simply everyone seeking a marriage license. Most states now require a compulsory blood test for syphilis and mandatory treatment as a protection for the newborn. Compulsory instillation of prophylactic eyedrops is also mandatory to protect the newborn from gonorrheal infection. The same justification might be used for compulsory genetic screening premaritally, prenatally when indicated, and postnatally. Since only some genetic diseases are detectable, such as Tay-Sachs and sickle-cell anemia, some groups may regard the screening as discriminatory. Another option, unthinkable to Libertarians, is that the state sterilize retinoblastoma victims with the dominant gene. Sixteen states still have compulsory sterilization laws.[28] Historically,

> . . . by 1931, thirty states had passed compulsory sterilization measures, some of which applied to a very wide range of "hereditary defectives" including "sexual perverts," "drug fiends," "drunkards," and "diseased and degenerate persons.[29]

The parallels to Hitler's program of purifying the race by the elimination of non-Aryans is inescapable. Such a view mistakenly emphasizes biological fitness and denies the negative and positive contributions of the environment to individual worth and capacity. An ethical concern is the responsibility of the individual or couple to society for the bearing and rearing of socially contributing offspring. This conflicts with the rights of individuals to procreate at will.

Moral Issues and Genetic Counseling

A number of serious moral issues arise with genetic counseling. Since retinoblastoma is generally associated with intelligence quotients of 116-128 and each case costs an average of $60,000, conservatively, to treat, we have here a classic case of tradeoffs between costs, benefits, and risks, sometimes called cost/benefit analysis. A question is whether society can afford to finance each case of retinoblastoma. A converse issue is that, given their relatively high intelligence levels, society cannot afford to deny treatment to such persons in view of their social, economic, and cultural contributions. A related question, aptly put by Marc Lappe, is: "What are our obligations to those children who are at risk for genetic disease and what are their parents' duties to society?"[30] What if a genetic disease was correlated with lower than average intelligence levels; would society still have an obligation to care for this population? Lappe asks what obligations a society has to the least well off. He also asks, "How do these obligations change when there are scarce medical resources to be distributed?"[31] Are individuals measured by their contribution to the social good? What role do parents have in bearing the cost of treating genetic diseases? Should affected individuals or their families pay for their own treatment? If society as a whole pays, does society have a right to constrain individuals from procreating "by withholding marriage licenses entirely from individuals with a heritable form of retinoblastoma?"[32]

These questions present moral and political issues for the relation of individuals and society, including issues of support and control. To give society a role in deciding who procreates may set a dangerous precedent in imposing restrictions that may not be rational or free from encouragement of selective breeding, a practice once championed by the Nazis. An immediate practical difficulty of any program of selective breeding involving either negative or positive eugenics is that restricting human variety lessens the chances for good as well as bad species modifications. We are left with moral dilemmas that have no satisfactory answers. Each answer implies some serious negative consequences.

These questions involve the issue of Libertarianism in opposition to Legal Paternalism and Legal Moralism. Libertarianism holds that a society is made up of individuals whose most important value is freedom from interference. According to Legal Paternalism, there are some common interests in society that call for justified interferences with individual liberties. These include a lifeguard at public beaches, safe drinking water (presently available to only a small fraction of the earth's population), requirements to wear seat belts in autos and helmets on motorcycles, rules providing for safe production and use of foods and drugs, rules restricting the underaged from voting and drinking. According to a third position, Legal Moralism, society is viewed as a "seamless web," with individuals regarded as parts of larger wholes. Each individual's place depends on compliance with the requirements of a centralized decision-making group. On this view, the antithesis of Libertarianism, individuals have no private lives free of moral correction. Every social virtue becomes a law, and every sin becomes a crime. Free will is at a minimum. Such a society is somewhat like the order found in the Ownership Model of family ethics.

The Nurse's Role in Genetic Counseling

We apply these positions, then, to the role of the nurse in genetic counseling. In this connection, Marc Lappe argues against any restrictions "constraining individuals from procreation." He opposes "intrusion into the privacy of reproductive decision making by the state, which . . . constitutes a greater harm than leaving such decisions to the couples at risk."[33] The nurse, on Lappe's view, does not constrain a retinoblastoma couple against procreation but leaves the decision to them. Lappe prefers "voluntary genetic counseling," which he regards "as superior to compulsory counseling in both outcome and compliance."[34] He is concerned about some state restraints. Blindness is a major health problem in the state; the costs of surgical care are escalating.[35] Lappe proposes a principle consistent with our moral traditions.

> First, recognize that virtually every prospective parent who puts a child at risk for retinoblastoma will have had the same tumor and will have experienced the pain, suffering and other burdens of that condition. [Lappe assigns] primacy to this unique experiential basis for judging over and against rules imposed by society from outside the family.[36]

Families at risk decide, even though Lappe concedes that "society" rather than the average individual family "has the financial resources to cope with the surgical cost of treatment."[37] Can the average family, for example, afford $60,000 per retinoblastoma member? At any rate, Lappe sides

> . . . with Montaigne who said "I have never seen a father who failed to claim his son, however mangy or hunchbacked he was. Not that [the father] does not perceive his son's defects . . . but the fact remains, the boy is his." . . . love and parental bond establish the grounding for a procreative decision, one which works to the best interests of the child.[38]

Lappe concludes that

> . . . the right to decide [therefore] must be vested exclusively with parents that are involved. We would be best investing the moral authority for making this decision not with the state but with these individuals who primarily bear the burdens of perpetuating their own genes. [Lappe sees the alternatives as] placing the state over the individual [which denies] the deepest feelings that parents have for their children.[39]

Lappe's message is to trust the parent who has had similar experiences. There is something inherently good and wise in parents. With a little care, one hears the refrain "Parents know best" in the form of genetic and moral counseling.

One may note the love-based ethics that provides an important moral premise for Lappe. The bond of love between parent and child suggests an innate wisdom and goodness, which parents, following Montaigne's reasoning, show in their decisions. Leave procreative decisions to parents, therefore. Lappe's advice to nurses may be regarded as a form of love-based ethics. His hypothetical advice to nurses is that in their genetic counseling they leave the option rights concerning procreation basically to prospective parents rather than to the state in either a Legal Paternalist or Legal Moralist form. This view is also identified as a moral-sentiment view, expressed alternatively by Jean Jacques Rousseau (1712-1778) and Leo Tolstoy (1828-1910), both of whom valued the moral sentiments that are found among ordinary people, including peasants, who are viewed as "noble savages." This innate moral folk wisdom is the love parents have for their children. It reveals wise and untutored forms of public and private decency.

But is this view of the goodness and wisdom of parents borne out by evidence? One has only to look at public institutions, such as those for the retarded and abandoned, rejected or abused children, to learn of all the despised and rejected physical, emotional, and mental "hunchbacks" unwanted by parents. The parent does not always know best. Persons in authority, such as physicians, judges, nurses, and other representatives of society have a role in sustaining good family relations even on the basis of paternalistic inteference.

CONCLUSION

A family can be positive if it enables individuals in the family to flourish separately and together. If the realtionships are destructive or unwise, intervention by nurses and other relevant persons is appropriate. The nurse can help by supporting positive human relationships. One reason for nursing intervention is that in relations between spouses or parents and children, the stronger does not always know best.

REFERENCES

1. Burgess E.W., Locke H.J., Thomas M.M.: The Family, 4th ed. New York, Van Nostrand Reinhold, 1971, p. 1.
2. Ibid., p. 2.
3. Thomson J. J.: In defense of abortion. Philosophy and Public Affairs 1(1): 47-66, 1971.
4. Goldman A.: The Moral Foundations of Professional Ethics. Totowa, N.J., Littlefield, Adams, 1980, p. 2-8, 20-22, 34-37, 49, 58-61, 65-69, 88-91, 109, 113, 273, 277-278, 281, 282.
5. Robbins M., Schacht T.: Family hierarchies. Am J Nursing 82(2): 285, 1982.
6. Ibid.
7. Benoliel J.Q.: The nurse-family relationship. In Curtin L., Flaherty M.J. (eds.), Nursing Ethics: Theories and Pragmatics. Bowie, Md., R.J. Brady, 1982, p. 103-123.
8. Feinberg J.: The child's right to an open future. In Aiken W., LaFollette H. (eds.), Whose Child? Totowa, N.J., Littlefield, Adams, 1980, p. 125-153.
9. Benoliel J.Q.: The nurse-family relationship, p. 121.
10. Mill J.S.: Utilitarianism, Liberty and Representative Government. London, Dent, 1948, p. 79.
11. Benoliel: The nurse-family relationship, p. 121.
12. Toulmin S.: The tyranny of principles. The Hastings Center Report 11(6): 31-39, 1981.
13. Ibid.
14. Governor's Task Force on Domestic Violence: Findings presented at the New York State Nurses' Association Convention. Rochester, New York, October 25, 1981.
15. Bloom B., Asher S. White S.: Marital disruption as a stressor: A review and analysis. Psychological Bulletin 85:867, 1978.
16. Feldman J.: Divorce and the children. In Getty C., Humphreys W. (eds.), Understanding the Family: Stress and Change in the American Family. New York, Appleton-Century-Crofts, 1981, p. 336.
17. Ibid., p. 333.
18. McCormick R.A.: Reproductive technologies: Ethical issues. In Reich W.T. (ed.), Encyclopedia of Bioethics. New York, Free Press, 1978, vol. 4, p. 1456.
19. Ibid.
20. Ibid., p. 1463.

21. Taber's Cyclopedic Medical Dictionary, 14th ed. Philadelphia, F.A. Davis, 1981, p. 1427.
22. Ibid., p. 1089.
23. Lappe M.: Genetics and our obligations to the future. In Bandman E.L., Bandman B. (eds.), Bioethics and Human Rights: A Reader for Health Professionals. Boston, Little, Brown, 1978, p. 84.
24. Lappe M.: Genetics and our obligations to the future, p. 86.
25. Ibid.
26. Taber's Cyclopedic Medical Dictionary, p. 1246.
27. Lappe M.: Genetics and our obligations to the future, p. 87.
28. Ibid., p. 91.
29. Ludmerer K.M.: Eugenics: History. In Reich W.T. (ed.), Encyclopedia of Bioethics. New York, Free Press, 1978, vol. 1, p. 459.
30. Lappe M.: Genetics and our obligations to the future, p. 89.
31. Ibid.
32. Ibid., p. 91.
33. Ibid.
34. Ibid., p. 92.
35. Ibid.
36. Ibid., p. 92.
37. Ibid.
38. Ibid., p. 93.
39. Ibid.

CHAPTER 8

Nursing Ethics and the Problem of Abortion

Through study of this chapter, the student will be able to:

1. Appreciate the moral significance of a couple's decision regarding procreative choice
2. Understand the Supreme Court and legislative decisions regarding abortion
3. Identify the physiological process of fetal development in its relations to abortion arguments
4. Utilize the ethical arguments in opposition to and in support of abortion as the basis for forming an individual position regarding this problem
5. Participate in policy formulation regarding abortion on the basis of ethical reasoning and arguments

INTRODUCTION

The procreative family has a most important decision to make. To paraphrase a Shakespearean question in *Hamlet*, "To be or not to be," the new family asks: To begin or not to begin a new life? Several diverse moral arguments provide justifying reasons in deciding whether to initiate a new life—a decision surrounded by enormous responsibility.

"In the beginning was the word," goes an important Biblical saying. More than one thinker has remarked about the importance of the beginning of any process or event. In the life process, deliberate abortion is the decision to terminate pregnancy, which, to some people, means the decision to end life. So the question whether to begin life or not becomes the question. "To end or not to end life?" In any event, the power of life and death is in the hands of those who decide. For this reason all problems in bioethics, in Willard Gaylin's view, keep coming back to abortion. Moral principles are designed to answer whether to end a life or not. As we shall see, these principles, while helpful, do not always work. For this reason, abortion continues to be a problem, one with no satisfactory answer.

LEGAL STATUS OF ABORTION

On January 22, 1973, in the landmark cases of *Roe* v. *Wade* (410 U.S. 113) and *Doe* v. *Bolton* (410 U.S. 179), the Supreme Court established the right of every woman to have an abortion legally. *Roe* v. *Wade* struck down the Texas statute restricting abortion to instances necessary to save a woman's life. The *Doe* v. *Bolton* case struck down a Georgia statute permitting abortions only if necessary to the woman's health, to prevent the birth of a malformed child, or to terminate pregnancy from rape. The Court's decision invalidated similar laws in other states that restricted abortion.

In the report of the majority opinion, the Supreme Court noted that there is no history in this country of ever prosecuting women for abortions, even for those performed after the fetus entered the "quickening period" (first felt movements of the fetus occurring from the 18th to the 20th week of pregnancy).[1] Moreover, the justices said that, since the adoption of the Constitution and through the 19th century, abortion was in less disfavor than it now is. The Court offered three reasons for the change from the historical right of a woman to terminate pregnancy to the criminal abortion laws then in existence in some states. Primarily, the laws were meant to discourage illict sex on Legal Moralist grounds. Secondly, the laws were meant to prohibit abortion as highly dangerous to women who died in large numbers from fatal infections. In regard to this argument, the justices admitted that early abortion mortality rates are now even lower than the rates for normal childbirth. The third reason given is the state's supposed interest in protecting the unborn life, based on the argument that life begins at conception.[2] Historically, however, most laws against abortion have been meant to protect the woman from a very risky procedure.

In the decision favoring abortion, the Court recognized the right of personal privacy in the Constitution, with roots in the First, Fourth, Fifth, Ninth, and Fourteenth Amendments, as well as in the Bill of Rights. The majority of justices said that only fundamental personal rights extending to marriage, procreation, contraception, child rearing, and education can be included in the right to personal privacy.[3] On the basis of these amendments, a woman's absolute, unrestricted right to terminate pregnancy was argued. The Court, however, could not agree to the woman's absolute right to privacy without the state asserting its interests in safeguarding health through maintaining standards of medical practice and "in protecting potential life."[4] The Court refused to accept the fetus as a person because of substantial disagreement on the concept of personhood and the omission of the unborn from consideration in the Fourteenth Amendment. "The unborn have never been recognized in the law as persons in the whole sense."[5]

Without resolving the question of when life begins—whether at birth, at conception, at quickening, or at viability—the Court recognized states' interests in the woman's health and the potential human life approaching term as compelling. The Court summarized its decision in the following provisions:

1. Any state criminal abortion laws such as the Texas type, which "excepts from criminality only a lifesaving procedure on behalf of the mother, without regard to pregnancy state and without recognition of the other interests involved,"[6] violate the due process clause of the Fourteenth Amendment.
   a. The abortion decision in the first trimester is between the woman and her physician.
   b. The state may regulate the abortion procedure to protect the mother's health after the first trimester.
   c. Following the stage of viability (a fetus usually 28 weeks or older, capable of living outside the uterus), a state may regulate, or even prohibit, abortion except where medically necessary to preserve the life or health of the mother.
2. Only licensed physicians are permitted to perform abortions.

Common sense might consider this decision from the highest court of the land to be authoritative and final. Not so. The controversy over abortion continues, and two more Supreme Court decisions affect the implementation of the *Roe* v. *Wade* (1973) decision.

On June 20, 1977, in two cases (*Beal* v. *Doe*, U.S.L.W. 4781 and *Maher* v. *Roe*, 45 U.S.L.W 4787) involving Pennsylvania and Connecticut, the Supreme Court ruled that states are not required to spend Medicaid funds for elective, nontherapeutic abortion. Congress then promptly banned the use of federal funds for abortions, with some exceptions. Thus, quite effectively, the Supreme Court's 1973 decision permitting abortion was seriously restricted by withholding funds for abortions from poor women, the recipients of Medicaid funds for health care, as unnecessary medical service. Thus, one social class, the poor, is singled out for the restriction of the fundamental right to abortion because of the inability to pay. Moreover, the justices' majority opinion argued for the states' "valid and important interest in emergency normal childbirth."[7] On the grounds of the state's significant interest in a woman's pregnancy, the state funds childbirth but need not fund elective abortions.

The Court said that while the state may not prevent abortions, it need not help poor women obtain them as a remedy for social and economic ills.[8] The Court left the federal government and the states free to provide or to withhold funding for abortions. Segers reports that about 300,000 of the 100,000,000 abortions performed in 1976 were paid for by Medicaid.[9] Critics of the decision called it a political response to antiabortion groups. Public opinion polls of random and of religious groups show a large majority of those polled in favor of legal abortion and freedom of choice.[10] Even on this point, we do well to remind ourselves of the "is-ought" fallacy, which may be committed if one argues that what people favor therefore justifies a moral policy.

ETHICAL ISSUES IN NURSING AND THE PROBLEM OF ABORTION

> Jane Smith is a 17-year old freshman student at a large state university. She is a graduate of a small-town high school in a rural county, sexually inexperienced and socially naive. She becomes pregnant and is rejected by her lover as "irresponsible and dumb." She does not inform her parents, who are against premarital sex and abortion. She cannot provide for a baby, has never worked, and is without skills. She comes to the college health service for advice. What kinds of moral justification could you provide for and against abortion?

In response to the unhappy situation just depicted, the first step might be for the nurse to help the young woman give careful consideration to the alternatives of aborting or continuing the pregnancy. What are the main arguments relevant to the issue of abortion on a personal and on a social policy scale? What are the arguments for and against abortion useful to the nurse as a counselor?

Before engaging in the controversy surrounding abortion, let us examine some of the terms used. Pregnancy normally lasts 38 weeks, but considerable variation occurs, which appears to be related to the time a fetus requires to develop.[11] The first stage of pregnancy is conception. This consists of the fertilization of the ovum by the sperm and implantation in the uterine wall. The combination of maternal and paternal genes and the multiplication of cells occurs in the first week. The embryo is formed in the second to the eighth weeks of development. The next stage is characterized by the growth of the fetus, in which some human characteristics, such as sex, can be identified by the end of the fourth lunar month (16 weeks). The mother may become aware of slight fluttering movements in her abdomen known as "quickening" by the end of the fifth lunar month (20 weeks). The fetal heart may be audible. At the end of the seventh lunar month (28 weeks), the fetus weighs about 2½ pounds and has some chance of survival (viability), depending on its condition and the hospitability of the environment. The fetus born at the end of the eighth lunar month (32 weeks) has an even better chance to survive. At the end of the ninth month (36 weeks) or the middle of the tenth month (38 weeks), the fetus has reached full term. As previously stated, the length of even full-term pregnancy varies considerably.

Positions on abortion are largely justified by opinions held on the status of the product of pregnancy. At one end of the spectrum, the Catholic church, through its Popes Pius XII and Paul VI, views life as sacred and to be preserved from the moment of its conception. All abortions, even for therapeutic reasons, are illicit.[12] This view holds that a human being emerges at conception through the parental combination of genetic packages with all of the potentialities of a person in the zygote. Counterarguments to this most basic position point to the fact that a

> zygote is not irreversibly an individual until around the end of the second or the beginning of the third week of life. During this time it may split, forming identical twins (or triplets, etc.) . . . there is evidence that twinned individuals may recombine, forming again a single genotype.[13]

This weakens the argument that a human exists from the moment of conception.

An argument favoring abortion is that, since the embryo lacks electrical activity in the brain, it is simply living tissue, which may be eliminated like other unwanted tissue, such as the appendix or tonsils. The counterargument of those opposing abortions is that reflexes are present in the embryo and, although lacking in brain activity, "its potentialities for full human life and personhood set it apart as quite different from a being whose permanently nonfunctioning brain signals that he is dead."[14] The counterargument is that, as Dedek and the Supreme Court decision point out, the fetus is a potential person and not actual, "just as the acorn is potential but far from the reality of an oak tree. Acorns are not oak trees"[15] after all. Thus, the counterargument against abortion rests on the potential personhood of the fetus, who has the same right to life as any other person.

Judith Thomson, a philosopher who defends abortion, confronts the premise of the fetus as a human being from the moment of conception. She acknowledges that human development is continuous and to draw a line of personhood at any point, whether at conception, quickening, viability, "understanding," "reasoning," or "life projects," is to make an arbitrary choice. Thomson assumes, for the sake of argument, that the fetus is a person from the moment of conception. The same kind of thing might be said about the relation of the acorn to the oak tree, but, she argues, "it does not follow that acorns are oak trees."[16] Arguments of this sort are notorious examples of the slippery-slope fallacy.

For the sake of developing both sides of the argument, Thomson grants that if the fetus is a person from the moment of conception, then, like every other person, it has a right to life. Likewise, the mother is a person and has a right to her life and to decisions determining what is allowed to happen in and to her body. At this point, the antiabortionists believe that a person's right to life, in this case the fetus's, outweighs "the mother's right to decide what happens in and to her body. . . . So the fetus may not be killed; an abortion may not be performed."[17]

Thomson responds to this point with her well-known analogy of waking up back-to-back with a famous unconscious violinist. The violinist has a lethal kidney ailment and is plugged into your compatible circulatory system. To unplug him would be to kill him. The hospital director soothingly tells you, "But it's only for nine months." But do you have to agree to it? Thomson asks. And what if it were nine years or your lifetime? The hospital director says, "Too bad. Everyone has a right to life, and this violinist is a person. His right to life outweighs your right to your own body. Therefore, you cannot be unplugged from him ever."

This is an outrageous argument, in Thomson's view. It is especially outrageous in instances of pregnancy through rape or when the mother's life is in danger because of pregnancy. If, on this view, the mother and the fetus have an equal right to life, why not flip a coin, or grant that the mother's right to life plus her right to what happens in and to her body outweighs the fetus's right to life?

The antiabortionist view is that performing an abortion is direct killing, whereas not doing anything is only letting the mother die and not killing an innocent person, namely the fetus. The direct killing of an innocent person, such as the fetus, is regarded as murder and therefore not permitted as preferable to letting either the mother or the fetus, or both, die. Thomson responds that it cannot be murder for the mother to save her life by performing an abortion. No woman need sit by passively waiting for her death. All she need do is to unplug herself from the violinist of the analogy. Thomson believes that to refuse an abortion to such a mother "is to refuse to grant to the mother the very status of person which is so firmly insisted on for the fetus."[18]

Thomson sees this situation as analogous to that of a mother trapped in a very tiny house with a rapidly growing child; she will be crushed to death by the lack of space. Thomson argues that third parties, such as health providers, may refuse to choose between the mother's life and the fetus's life, but the mother, who is the person housing the child, has the right of self-defense against threats to her life. She owns the house.

Thomson likens the houseowner analogy to that of two people freezing to death, with one the owner of a coat that will save his life. The coat owner has the right to the coat. So does the pregnant woman own her body, which houses the fetus. Therefore, the health provider can refuse to act in not performing an abortion, but someone needs to protect the rights of individuals both to their own bodies and to their own coats.

Thomson then considers the case for abortion when the mother's life is not at stake. She sees the antiabortionist argument here as resting on the fetus's claim to a right to life. This view regards the right to life as unproblematic. Thomson says that life is not unproblematic. In her view, the right to life includes the right to the "bare minimum ... for continued life."[19] But what if the bare minimum is something to which the person has no right, such as continuous free food, clothing, shelter, health service, and loving care?

Thomson raises the counterargument to this position, which is that even if no one has a right to be given anything, there is a right not to be killed by anyone, by unplugging, shooting, or knifing. But to refrain from unplugging the violinist is to allow him to continue the use of your kidney. Although he has no right to the original use of your kidneys, the antiabortionist arguments says that the violinist has the right against you "not now to intervene and deprive him of the use of your kidneys."[20] The right to life in Thomson's view does not guarantee the use of another's body even if such use is lifesaving, contrary to the antiabortion position. Thomson uses the example of a gift box of chocolates to two brothers to illustrate her case. If the gift was to both jointly and the older brother eats the whole box without giving any to his brother, he is unjust, for the younger brother was given half. Contrariwise, unplugging the violinist is not unjust, since you gave neither him nor anyone else the right to the use of your kidneys. Unplugging him would surely kill him, but not unjustly and without violation of his right to life, since the use of another's body is not guaranteed in the right to life.

Thomson then responds to the charge of abortion as unjust killing. Certainly the rape victim has not given the fetus "a right to the use of her body for food and shelter."[21] But isn't there some sense in which a woman engaging in intercourse who then becomes pregnant is at least partly responsible for the life within, even if she did not invite it in? (It is a statistical fact that not all contraceptives are 100 percent effective.) Does the woman's partial responsibility then give the fetus the right to the woman's body, and can the woman now kill it even to save her own life? Thomson points to the argument that a fetus's right to life as an independent person is fallacious since, in fact, the fetus is dependent on the mother and the mother has a special kind of responsibility for its well-being. Nurses know the significance of the mother's nutrition, health habits, and life-style in supporting the fetus's proper growth and development. Thomson uses other analogies to support her arguments in defense of abortion. If, for example, I open the window of my home and a burglar climbs in, it would be incorrect to say, "Ah, but you opened the window and now he's in, and therefore you're partly responsible and must let him stay."[22] Or, for example,

> People seeds drift about in the air like pollen, and if you open your windows, one may drift in and take root in your carpets or upholstery. You don't want children, so you fix your windows with fine mesh screens, the very best you can buy. As can happen, . . . one of the screens is defective; and a seed drifts in and takes root. Does the person plant who now develops have a right to the use of your house?[23]

The required move might be to seal your windows and doors and to live with bare floors and without furniture. Surely a person plant who enters your house does not have a right to a place in the house, any more than a burglar has who came into your house without permission. A woman could have a hysterectomy to avoid unwanted pregnancies, but like the person who keeps the person plants out of her home, a woman who wishes to avoid rape would never leave home without an army. Since this is virtually impossible for most persons, abortions of unwanted pregnancies are justified.

Some difficulties arise for several aspects of Thomson's argument. One is that to have a right in and to one's body, compared to owning a house, is not absolute. There are exceptions to one's rights in and to one's body. If one has a contagious disease, such as typhoid or smallpox, one cannot go anywhere one pleases. Nor can one use one's body to swim in the community drinking water supply. The "landlord" analogy, to use a metaphor of Stephen Toulmin's about certain abortion arguments,[24] implies that a pregnant woman has the right to decide whether to evict her tenant, and it presupposes that a woman owns her offspring. Some writers even go so far as to assert that a "pregnant woman makes a baby, presumably like a carpenter, sculptor, or architect."[25] Viewing a pregnant woman as a landlady, factory owner, or sculptor begs the question at issue and gives the case away to those who argue that a pregnant woman may do with her body as she pleases. A criticism of the property or artifact metaphor is that a life growing within another person is not quite like somebody's property or factory or simply clay in someone's hands, contrary to the claim of those who write that a mother makes a baby.

A mother does not make a baby, since there are factors outside a mother's power to control affecting the development of the fetus. A mother's contribution to the fetus's physical development is largely involuntary, unlike a carpenter's, sculptor's, or architect's, whose will and design has more to do with shaping the outcome. The mother cannot decide the sex, size, color, or genetics of her offspring, for example. Opposed to the landlady, factory-owner, or sculptor metaphor of a mother-fetus relationship is the comparison of a pregnant woman to a passive receptacle, such as a flower or oven, who does not create the life within her. On this view, God alone makes or creates a baby. The mother is only the one who will help it grow, like a plant growing with the help of water and sunlight. A woman's role is to receive male sperm, which then develops inside her womb. But "the gift of life," to use St. Thomas Aquinas's metaphor, is not any human being's to take or to destroy under any circumstances. According to Aquinas, "Life is God's gift to man and is subject to His power who kills and who makes to live."[26]

The woman-as-flower analogy also has difficulties. How could one test the assertion that God makes a baby, for example? What kind of gift is life that it cannot be refused or destroyed by anyone else? Is life necessarily or always a gift, even for an infant or older person with multiple physical or mental deformities such as spina bifida, myelomeningocele, or cancer? Another view denies the essentially passive role of women in pregnancy and child rearing. A woman, on this view, has a role and a stake in the outcome. She is no mere receptacle to be filled at will by a male who owns and controls her nature and destiny. To compel a woman to bring to term an unwanted pregnancy is regarded by one writer as "forced labor."[27] This position implies that a woman has an important role in deciding whether or not to have a baby.

The analogy of "forced labor" has been used to describe the compulsory labor of political dissenters banished to Siberia. Black slavery in the United States fulfills the "forced-labor" analogy. Whether practiced in the USSR or pre-Civil War America, in migrant labor, or in big-city sweatshops, or in being forced by society to have an unwanted child, the expression "forced labor" has a justifiably negative value connotation equivalent to "morally wrong." If there are any *a priori* truths in morals, they include the statement that "forced labor" is morally wrong.

But whether a given practice counts as "forced labor" may be philosophically debatable. For example, Robert Nozick, a prominent recent philosopher, argues that taxation beyond that which is necessary for a minimal state—one that protects individuals against one another—is "forced labor."[28] Ingenious as is Nozick's idea of forced labor, there is room for debate. His argument does not present us with a fixed truth. For example, taxation for libraries, museums, parks, colleges, or public preservation of the wilderness, as Joel Feinberg previously pointed out,[29] hardly constitutes "forced labor."

Prior to Nozick's example of "forced labor," another ingenious but debatable example is implied by Karl Marx and Friedrich Engels. In the *Communist Manifesto*, they contend that any person who works for private employers in a capitalist society is a "wage-slave."[30] Ingenious as this example of "slave labor" is, like the previous example by Nozick, it too is philosophically debatable. Surely, one can work in some capitalist institutions, including some hospitals, without feeling that every working person is a "wage-slave," who is solely a subject of forced and unfree labor. What is less debatable is that the use of the expression "forced labor" implies that it is morally impermissible, a violation of one's basic rights as a woman, to be compelled to bring an unwanted pregnancy to term.

The use of the property and the flower metaphors attempts to answer the question, "When does life begin and end?" This question presupposes an answer to the metaphysical question, "Is a pregnant woman one being or two?"[31] To individuate the fetus very early in pregnancy or at the moment of conception is to regard a pregnant woman as two persons, each with equal rights. A conflict then develops between the rights of each, calling for a settlement by a third party such as the church or state. To individuate later in the pregnancy or near the time a woman gives birth is to regard a pregnant woman as one person and, therefore, as the only rightholder. Against this one pregnant person, a growing fetus may be conceived of as an intrustive invader if that fetus is unwanted. The mother decides whom to let into her house or body, as one chooses whom to invite to one's party. On this view, the decision is hers to make. She owns her body and everything in it. The force of the ownership model, is again an intuitively powerful source of appeal when it comes to a woman claiming her rights; for if she owns anything, it is her body, to which she therefore has rights.

In opposition, Brody argues that humanity begins with a fetus. A human fetus has the same moral status as a mother, and therefore the same right to live. This means abortion is not morally justifiable, even in cases that threaten a mother's life. By analogy, a bigger, stronger person has no right to kill a weaker one. To Brody, Thomson's self-defense argument does not work, because the fetus is not the mother's pursuer.[32] Instead, the fetus is a miniature human in the sense that it has an essential property of being human, namely a brain,[33] which it develops sometime between the second and twelfth week after conception.[34]

There are strengths and difficulties in Brody's argument. One strength is that his argument refutes Thomson's self-defense argument. Another strength is his appeal to the obvious resemblances between a fetus and an infant human being. A third strength is the respect Brody engenders for the living and the moral wrongness of killing.

A difficulty with Brody's argument, however, is that he is nowhere able to equate human life as a set of conscious acts with the undeveloped fetuses' states of mind. This discrepancy between ordinary humans and fetuses undermines his claim that fetuses are human.

The philosophical point is that, while each side has its devotees and battalions, neither side has as yet delivered a decisive refutation of the other. There is not sufficient evidence to show that either God or a mother makes a baby. Neither the receptacle nor property metaphors will do in answering the objections raised by the other side. An acorn may not be an oak tree, and a fetus may not be a person, but without acorns and fetuses it is unlikely that there will be oak trees or persons. Appeal to the principle of potentiality cannot be lightly dismissed.

Nor, however, can one dismiss the woman's role in our culture in caring for and carrying the burden of bringing up her offspring long after its birth. She ought therefore to have a large decision-making role in deciding whether to foster or terminate the life inside her. For if the mother cannot sustain the life once born and promote the child's actualization of its potential for full personhood, then she might do better to terminate such a being earlier in its development rather than later.

A recent variation on the pro-choice argument claims that in our culture only a woman and not the male parent, physician, nurse, or any other person has a right to decide whether to abort. The decision is the woman's, the argument goes, not because of her right to her body, but rather, according to a view recently put forward by Allison Jaggar, on the basis of two other principles.[35] The first principle is that the right to life means "the right to a full human life." Jaggar contends that a newborn has the right to a full human life, and if the woman is unable or unwilling to provide such a life, she has a right to terminate her pregnancy. The right to life of a fetus is not merely a right to be born. A person's right to life is a right to the means necessary to a full life, such as adequate nutrition, shelter, clothing, education, health care, love, and affection. A newborn being's right to a full life and to all the means necessary to achieve it leads to Jaggar's second principle, "decisions should be made . . . only by those importantly affected by them."[36] Since in our culture the main onus and responsibility of parenting rests on a woman, she, being most importantly affected, is the one to decide. "This principle provides the fundamental justification for democracy."[37] A woman's role in giving birth terminates approximately 20 or more years after birth, after a mother has provided the major conditions for the child's being on the way to achieving the right to a life of fulfillment and decency.

To Jaggar's argument we would add this further post-Malthusian point. (Thomas Malthus [1766–1834] argued that, while the earth's food supply goes up in an arithmetical progression, the population moves up in a geometric progression.) Abortion is regrettable and may well be a serious trauma to a woman. To abort goes against the drive to support life. Contraception is preferable to abortion in controlling population growth. However, abortion is morally more desirable than serious overpopulation, in which each individual cannot be given an opportunity and the conditions for "a decent and fulfilling human life." A family that has more members than it can amply provide for has to give each individual fewer resources, including love. A consequence of placing no restrictions on reproduction is to have too many people struggling over meager resources, with a consequent increase in violence.

SOCIAL-POLICY IMPLICATIONS OF ABORTION

Both pro-choice and antiabortion supporters justify their choice by marshalling arguments considered favorable. In Senate Judiciary testimony, Alfred F. Moran, executive vice-president of Planned Parenthood, discussed the problem of birth control and abortion as one that concerns 58.5 million American women aged 15 to 50. The youngest face 25 to 35 years, 300 to 400 months, of risking pregnancy in addition to bearing the number of children they actually want. Virtually every young woman of this group will have at least one unwanted pregnancy during her child-bearing span. For this group, more successful means of avoiding unwanted, unintended pregnancies is needed. Attempts to stop abortion will simply drive it underground.[38] Increasingly, Moran argues, couples value children for their own sake. Each child is valued as an individual, not as property or working hands, not as social security for old age, or as punishment for sex and for the misfortune of being a woman.[39] The benefits of the public policy for legalized abortion have been twofold. According to Moran, legalized abortion has virtually eliminated the deaths and complications of illegal abortions. Moran believes that fewer teenagers are parents. Those babies born are healthier, with a decline in both infant and maternal mortality.

Moran's argument for legalized abortion as public policy is that the majority of women and couples are determined to bear only those children whom they can love, nurture, and support. Increasingly families aspire to a minimally decent standard of living in which each child is decently fed, clothed, housed, educated, and given essential medical and dental care. The cost of raising a child under even minimum standards of decency from birth to age 17 or 18 is straining the resources of most American families. As a consequence, both spouses engage in family planning through whatever means they consider appropriate. Thus, childbearing, for rich and poor alike, is now a deliberate action. Value is placed on each child as an individual, largely through such measures of family planning as contraceptives and abortion.

THE NURSE'S ROLE IN ABORTION

The nurse primary-care practitioner cited in our case study has at least three positions he or she may take regarding the college student's request for advice regarding an unwanted pregnancy. The nurse should have reflected earlier on the ethical issues so that he or she has thoughtful, deliberate ethical justifications and not scattered reasons for counsel to the troubled young student. If the nurse assumes that human life begins at conception and that this person has a right to live that overrides the unwed mother's right to rid herself of an unwanted pregnancy, the nurse concludes that abortion is wrong. The nurse's conviction that abortion is morally wrong does not, however, mean that abortion is legally wrong. Abortion is now legal in all states, according to the Supreme Court decision of *Roe* v. *Wade*, previously discussed. However, not all states fund abortion for poor women through Medicaid. Nor does the nurse's belief that abortion is morally wrong free him or her of professional obligations to advise the young woman. The nurse's responsibility is to give the patient objective information and referrals to appropriate resources before, during, and after an abortion.[40] The Division on Maternal and Child Health Nursing Practice of the American Nurses' Association recognizes the woman's right to seek a legal abortion free from the imposition of anyone else's judgments or beliefs. This position is consistent with the American Nurses' Association *Code for Nurses* which says that

> Each client has the moral right to determine what will be done with his/her person; to be given the information necessary for making informed judgements; to be told the possible effects of care; and to accept, refuse, or terminate treatment. These same rights apply to minors. . . .[41]

Clearly, then, the young woman with the unwanted pregnancy has the right to information and counseling, with consideration given to all the alternatives to abortion as the basis of informed consent. The patient who chooses abortion has the right to information and counseling in an environment of mutual respect, trust, privacy, and confidentiality. Referrals are expected to be made to facilities where expert nursing and medical care is provided.

The nurse, too, has a right to his or her own moral and religious values. However, these values and beliefs do not give the nurse license to impose or to influence the already frightened, worried, and vulnerable client to accept the nurse's value preferences. Nor should the client's self-esteem be lowered by implication that her decision is less than morally acceptable. The nurse in any situation, except an emergency where the patient's well-being is at stake, has the

> . . . right to refuse to participate in a voluntary interruption of pregnancy . . . and . . . a right not to be subjected to coercion, censure or to discipline for reasons of such refusal.[42]

A nurse in New Jersey, Beverly Jazelik, assigned to the obstetric floor, refused to participate in procedures related to abortion. The state's law supported her refusal. The hospital then transferred her to another unit where she would have no contact with patients undergoing abortion. Ms. Jazelik objected to the transfer and sued the hospital. The Court ruled in favor of the hospital's right to transfer Ms. Jazelik to a nonabortion area.[43] Thus, the patient's right to interrupt pregnancy and the nurse's right to refuse to participate are both upheld. But moral questions arise if the nurse who opposes abortion is the only nurse available and a patient decides to have an abortion.

Nurses who defend or oppose abortion have similar responsibilities to provide information concerning the alternatives as the basis for informed consent and appropriate referral to resources. Alternatives include prenatal care and adoption.

Clearly, abortion in the case of the college student, as in so many others, is a concern and responsibility primarily for women in our culture. Tragic choices such as this require the utmost kindness and consideration from the nurse in support of the patient's struggle with the decision. Providing conditions of calmness, free from pressures of time and place, in which the alternatives can be thoroughly explored is helpful to the process of deliberation and decision. Few women want abortion. Some women are forced into securing abortions because of socioeconomic, psychological, or physiological circumstances unsupportive to a minimum decent life for themselves and the child. For them, there is no alternative. Other abortions are performed because of contraceptive failure. The intent was not to have a child. Increasingly, humans have exercised control of their procreative functions. Much remains to be done in the way of medical research to enable each couple to bring each new life into the world by deliberate choice and design and as a consequence of mutual love, respect, and desire for a family.

The nurse who assists with abortions on a regular basis may understandably be saddened by the loss of so much potential life; yet the nurse's concern properly belongs with the woman who, in the last analysis, must part with a potential life in which she is deeply invested. In most cases of abortion, the woman is the victim of her biological and social vulnerability and deserves the respect and help accorded all human beings by reason of their humanity.

Beyond the individual level, the nursing profession has the collective responsibility in policy formulation. An example of how this may be done is the New York State Nurses' Association support of the repeal of a restrictive state abortion law. The Association cited two reasons for liberalizing the law. The first is that the law "encourages poor health practices"[44] because the woman is forced to resort to illegal and hazardous abortions. The second reason given is that the restrictive law "deprives certain segments of the population of adequate medical care."[45] Poor women are simply unable to pay for safe and legal abortions. The Association stated unequivocally that it "takes no position on the moral aspects of abortion"[46] and supports the law that protects the rights of individuals refusing to participate in any procedure "contrary to their religious beliefs or conscience."[47]

CONCLUSION

A consideration of alternative metaphors associated with the moral problem of abortion and the role of nursing reveals difficulties in the way of resolving this issue. Competing metaphors are at work. Legal restraints on abortion or a lack of them reveal deep moral differences on the abortion issue. On some issues, one or the other tends to be or is right. On other issues, there is a stalemate. On still other issues, both sides may be "talking past each other." The abortion issue seems to us to be either a stalemate or a case of communicating on different levels. Perhaps when antiabortionists speak of the beginning of life, they refer to the moment of conception whereas prochoice supporters refer to newborns.

In saying this, however, we do not wish to hide behind the banner of neutrality; we have supported the argument on behalf of a woman's right to choose. But we also think it only circumspect to point out that the problem of abortion has not been solved with a conclusively justifiable or morally compelling answer. The reason is that, on such questions, no such answer is forthcoming.

REFERENCES

1. Tabers' Cyclopedic Medical Dictionary, 14th ed. Philadelphia, F. A. Davis, 1981, p. 1206.
2. *Roe* v. *Wade*, 410 U.S. 113.
3. Ibid.
4. Ibid.
5. Ibid.
6. Ibid.
7. Segers M.C.: Abortion and the Supreme Court: Some more equal than others. The Hastings Center Report 7(4):5, 1977.
8. Ibid.
9. Ibid., p. 6.
10. Ibid.
11. Fitzpatrick E., Reeder S.R., Mastroianni L. Jr.: Maternity Nursing, 12th ed. Philadelphia, Lippincott, 1971, p. 87.
12. Dedek J.F.: Abortion. In Ethical Issues in Nursing: A Proceeding. St. Louis, Mo., The Catholic Hospital Association, 1976, p. 77–78.
13. Ibid., p. 81.
14. Ibid., p. 82.
15. Thomson J.J.: A defense of abortion. Philosophy and Public Affairs 1(1):47–66, 1971.
16. Ibid.
17. Ibid.
18. Ibid.
19. Ibid.
20. Ibid.
21. Ibid.
22. Ibid.
23. Ibid.
24. Toulmin S.: The tyranny of principles. The Hastings Center Report 11(6):31–39, 1981.

25. Held V.: Abortion and the rights to life. In Bandman E.L., Bandman B. (eds.), Bioethics and Human Rights: A Reader for Health Professionals. Boston, Little, Brown, 1978, p. 108.
26. St. Thomas Aquinas: The sin of suicide. In Abelson R., Friguegnon M.L. (eds.), Ethics for Modern Life, 2nd ed. New York, St. Martin's, 1982 p. 25.
27. Held V.: Abortion and the rights to life, p. 105–107.
28. Nozick R.: Anarchy, State and Utopia. New York, Basic Books, 1974, p. 169.
29. Feinberg J.: Social Philosophy. Englewood Cliffs, N.J., Prentice-Hall, 1973, p. 54.
30. Marx K., Engels F.: The Communist Manifesto. In Marx and Engels: Basic Writings on Politics and Philosophy. New York, Anchor, 1959, p. 6–41.
31. Ruddick W.: Parents, children and medical decisions. In Bandman and Bandman, Bioethics and Human Rights, p. 165.
32. Brody B.: Opposition to abortion: A human rights approach. In Arthur J. (ed.), Morality and Moral Controversies. Englewood-Cliffs, N.J., Prentice-Hall, 1981, p. 200–213.
33. Brody: Opposition to abortion, p. 211.
34. Ibid., p. 212–213.
35. Jaggar A.: Abortion and a woman's right to decide. Philosophical Forum 5:351, 1973–1974.
36. Ibid.
37. Ibid.
38. Moran A.F.: Avoidable Births. New York Times, January 25, 1982, p. A31.
39. Ibid.
40. Executive Committee on the Division on Maternal and Child Health Nursing Practice, Statement on Abortion. Kansas City, Mo., Association, June 12, 1978.
41. American Nurses' Association: Code for Nurses with Interpretive Statements. Kansas City, Mo., The Association, 1976, p. 4.
42. Executive Committee on the Division on Maternal and Child Health Nursing Practice, "Statement on Abortion."
43. Curtin L., Flaherty M.J.: Nursing Ethics: Theories and Pragmatics. Bowie, Md., Brady, 1982, p. 254.
44. NYSNA Legislative Bulletin, no. 14. Albany, N.Y., New York State Nurses' Association, April 27, 1972.
45. Ibid.
46. Ibid.
47. Ibid.

CHAPTER 9

Ethical Issues in the Nursing Care of Infants

Through study of this chapter, the student will be able to:

1. Utilize ethical arguments for and against saving premature and deformed babies in facilitating the family's decisions regarding alternatives
2. Formulate the nurse's role as patient advocate for protecting the infant's right to care and safety and the family's well-being
3. Understand the significance of such moral issues as quorum features and the potentiality/actuality distinction
4. Discriminate among relevant principles of Utilitarian, deontological, and rights-based ethics in relation to each problem infant

INTRODUCTION

A tiny, helpless infant may be the ultimate appeal to the strength and benevolence of an adult. The newborn's obvious and total dependency on a supportive environment and a loving family matrix for its growth and development evokes adult nurturing and protective responses. As a totally dependent human, the newborn child needs a healthy and friendly environment. One of the best friends a newborn child has is a good nurse—one who cares for it, who can identify and respond to the newborn's feelings of discomfort from wetness, hunger, and thirst, and to its desire for warmth, closeness, and gratification.

Appreciation of the feelings of another is necessary to be an effective nurse. To be sensitive to the feelings of another is to want to help that person feel better. Infants, young children, and sometimes even older children and adolescents are unable to express feelings and needs verbally. They are often defenseless against imposition of painful treatments or the withholding of treatment by parents and health professionals. Children and even adolescents provide opportunities for implementing the nurse's role as advocate of the patient's rights to respect and to receive treatment. These young patients are the most vulnerable to neglect, indifference, rejection, or manipulation and abuse. Even more serious may be the moral conflicts that arise when the child is either physically or mentally abnormal. Ethical dilemmas arise when the parents want a normal child and the newborn is severely retarded or has physical abnormalities, such as trisomy 18, meningomyelocele, or Down's syndrome. Does the nurse comply with the parents' wishes if they refuse treatment for the child as their right, or does the nurse exert initiative to save the infant's life as the child's right?

If family and community resources are scarce, competing interests may call for other moral values to be given priority over the interests of preserving the life of a severely abnormal newborn. Some people call the failure to save a life "murder." Others condemn preserving infants that show few or no prospects of becoming independent, self-sufficient persons. The question is: How to decide who lives and who dies, and who is given quality care and who not? The issue of treatment for the abnormal infant is one filled with moral concerns and conflicts and with considerable potential for good or harm.

The pediatric nurse has a special role in being sensitive to the viability of the infant. Systematic assessments of the infant's functional assets and deficits as well as responsiveness are useful data in the final decisions of whether to care for, treat, or place with the family or in an institution. Each nurse caring for the infant is a vital link in compiling the data to be considered in making that ultimate decision. Nurses' interactions with parents provide data regarding parental perceptions of their ability and desire to cope with the problematic situation. Despair may be profound. Parents may be overwhelmed, guilty, angry, and ambivalent about what to do. Their moral conflicts may be acute. The advice given them may be conflict-ridden. The time for decision may be short and pressured. Parents may turn to the nurse for advice, support, and help. The nurse's role as advocate of the child's right to live and to be treated under all conditions may conflict with other moral principles holding that the happiness of the greatest number, in this case the family, may be in direct contradiction to saving the child. Careful consideration of all the variables relevant to the infant's capacities and potential as well as those of the family's abilities and willingness to cope with a painful, problematic situation of an abnormal child are determining factors in the final decision. In some situations with which some nurses are in agreement, the principle of the sanctity of life may prevail over all other considerations. Here, again, the nurse may play a significant role.

However, the "sanctity-of-life" principle, that human life is to be preserved under all conditions, conflicts with another principle, "the quality of life." This principle holds that there are conditions, sometimes referred to as *quorum features*, such as the presence of consciousness, that define a worthwhile human life. Thus, not all life is to be preserved if it fails to comply with "quality-of-life" standards. Consequently, five sometimes conflicting principles govern health professionals' first encounters with newborn infants. One principle is to preserve human life under all conditions. A second principle is to promote worthwhile human life, the "quality-of-life" argument, with the implication of productivity and independence. A third principle is to prevent or minimize harm. A fourth principle is to alleviate suffering. A fifth principle is to seek to do good, as by giving skilled nursing care. These principles will be considered in relation to examples of moral dilemmas in the nursing of infants.

ARGUMENTS FOR AND AGAINST SAVING PREMATURE AND DEFORMED INFANTS

Infanticide of deformed and even normal female babies was an ancient practice for controlling populations. High infant mortality rates were accepted. The death of a deformed baby was often welcomed and perhaps assisted by midwives sympathetic to women's destiny of uncontrolled pregnancies.

The contrary principle, that life is the highest good, is supported by the Judeo-Christian tradition prohibiting abortion, infanticide, and euthanasia. Significantly, medical technology has now advanced to a level of saving an increasing number of premature, underweight, and underdeveloped infants by means of neonatal intensive care units. The most sophisticated forms of monitoring vital signs and regulating electrolytes, food, and fluid are keeping premature and deformed infants alive at an astonishing rate. The principle of saving all life is respected through routine application of extraordinary means to continue the living processes of these infants. The cost of continuous professional care, high-level technological equipment and supplies, and prolonged hospitalization is more than $400 a day per child in neonatal intensive care units. In these fully lighted, gleaming-surfaced, windowed enclosures, nurses adjust rates of flow of fluids and gases in response to readings of the monitoring devices attached to each infant. The operating principle and the goal are identical. These are to save all life with no regard for the quality of the life saved or the costs to parents and society. The infant is given care, in most instances, without regard for the present and later burden this may impose on families and society or even the suffering of the infant itself from necessary injections and intubations. Once the infant is received in the neonatal intensive care unit, the decision has already been made to treat fully and intensively, with no regard for such long-term consequences as brain damage or chronic cardiopulmonary disease.

However, not all premature or deformed infants are immediately transferred to intensive care units. Two examples of frequently occurring problems in newborn infants illustrate the scope and depth of the moral issues involved in decisions of treatment or nontreatment. These cases point to the usefulness of identifying short-term and long-term goals and consequences to the individual affected as well as the family and society.

The first frequently occurring example of a neonatal problem is the birth of very premature, underweight, underdeveloped babies as a result of spontaneous or induced abortion. On one view, the gasping infant is left to die in a surgical pail. On another view, that infant is resuscitated and admitted to an intensive care unit. On one view, the decision to seek an abortion is an automatic death sentence for the fetus; on another view, the abortion decision is one of ending the pregnancy. On one view, the viable fetus has the right to live and the nurse, as patient advocate, has the duty to protect the fetus's life above all other values. Questions arise as to who decides, and by what criteria, to either resuscitate or not resuscitate the infant. Other questions arise as to what difference voluntary versus involuntary abortion makes. Related questions concern the difference socioeconomic status, race, age, and the mother's marital status play in decisions to resuscitate and treat or not to resuscitate and treat.

The second example is that of the infant born with multiple defects that threaten life. One example is the baby on a respirator due to respiratory difficulty with evidence pointing to the diagnosis of trisomy 18. This genetic disorder leads to severe mental retardation, failure to grow, and many other abnormalities.[1]

Adapting the case somewhat, let's suppose one parent insists that the chief of pediatrics does nothing to keep a four-day-old trisomy 18 infant alive. A pediatric resident points out that another patient who has a slight respiratory difficulty cannot be put on a respirator because the trisomy 18 infant is using the only available machine. Without the respirator, the other infant, "who is otherwise healthy, runs a 50% risk of some brain damage."[2] The facts are that 87 percent of trisomy 18 infants die in the first year. At this point two nurses directly responsible for the infant's care interrupt. Nurse A insists that the trisomy 18 infant "has every right to live and should not be allowed to die by human hands." Nurse B disagrees with Nurse A and says that those beings with a meaningful life have the right to be given health care resources, that an infant with a slight respiratory difficulty should not be sacrificed for the trisomy 18 infant. Nurse A supports the principle of "the sanctity of life" under all conditions. Nurse B believes in the principle of "the quality of life"; she believes the trisomy 18 infant has poor prospects. If you are Nurse C, what do you advise the parents and Nurses A and B to do—save the trisomy 18 infant or leave it to die?

Further questions arise as to the original decision to start a life-support system and to continue it. Considering the evidence of multiple defects, a poor quality of life, and an expected life span of less than a year, questions arise as to what criteria for decision are relevant, who the decision makers are, and what the role of the nurse is in facilitating the decision.

A second case involves a baby boy who had Down's syndrome and who also had a surgically repairable duodenal obstruction. The parents, by not consenting to surgery, contributed to the death of their six-day-old Down's syndrome child.[3]

One writer who fictionalizes a similar account points out that "many nurses and physicians thought it was wrong that the baby was forced to die. . . ."[4] This writer adds this fictionalized scenario to the actual case.

> The burden of caring for the dying baby fell on the nurses in the obstetrics ward. The physicians avoided the child entirely, and it was the nurses who had to see to it that she received her water and was turned in her bed. This was the source of much resentment among the nursing staff, and a few nurses refused to have anything to do with the dying child.... But one nurse... was determined to make... [the baby's] last days as comfortable as possible. She held the baby, rocked her, and talked soothingly to her when she cried. . . . But even [this nurse] was glad when the baby died. "It was a relief to me," she said. "I almost couldn't bear the frustration of just sitting there day after day and doing nothing that could really help her."[5]

In actual fact, Dr. Milton Heifitz writes that "the world press in 1971 condemned the 'inhumanity' of a husband and wife and the staff of a major American medical center. A mongoloid baby was born with an intestinal obstruction at John Hopkins Hospital in Baltimore. The parents, who had two normal children, refused to give consent to correct the obstruction. The infant could not be fed and died within fifteen days."[6] According to Heifitz, "the child's death caused a furor in medical and lay circles. It was a major topic at an international symposium concerning medical ethics. Panelists disagreed with parents. They suggested the child's right to life, to the limit of happiness possible, was more important than the years of anguish and burden the child would bring the family."[7] Thus, "the sanctity of life" overrides all else.

ETHICAL CONSIDERATIONS IN THE NURSING CARE OF INFANTS

The nurse working with infants, like nurses working with any other age group, occupies a number of roles. Pediatric nurses, however, may perceive themselves as primarily patient advocates for the rights of the helpless, vulnerable infants in their care. They may see advocacy responsibilities as a significant feature in the delivery of quality care to each baby. The American Nurses' Association Code for Nurses defines the role of client advocate in sweeping terms.

> The nurse's primary commitment is to the client's care and safety. Hence, in the role of client advocate, the nurse must be alert to and take appropriate action regarding any instances of incompetent, unethical, or illegal practice(s) by any member of the health care team or the health care system itself, or any action on the part of others that is prejudicial to the client's best interests.[8]

The nurse dealing with the infant has an additional responsibility. He or she has to fulfill the role of a surrogate parent and clinician and consider the fragile state of the infant. This definition of the role of client advocate is tantamount to a mandate or command to safeguard the infant's life against those who would not treat or feed the infant because of a decision using a quality-of-life argument. But a question arises as to whether a nurse is an advocate of the infant client or the infant's parents. This becomes crucial if the infant's parents have conflicting interests between themselves or if their interests are not those of their infant. Pediatric nurses most in contact with the infant may feel the decision by parents to terminate an infant's life to be unfair or to be tantamount to an act of murder. These nurses perceive themselves to be advocates for the infant's right to life.

Patient advocacy may be expressed in a variety of ways. One way is to marshal the facts based on careful, systematic assessment of the infant's status as the basis for arguments favoring the continuation or termination of life on the basis of quorum features. The arguments may be then presented to the physician and family for consideration. Through contact with the parents, pediatric nurses may exert considerable influence on their decision. Sharing of nurses' knowledge of this child's estimated needs for care through the life span and the experience of other parents facing similar demands may be useful information in the parents' process of decision. In some cases, nurses as patient advocates comply with the directive of the *Code for Nurses* for being fully aware of institutional policies and procedures as well as state laws regarding unethical, incompetent, or illegal practice and taking necessary steps to initiate action through appropriate channels. It is important to provide careful documentation and to use established mechanisms for appeal so as to avoid reprisal. There have been instances in which the courts have directed that an infant be fed and treated where parents have refused treatment. Sometimes, custody of infants is taken from the parents at the instigation of a family agency on grounds of neglect when the parents refuse treatment. A counterexample occurred in 1982 in Bloomington, Indiana, where two Monroe County courts and the state Supreme Court all declined to force parents to feed or treat a baby born with Down's syndrome and an incomplete esophagus. The Monroe County prosecutor said he would not file charges in the death of the week-old baby despite plans for an appeal to the Supreme Court.[9] Those nurse client advocates who participate in securing legal advocacy for this and similar babies to whom nourishment, treatment, and life itself were denied are committed to the sanctity-of-life principle.

Other nurses may support the quality-of-life principle and appeal to the *Code for Nurses*, which directs the nurse to "take appropriate action regarding . . . incompetent, unethical or illegal practice(s) . . . prejudicial to the client's best interests."[10] Nurses committed to the quality-of-life principle may believe it cruel and unjust both to the child and the family to prolong the suffering of a severely handicapped child. Such nurses may support parental decisions not to treat the deformed infant while giving compassionate care to the hungry infant. Such babies can be kept sedated and comfortable until they die. Parents need the support of nurses and physicians in handling the inevitable guilt feelings concerning their decision not to treat or feed.

In still other examples, parents may not consent to treatment for correction of a minor deformity that will not interfere with the full potential of the infant. The nurse as patient advocate may in this instance be in the very best position to protect the "client's care and safety"[11] by persuading parents to permit treatment on the grounds of the child's right to a full human life. Nurses and physicians, in advocating infants' rights, may consider in extreme cases openly disagreeing with the parents by presenting morally cogent reasons and arguments. Nurses and physicians may also appeal to the courts, if necessary, to protect the right of a minimally deformed child to be fed and treated.

Another issue for the nurse advocate to consider is the principle to do no harm. Such a principle is as relevant for the physician as it is for the nurse. Some research done on infants may be justified in terms of benefit to the immature client. Other research may be done for the social benefit of others at some indefinite time without any benefit to the infant subject. We have all benefitted, after all, from research done on others at an earlier time or at some other place. So, on a reciprocity basis between generations and places, we owe it to others to submit to research, but not as our primary duty. The nurse who secures consent from the parents for research or experimentation involving their child needs to make the clear distinction between benefit to the parents, benefit to the individual, and social benefit. A truthful account would distinguish research for the benefit of one's child and research for the benefit of other children. Research that is of no benefit to the infant or to other children is nothing more than an assault against the tiny body of the infant.

Those nurses who agree with the quality-of-life argument and the need to minimize the suffering of the affected infant and family appreciate the integrity of the Duff and Campbell study. These two Yale University physicians reported that in a 30-month period, 43 infants judged by parents and staff to have little or no hope of achieving personhood were left to die by the withholding of essential medical treatment.[12]

The role of patient advocate for handicapped infants became a national issue in April 1982 when a six-day-old infant, "Baby Doe," of Bloomington, Indiana, died from lack of food and water. Treatment of the infant's tracheoesophageal fistula was denied by the parents, who were supported in their decision by the Indiana courts. Presumably the parents refused surgical repair of the condition because the infant also had Down's syndrome.

In response to the public outcry of indignation, the United States Department of Health and Human Services Office of Civil Rights issued a "Notice to Health Care Providers" on May 18, 1982. The notice quoted the Federal Law, Section 504 of the Rehabilitation Act of 1973.

> No otherwise qualified handicapped individual shall, solely by reason of handicap, be excluded from participation in, be denied the benefits of, or be subjected to discrimination under any program or activity receiving federal financial assistance. . . . It is unlawful for a recipient of federal financial assistance to withhold from a handicapped infant nutritional sustenance or medical or surgical treatment required to correct a life threatening condition, if: (1) the withholding is based on the fact that the infant is handicapped; and (2) the handicap does not render the treatment or nutritional sustenance medically contraindicated.

This notice directed that anyone with knowledge of the denial of food or customary medical care should immediately contact the Department's handicapped-infant hotline available 24 hours a day or the particular state's child-protective agency. Telephone numbers were provided, as well as a promise of confidentiality. The notice stated that failure to feed and to care for infants may also be a violation of state criminal and civil laws. Providers of health care to infants were required to post this Notice in conspicuous places where such care is given. Thus, nurses, physicians, and parents of handicapped infants were continuously confronted with this reminder of the stipulations of the advocacy role in delivery rooms, nurseries, and intensive care and pediatric units.

A suit against the Department of Health and Human Services and its secretary to prohibit the Notice from becoming final was brought by the American Academy of Pediatrics, the National Association of Children's Hospitals, and Children's Hospital National Medical Center. On April 14, 1983 the United States District Judge ruled the Health and Human Services regulation to be invalid because the Department did not follow proper procedures in making public the terms of a proposed law and inviting wide public comment.

The judicial decision simply postponed the inevitable clash of values between proponents of conflicting legal and ethical principles. The Department believes that posting of notices and complaint procedures is an effective means of deterrence and enforcement of the rule that a handicapped infant must be fed and treated. This is a sanctity-of-life position. Judge Gesell, who ruled on this regulation, pointed to elimination of the role of the infant's parents in selecting appropriate medical treatment as an infringement of privacy. Parents presumably know what the infant's best interests are, based on their knowledge of the economic, social, psychologic, and physical aspects of their situation. The judge described the regulation as "arbitrary and capricious." He recommended that "federal intervention in the delivery rooms and newborn intensive care units should 'obviously reflect caution and sensitivity.'"[13]

Medical critics point to several major difficulties in this proposed rule. First, major handicaps, such as major malformations of the brain along with the absence of kidneys, are a reason for withholding treatment because the child will not benefit from treatment and treatment is not in its interest.[14] (Adult patients who are hopelessly and terminally ill with pain and dysfunction are also not treated by resuscitation because treatment is not in such patients' interests.) The Department responded to this criticism by pointing out that "Section 504 does not require the imposition of futile therapies which temporarily prolong the process of dying of an infant born . . . with anencephaly or intra-cranial bleeding."[15]

The Health and Human Services Department suggested that health providers do not aid parental decisions "to withhold treatment or nourishment . . . by allowing the infant to remain in the institution." The possibilities of coercion of parents to change their minds, or of parental rejection of the infant or inadequate home care if the infant is discharged or transferred following a request for nontreatment, is another criticism of this proposed regulation. The major medical criticism remains that handicap alone is an insufficient "criterion for distinguishing justified from unjustified deaths. . . . The potential for human relationships or the capacity to survive infancy and participate in human experience may serve better."[16]

Nurses play significant roles in these decisions, both through their participation in the assessment and their participation in the judgment process as members of a team. If open-ended moral dialogue is regarded as an essential condition of the decision-making process, then that process is one of mutual respect. Mutual respect in this context means that the negotiation process is open and encourages reasoned arguments until some approximation of consensus is reached about the infant's right to live versus the benefit to the child, as well as to the family and society, which bear the cost. As caregiver and with understandable feelings of deep compassion for the short and tragic life of the tiny, defenseless patient, the nurse provides for the comfort of the dying infant to whom food and treatment are denied. If the nurse disagrees with this order or is unable to give skilled care and comfort to the infant because of resentment of the family's "dumping of their responsibility," the nurse may refuse to provide care.

Before the nurse takes individual action, he or she might benefit from institutional review. The need is for the development of institutional policies and review processes that apply broad rules to specific cases, such as the priority given to the best interests of the infant, with care not withheld solely because of mental retardation.

When the parents of a seriously ill newborn are disqualified from making decisions by incapacity, disagreement between them, or choices clearly against the infant's best interests, there are currently civil courts, state laws, child protection agencies, and even criminal penalties available to respond to the presumed neglect of the handicapped infants. Until such policies and processes are developed in each caregiving institution, the nurse is the best interim advocate protecting the interests of the handicapped infant.

The *Code for Nurses* states that if the nurse is

> . . . personally opposed to the delivery of care in a particular case because of the nature of the health problem or the procedures to be used, the nurse is justified in refusing to participate.[17]

The *Code* goes on to say that such refusal is expected to be made known in time for other arrangements for providing nursing care. According to the *Code*, the nurse can withdraw from a situation only when others are available to provide the care and comfort needed by the infant as its last demands. But two moral questions arise: (1) What if a nurse does not accept the conventional morality of the *Code* and refuses to participate before any other nurse is willing to help? and (2) What if there are no other nurses available who are willing to comply with the decision to facilitate a dying infant's last moments? There is the understandable moral ground that nurses may not concur with an act they regard as "murder." To such questions there may be no answers, only stalemate and tragedy, which the human race may have no choice but to accept.

ETHICAL AND PHILOSOPHICAL CONSIDERATIONS

Several Philosophical Moves

Moral and philosophical questions arise about these cases such as: Whose rights are to be taken most seriously? Since decisions concerning these cases involve values, either the sanctity or the quality of life, these questions cannot be settled by science, by evidence, or by verifying what is true or false only. Nor can one settle these questions by considering sociological factors, such as: "What do most people favor?" These are philosophical value questions. Value questions, if they are settled at all, are settled by showing that one moral value is more justifiable than another. One way to justify a moral argument that a trisomy 18 infant has fewer rights to live than a mild Down's syndrome or normal infant is to show that the consequences clearly favor one side over the other. Another way to justify a value preference is to show that one belief has more conceptual and practical difficulties than any other.

Quorum Features. Several philosophical moves have recently been developed in an attempt to clarify the right to life and parental, health professional, and nursing responsibilities. One move consists in applying the idea of "quorum features"[18] to the question, "When does a person's life begin and end?" A quorum at a meeting means that a previously agreed-upon number of persons have to be at a meeting for the meeting to take place. So one philosophical move consists in applying the idea of a "quorum feature" to the question, "When does a human life begin and end?" or to the question, "What is a person?" A being who lacks the quorum or majority of essential features of an ordinary person, such as one who has multiple deformities, or lacks consciousness, such as a trisomy 18 infant, does not satisfy the quorum features of being a person. What makes the refusal to save the life of the Down's syndrome infant morally questionable to some people and an outrage on the border of "murder" to others is that the Down's syndrome patient is more clearly a person than is the infant with trisomy 18. Some might say that the Down's syndrome infant has some prospects for a meaningful human life, whereas the trisomy 18 infant does not have such prospects.

Tracing and Examining for Appropriate Metaphors and Models. A second philosophical move consists of considering a viewpoint that purports to provide an answer to the question, "What is a person?" One then traces that viewpoint to some deeply acknowledged metaphor, word picture, or pictorial analogy on which defense of the viewpoint depends philosophically. One then examines the metaphor to determine how it applies or breaks down in practical discourse. One may consider next whether supplementary or alternative metaphorical analogies aid in the defense of a given viewpoint. One may, for example, regard any being born to be unconditionally worth preserving on the ground that "life is a gift,"[19] to cite St. Thomas Aquinas's insightful metaphor. One thus traces a viewpoint to a metaphor on which its philosophical defense partly rests. But one may next examine the metaphor to note what conceptual or practical limits or difficulties it implies. A difficulty immediately becomes apparent. Is life always a gift? Is it necessarily a gift, so that there could be no instance of life that was not a gift? One has only to consider some terminal patients or seriously maimed or wounded persons to note that there are exceptions to life always being a gift. Furthermore, in ordinary language, if one gets a gift, one may keep it, give it to someone else, or discard it in the wastebasket. But the gift of which St. Thomas Aquinas speaks, because it is given, may not be taken. This is a strange requirement for any gift. And yet one can appreciate that the recognition that life is a gift spurs health professionals to save it. A metaphor may thus be examined for its illumination as well as for its implied difficulties. Life is not always a gift, as the trisomy 18 case amply shows.

The Potentiality-Actuality Distinction

A related effort to answer "What is a person?" is to regard any potential person as a person. Thus, an acorn is potentially an oak tree and therefore is to be accorded the recognition that someday it will be an oak tree. Similarly, a girl is a potential woman. Since a rock, stamp, or oak tree is not a potential person, one need not confer personhood status to these entities. But even a seriously deformed person enjoys the status of being a person, according to the potentiality principle. This is not true, however, if one shows that the potentiality principle has limits. According to one philosopher, Stanley Benn, "A potential president of the United States is not on that account Commander in Chief of the U.S. Army and Navy."[20] According to another philosopher, Joel Feinberg, "A dog is closer to personhood than a jellyfish, but that is not the same thing as being 'more of a person.' . . . In 1930, when he was six years old, Jimmy Carter didn't know it, but he was a potential president of the United States. That gave him no claim then, not even a weak claim, to give commands to the U.S. Army and Navy. Franklin Roosevelt in 1930 was only two years away from the presidency, so he was a potential president in a much stronger way . . . than was Jimmy Carter. Nevertheless, he was not actually president and he had no more of a claim to the prerogatives of the office than did Carter."[21] One could, however, criticize this analogy by pointing out that a fetus's becoming a person is a biological process rather than a social or political process, unlike a candidate for president's becoming president. The point nevertheless remains that potentiality does not imply actuality; and the potential person may be discounted from being regarded as an actual person. A trisomy 18 infant who has multiple deformities, while *potentially* a normal person, is not *actually* a normal person. The analogy one appeals to is to show that a presidential candidate, who is a potential president, while closer to being a president than a potential candidate who is six years old and therefore under age, is not an actual president, who alone has the rights and responsibilities associated with being a president. The analogy of president to person shows that as a potential president is not an actual president, a potential person is not an actual person.

Traditional Ethical Viewpoints Applied to the Infant Cases

A fourth and last philosophical move one might consider is to examine how the ethical principles previously considered apply to resolving the question of what to do about infants with abnormalities. A Utilitarian, for example, would adopt the quality-of-life principle. In relation to competing demands for the available respirator, the Utilitarian ethicist would say that considering "the greatest happiness of the greatest number," one ought to give preferential treatment to the one normal infant with respiratory difficulties over the infant with trisomy 18. A Utilitarian might even defend the refusal to consent to surgical repair of a duodenal atresia in the case of a Down's syndrome infant. However, on a Christian or Agapist or love-based ethical view, which favors "the sanctity of life," one does all one can to save the life of a trisomy 18 infant or one with Down's syndrome, on the ground that "they are all God's children," to cite yet another metaphor.

One might think a Kantian deontological ethics commits one to a similar ethical conclusion, but Kant confines his ethics to rational beings. The point about Kant's deontological ethics is that appeal to universalizable principles requires the same treatment for all individuals within a given group without exception, allowing exception only if relevant differences are shown.

From a rights point of view, if persons alone have rights, and a seriously deformed being is not regarded as a person, then such a being, including a trisomy 18 infant, is not a person, and hence has no rights. The mild Down's syndrome infant who falls within the quorum feature of being human—that is, satisfies the requirements of personhood—does have rights, including the right to live. The violation of the Down's syndrome infant's right to live is an indication of its moral wrongness.

Since one cannot always reconcile these alternative moral points of view, one has to consider the place both of tragedy in human life and of stalemate in the effort to resolve sometimes unresolvable problems.

Application of Philosophical Moves to the Infant with Handicaps

We have seen that the federal regulation issued as a "Notice to Health Providers" on May 18, 1982, required health providers "to meet the immediate needs that can arise when a handicapped infant is discriminatingly denied food or other medical care."[22]

In regard to this handicapped-infant ruling, goal-based ethics (see Chapter 4) says: Consider the consequences. A consequence to future generations is to be borne in mind. For every pregnancy, two questions are relevant: Who will provide? and How will it be provided for? On an aggregate macrolevel, there must be enough people with the capacity to develop into persons of adequate achievement to contribute to advancing levels of knowledge, science, and technology for everyone. One might refer to the principle to "produce as many socially useful individuals as possible" as the Aggregate-Capacity Principle. The need to provide persons of social and moral merit is basic to the dictum that people generally have to pay their way in the world. Future health care and human service providers will be decreasingly able to cope effectively with excessive numbers of essentially dependent people.

Infant health care policies consequently cannot be oriented solely toward the principle of saving every infant, no matter how handicapped. Nor, however, can health care policies be oriented toward saving only those some people deem as fit to lead a high-quality life.

A problem for both those who strive to save everyone and those who exclude those with less than optimum human qualities is analogous to having either too many or too few people at the world's dinner table. If there are too many at the table, then everyone will not have enough to eat. If one excludes too many, those excluded will have nothing to eat. Moreover, the principle of selection and the basis for excluding are apt to be arbitrary. A difficulty of including or excluding too many beings is illustrated by having to decide whether to treat infants with myelomeningocele, hydrocephalus, mental retardation, and other serious anomalies.

One can picture this dilemma of distributing resources to people by drawing concentric circles, one inside the other. Let the inner circle represent available resources and the outer circle represent people and their needs and desires. The larger the inner circle is made in relation to the outer one, the smaller will be the shares for each person. But if the inner circle is kept small, more people will be excluded. One possible resolution of this dilemma is to limit the outer circle, the number of people, keeping the inner circle representing resources as close to the outer circle as possible. A dynamic equilibrium between the world's population and available resources calls for both circles to be as close as possible.

On this ground, Utilitarianism or goal-based ethics seems to have a claim on future societal needs. Decisions have to be made employing fair, rational, and relevant criteria as to whom to help and save. To save blue-eyed infants, for example, seems to be irrelevant and/or unfair. It is fairer to save those who have the best chance of leading socially useful lives. In addition to observing this dictum, one works to achieve a balance between extreme positions, regard for merit and for the equal distribution of socially useful resources.

The appeal to the achievement of merit calls for exclusions of those who show little or no merit. Exclusions of this or that group may be painful. Such exclusions may also be unjust. Including everyone, however, means resources may be too thinly distributed to do much good, especially if those individual beings included are too numerous in relation to available resources. A policy, like Section 504, may tip the scale in favor of attempting to save too many infants, and also more infants than can be provided for throughout the life span, who require continuous medical care, special education, and housing and financial assistance.

One strikes a balance not by ignoring the claims of each position, but by attending to both claims, "prevention of harm" and "caring for quality of life."

There is no innate obligation to favor the prevention-of-harm or quality-of-life principle. Both are good because of the good they bring, in the estimation of people who have good reasons for juidiciously applying both these principles.

According to Aristotle, the good is "that at which all things aim."[23] One may amend this to read: The good is that which attempts to reconcile the goods at which people aim. One aim that is believed good is the prevention of harm. Another is fostering the quality of life. One route is to realize that, as with life, there are moral polarities, intermediate positions, priorities, and criteria for selection. Striking a balance between these calls for rational criteria, inferrable by reasoning with Kantian principles rather than solely with Utilitarian considerations, such as impartiality and consistency. A health care policy, for example, may take the form, "Every baby having features A, B, C . . . is regarded as a person and every baby with features D, E, F . . . (medically untreatable) does not qualify as a person. Every person shall be adequately cared for and treated. Therefore, babies having features A, B, C . . ., being persons, shall be treated; and babies with D, E, F, (and medically untreatable), not being regarded as persons, shall not be treated." Invoking a Kantian appeal to a universal moral principle minimizes (but may not eliminate) arbitrariness as to what counts as a person. Specifying features, such as A, B, and C (drawing a justifiable and useful distinction between these features of a "person" and those without such features), may reduce arbitrariness somewhat.

On this view, a health care policy would be a health care guideline to health providers. Details of the features of persons and nonpersons would be worked out in health care ethics committees by relevant professionals, including nurses, with input from public policymakers, parents, and other representatives of society. A so-called hotline would go, not to a centralized bureaucratic government agency, but to an appropriate impartial patient advocacy group. Its functions would be to guide present and future decisions effectively rather than blaming or punishing health providers for past decisions.

CONCLUSION

Ordinarily, the wonder and joy of human life begins with the birth of an infant. The mother of the new infant is apt to feel the emotion of participating in the creative process of life. But the infant is fragile, helpless, and dependent. It will need the highest quality of nurture a mother and father are prepared to give it in order to grow into childhood, adolescence, and responsible adulthood. Not all newborns, however, are normal at birth. Some are born with minor deviations from health. Others are born with gross abnormalities. Nurses are involved in the health care activities and processes of decision making for all infants. Therefore, nurses contribute their observations regarding the infant's health status when decisions are to be made regarding who lives, who receives special consideration, and who is left to die.

The quorum feature or majority features of a human life, including evidence of consciousness, helps parents and health professionals, including nurses, to make ethically justifiable decisions. The sanctity-of-life principle, under which life is regarded as sacred under all conditions, may conflict with a quality-of-life principle in those instances when not all can be effectively helped to live decent, fulfilling lives. If resources are scarce and not all can be saved, the sanctity-of-life principle may appear impractical, inflexible, and unworkable. If the quality-of-life principle is then invoked, questions of arbitrariness arise. How to decide on just grounds who lives and dies is the question continuously considered by morally reflective people. Therefore, while both principles, the sanctity and the quality of life, have a claim on nurses, neither principle is satisfactory in every case, nor is either quite free from fault, nor is either able to withstand further questions.

REFERENCES

1. Brody H.: Ethical Decisions in Medicine, 2nd ed. Boston, Little, Brown, 1981, p. 116.
2. Ibid.
3. Shaw A.: Dilemmas of "informed consent" in children. In Hunt R., Arras J. (eds.), Ethical Issues in Modern Medicine. Palo Alto, Calif., Mayfield, 1977, p. 184–186.
4. Munson R.: Intervention and Reflection: Basic Issues in Medical Ethics. Belmont, Calif., Wadsworth, 1979, p. 94–97.
5. Ibid., p. 96–97.
6. Heifitz M.D., with Mangel C.: The Right to Die. New York, Berkeley, 1975, p. 59–60.
7. Ibid., p. 60.
8. American Nurses' Association: Code for Nurses with Interpretive Statements. Kansas City, Mo., The Association, 1976, p. 8.
9. The prosecutor closes case in death of Indiana baby. New York Times, April 20, 1982.
10. American Nurses' Association: Code for Nurses, p. 8.
11. Ibid.
12. Duff R.S., Campbell A.G.M.: Moral and ethical dilemmas in the special care nursery. N Eng J Med, 289:885, 1973.

13. Annas G.J.: Disconnecting the Baby Doe hotline. Hastings Center Report 13(3):14, 1983.
14. Fost N.: Putting hospitals on notice. Hastings Center Report, 12(4):5, 1982.
15. Federal Register 48(129):30846, July 5, 1983.
16. Fost: Putting hospitals on notice.
17. American Nurses' Association: Code for Nurses, p. 5.
18. Hospers J.: An Introduction to Philosophical Analysis. Englewood Cliffs, N.J., Prentice-Hall, 1967, p. 71–73.
19. St. Thomas Aquinas: The sin of suicide. In Abelson R., Friquegnon M.L. (eds.), Ethics for Modern Life, 2nd ed. New York, St. Martin's, 1982, p. 25.
20. Benn S.: Abortion, infanticide and respect for persons. In Feinberg J. (ed.), The Problem of Abortion. Belmont, Calif., Wadsworth, 1973, p. 102.
21. Feinberg J.: The problem of personhood. In Beauchamp T., Walters L. (eds.), Contemporary Issues in Bioethics, 2nd ed. Belmont, Calif., Wadsworth, 1982, p. 113–114.
22. Federal Register 48(45):9630–9632, March 7, 1983.
23. Aristotle: Nichomachean Ethics. Martin Ostwald, tr. Indianapolis, Bobbs-Merrill, 1962, p. 3.

CHAPTER 10

Ethical Issues in the Nursing Care of Children

Through study of this chapter, the student will be able to:

1. Identify the ethical issues involved in problematic situations involving children's rights to health care, safety, and well-being
2. Facilitate the parents' participation in shared decision making regarding the well-being of the child in relation to the whole family
3. Distinguish between a biological and a biographical life as criteria for personhood
4. Clarify the role of children's rights in relation to parental and societal rights and duties owed dependent children
5. Evaluate the role of the nurse as patient advocate in nursing practice with children

INTRODUCTION

Children are almost universally regarded as the hope of the future for a better world. Yet in parts of this globe, large numbers of children are ill-fed, inadequately clothed, housed, and educated, and in dire need of curative, preventive, and rehabilitative health care. Children are perceived in the light of cultural values and mores. It is the culture that defines "the length of childhood, the essential nature of childhood, and the meaning of childhood."[1] At least one writer claims that childhood is a European invention of the 16th century. This means that from that time on children were taken more seriously as distinct beings.[2] But in view of child labor laws and cruelty and abuses inflicted on children since then to the present, this assertion is debatable.

Predictably, the pluralistic culture of the United States at present supports a wide range of values regarding children reflected in child-rearing practices. Children are incorporated into various family models. One model of parent-child relations is that of Ownership. According to this model, children are perceived as being possessions of their parents. A second model, Partnership, implies that children are more nearly equal with their parents. A third model, widely practiced, especially in remarriages, is that of Club Membership. Here, the members of the family are not cared for very much as individuals. They are essentially left on their own. Family socioeconomic differences are usually reflected in the prevalence or absence of family planning, numbers of children, and the desirability of the birth of each child. Middle- and upper-class families in the United States are usually child-centered, attempting to meet each need and foster individuality. Poor families may struggle to provide basic necessities of life with little concern for the special needs of each child. Nevertheless, affluent and poor families may each have difficulty in meeting children's rights, due to the parental tendency to prefer either the Ownership or Club Membership models over the Partnership model.

In response to the largely dependent and vulnerable status of children all over the world, several lists of rights have been developed. The most controversial list is that put forth by John Holt[3] in 1974. This list includes rights to vote, "to work for money," to receive equal treatment under the law, to be financially responsible for oneself, to privacy, to self-directed education, to travel, to choose a residence, to a minimum income equal with adults, to "quasi familial relationships outside one's immediate family," and to mutually consenting relationships.

A less controversial but nevertheless utopian set of rights was *The Declaration of the Rights of the Child.* This rests on the recognition of human rights and in the worth and dignity of each human being; it was developed by the United Nations in 1959. This declaration recognizes the special protection needed for enabling the immature child's physical, mental, moral, social, and cultural growth and development to proceed. Humankind "owes to the child the best it has to give . . . to the end that he may have a happy childhood and enjoy for his own good and for the good of society, the rights and freedom . . . set forth."[4] The rights set forth are for nondiscriminatory entitlement to rights, which recognize the interests of the child. At birth, the child has a right to a name and a nationality. The child has the right to adequate food, shelter, recreation, and health care. The handicapped child shall be given special care, treatment, and education, according to the *Declaration.* Every child's need for love and understanding, parents, and security will be supported by state assistance to families and care of children without families. The child has a right to education, at least through the elementary grades, free of cost but on the condition of compulsory attendance. This requirement built into the rights declaration is purportedly justified by the need for the child to develop his or her abilities and to contribute to society. The child has the right to special protection from neglect, cruelty, and exploitation in the form of traffic or employment detrimental to health and development. Lastly, the child will be protected from discriminatory practices and be reared in "peace and universal brotherhood."[5]

Wieczorek and Natapoff point to the United Nations *Declaration* as omitting rights "to love from a significant adult . . . to a safe environment . . . to reach individual potential . . . to be a wanted child in a situation that has resources . . . to respect the individual autonomy of the child, and . . . to personal space that may include sexual expression."[6] All of the rights listed have the dual function of both enhancing the child's personhood and protecting the child's fundamental needs in its growth and development toward humanity.

ETHICAL ISSUES IN THE NURSING CARE OF CHILDREN: SOME CASES

Some major ethical issues concerned with children between 1 and 12 years of age involve the principle of informed consent, its scope, and its limits when applied to children. Other issues concern parental control versus the child's growing autonomy. Another moral concern is that of the abuse of children directly and through neglect or denial of the child's rights to the truth, to proper health care, education, and a safe environment, as well as by direct inflicting of harm and injury of children.

Selective cases will illustrate the importance of these issues to the child's survival as a person. As these cases illustrate, there is a continuum of decision regarding children's rights. At one end there is absolute parental control, with complete child autonomy at the other end. This gives rise to conflict in making health care decisions when there is disagreement between parent and child or parent and health care provider regarding the child's best interests. The process of making decisions for and by the child is also related to the quality of child-parent relationships and family values, the age and maturity of the child, the diagnosis, and the significance of the treatment to the future of the child.

Some decisions to treat or not treat are uncomplicated. For example, a pediatrician does not prescribe drugs for a hyperactive child at the request of the teacher or school nurse without parental consent.[7] One might also expect that the decision for tonsillectomy in a 6-year-old would be the sole decison of the parents. On the other hand, one would expect sensitive parents to seek the informed consent of a 10-, 11- or 12-year-old child to the same surgery. Where parents are divorced, the parent with legal custody of the child is legally responsible for informed consent to treatment.[8] Moral considerations, however, are complex when parents, either married or divorced, have an honest difference of opinion regarding the desirability of treatment, such as tonsillectomy or amputation for a malignant tumor. Here the principle of beneficence, that is, to do good, directly collides with the principle of "Do no harm," or nonmaleficence. This is a common problem in the example of tonsillectomy, where the tonsils are not a focus of infection but where frequent colds and sore throats occur. The evidence on either side, for tonsil removal or retention, is inconclusive.

The situation becomes even more complex when the child disagrees with the parents. Holder says that when a genuine emergency occurs, the child is to be treated even without parental consent.[9] In a nonemergency, for example, when a 10-year-old wearing glasses requests contact glasses from the ophthalmologist to participate in sports, parental consent is morally indicated. The parents and the child need information regarding the benefits, risks, and costs of the procedure as the basis for informed and judicious consent. In contrast, an 11-year-old with venereal disease seeking treatment who refuses to name or to notify her parents has the moral and legal right to receive treatment, since the consequences of nontreatment to the child, to others, and to society override the rights of the parents to know of the infection and to agree to its treatment. Generally, any communicable disease is an emergency to be treated without parental consent if necessary.[10] Holder maintains that the physician who refuses to treat a drug-addicted child refusing treatment if parents are notified is "himself guilty of contributing to the delinquency of his patients."[11] The trend appears to favor the consent of the minor to health services. This is reflected in the proposed Model Act of the American Academy of Pediatrics permitting the self-supporting and separated minor to consent to treatment. The Act also calls for treatment of any pregnant, infected, or addicted minor without parental consent.

The proposed Model Act provides that any minor with physical or emotional problems who is capable of rational decisions and who refuses help if parents are notified may consent to treatment. The health professional may legally thereafter tell parents or guardians unless it jeopardizes the patient's life or treatment results.[12] If serious health care procedures are to be given without parental consent, approval is sought from another physician. Thus, the Act seeks to protect the minor's rights to treatment, the parents' right to be informed of the health of their child, and the physicians's right to provide treatment without legal consequences.[13] The Act strives to protect the child's right to privacy and confidentiality.

The following two cases present moral dilemmas. The first case is that of a mass screening program for iron-deficiency anemia in children that requires the direct participation of nurses. The focus of concern is for the nutritional status of lower-socioeconomic-class children whose mothers use food stamps to purchase foods that are less nutritious and contribute to dietary deficiencies. The plan is to secure finger-prick blood samples for hematocrit from the children by requiring the child's blood test for the mother to secure food stamps. Anemic children would be immediately provided with free iron supplements.[14] Nurse A argues in favor of the test, since it is the same used in the well-baby clinic. She points to the inadequacy of current detection of iron deficiency of children, the free treatment, and to each child's right to health care. A signed consent form will be requested of each mother. Nurses are the only available health professionals to do this test.

Nurse B argues against the compulsory nature of the screening and invokes other moral arguments favoring truth-telling and the client's moral right to self-determination, in this case the mother's deciding for her child. The issue is whether the coercion used in this screening program is ever morally justifiable, even though the predicted consequences are beneficial to the child.

Another case adapted from Brody is that of 10-year-old Janie, who was admitted for routine observation following a fall against the corner of the fireplace. Her head wound was superficial. No skull fracture was found. On a routine check, the nurse discovered her not breathing, blue, and with fixed and dilated pupils. She was immediately intubated, given drugs, and hooked to a cardiac monitor. The heartbeat returned in a half hour, but the pupils remained fixed and dilated. The evidence points to a considerable period of anoxia of the brain "with irreversible damage, but you cannot be sure."[15] The issue becomes one of treating or not treating by transferring Janie to a respirator in the intensive care unit. Here tests will be made to diagnose brain death or irreversible brain damage. Supposedly, this diagnosis will be followed by turning off the respirator.

The counterargument is that once Janie is on the respirator and treatment is started, it will be continued regardless of Janie's diagnosis or condition. Nurse A argues in favor of pronouncing the child dead for the sake of the greater good of the family and society. Nurse B argues for giving the child every help and every chance regardless of the consequences to Janie, the family, or society.

A third case illustrates the ethical problems of organ donation of one sibling to another. It raises the further issue of whether one sibling or child should be used to help another when there is no benefit to the donor. One of a pair of 8-year-old identical twin girls suffered from a life-threatening kidney disease necessitating the removal of both kidneys. The identical twin sister was the ideal donor. She appeared to understand and to agree with the procedure. The issue for the nurse as a member of the transplant team is on what grounds the healthy sibling is permitted or denied the donation of a kidney to her sick sister at some risk to herself.

Nurse A argues for donation on grounds of the greatest happiness of the greatest number. Nurse B argues against the donation on Egoistic grounds of no benefit to the donor, but certain risk and pain. Nurse C argues for donation on the grounds of the child's autonomy and self-determination. The 8-year-old donor appears to understand the issues and to be closely identified with her sister. The moral dilemma is whether to permit or deny the kidney donation.

Abuse of young children is a frequent problem of deep concern to nurses in emergency rooms, crisis centers, hospitals, schools, and public health agencies. The abuse may be physical, sexual, or emotional. One not infrequent example is that of an intimidated wife and a sexually abused 9-year-old daughter with whom the husband and father is having intercourse. In a routine exam, the school nurse discovers signs of penetration, and upon questioning, the child admits to intimacy. She begs the nurse not to tell anyone of her secret, since the father has threatened to kill mother and child if he is exposed. The child fears her father and is convinced that he will carry out his threats. The nurse is horrified at the exploitation of this child and all other defenseless, vulnerable children who are abused and neglected. She views her role as that of patient advocate with her "primary commitment . . . to the client's care and safety."[16] The nurse is aware of the laws protecting children from abuse and the sad lack of implementation by way of child and family welfare agencies and child placement facilities. The incest is clearly "prejudicial to the client's best interests" by interfering with the child's normal psychosocial growth and development. The father-daughter relationship will undermine the child's perception of the security and trust expected of parents and other authority figures. The incest may seriously warp the child's future relationships with intimates. Despite these serious misgivings, the nurse weighs the child's present security against an uncertain future in a foster home, separated from the family. The nurse is filled with doubt regarding the pledge of confidentiality to the child and the moral problem she faces.

MORAL IMPLICATIONS IN THE NURSING CARE OF CHILDREN

For the nurse working with children, the role necessarily involves consideration of the parents' significant contribution to the child's well-being. It is the parents who generally carry the lifelong burden of a seriously handicapped child. Parental responsibilities include investment of their energies, emotions, time, and finances in the care of the disabled child. Continuous health care, frequent hospitalizations, and special education are usually indicated throughout the life of the child. Some parents may fear the birth of another defective child and so devote the rest of their lives to the care of this one. Siblings, where they exist, may be deeply hurt and resentful of the disproportionate share of parental involvement and family resources taken up by the afflicted child. Mothers, especially, may be forced to give up career aspirations in order to give continuous care to the child. Parental conflict and even divorce may occur as a consequence of spousal guilt, frustration, and rage in this troubled situation.

Thus, the *Code for Nurses*' description of the nurse as advocate with "primary commitment . . . to the client's care and safety"[17] can be in conflict with other moral principles, such as the greatest good of the greatest number of family members. The nurse may be in a genuine dilemma regarding the conflicts of the infant's right to life and the family's right to a full human life without the lifelong burden of a child with little potential for personhood. The sensitive nurse ponders the identity of the client: Is it primarily the child, the family system, or the interests of the whole society? The nurse can muster persuasive arguments favoring the family system and still other arguments favoring the individual child as the client in need of advocacy. If the nurse gives serious and primary consideration to the children's bills of rights previously discussed, then the role of advocate as "primary commitment . . . to the client's care and safety"[18] is the only morally permissible alternative.

If the statement in the *Code* is to be taken literally, then all deformed children will be treated and no respirators turned off. Moreover, no thought will be given to the burdens of the handicapped child to the parents and the negative consequences to the family. On the other hand, no child will be deprived of the chance to live in the state to which he or she is restored, whatever that may be. Much more can be done by official and voluntary agencies to help families care for the retarded and the handicapped at home. The mother deserves compensation for her care. Allowances are needed for special foods, special clothing, and extra transportation to clinics and schools for the child. The overburdened family would thereby be helped in concrete ways, with considerable saving to the state. Most important, life will be saved, and each child will live to the extent of its potential.

A difficult situation for nurses is that in which the parents have opposing opinions about whether or not to treat. The tendency is for deeply troubled parents to turn to nurses caring for their child with such questions as, "What would you do if this were your child?" The child does not belong to the nurse, of course. Nor can the nurse put himself or herself in the parents' shoes. The nurse does not know the parents' circumstances, their values, commitments, feelings, or relationships as they do.

The nurse can facilitate parents' careful assessment of the relevant facts of the case, the parents' values, family resources, and the deep concerns of each parent. Identification of the problem, facts, values, and concerns are useful steps in helping parents resolve ambiguities and ambivalence in problem situations. Parents can be encouraged to talk together alone and with pediatric or family-practice nurses, physicians, clergy, lawyers, children, and relatives. Other families who have experienced similar problems may be consulted regarding their experiences with a handicapped child. Nevertheless, after all possible help is given parents, there remains the tragic choice of sustaining the fragile life with the utmost commitment to the child's right to life or the denial of that right based on the principle of the greatest happiness for the greatest number. Although some physicians and nurses tend to make that decision to treat or not treat for others, it can be viewed as the parents' rightful decision, since they bear the lifelong burden. If, however, the parents' decision is seen as improper, inappropriate, unethical, or illegal, the nurse as patient advocate has the duty to appeal that decision in the most effective way possible.

The nurse in contact with families in which there is abuse seeks information concerning laws protecting children, local regulations surrounding reporting of abuse, law enforcement agencies, child and family welfare agencies, and measures for protection of the child. The nurse may view his or her role as primarily one of patient advocate committed to the child's care and safety. In that case, the regulatory and child-caring resources can be utilized to the utmost on behalf of the child. If the nurse views him/herself as an advocate of the family, she or he can then secure the resources of community family agencies in enlisting the family's participation in family therapy or counseling.

As advocate of the child, the nurse has an important role in facilitating the child's participation in ethical decision making regarding its own health care. The Partnership Model of relationship (cited in Chapter 7) recognizes children as full human beings due respect for their thoughts, feelings, interests, and desires in relation to their own health care. Ideally, the Partnership Model of relationships is based on an open, shared decision-making process, in which children's growing autonomy is supported to the extent of each child's cognitive maturation, personality, and thought processes. This model recognizes children's rights to information about their health status and to truthful answers concerning diagnosis, hospitalization, treatment, intensive procedures, chronic disease, and even impending death. Such knowledge is shared in words and at times by persons appropriate to the child's age, understanding, emotional state, and relationship with the nurse and significant others. Wieczorek and Natapoff recommend interviewing children regarding their health status. Some children will readily respond; a few will not. The process reveals whether the parents use the Ownership, Partnership, or Club Membership models of family relationships. Some parents answer for the child. Other parents qualify the child's answers. Parental interference is consistent with the Ownership Model. Some parents support the child's expression of his or her thoughts regarding the health problem; this is consistent with the Partnership Model. The nurse who practices within this model believes it important to find out what children think is causing their health problem and the nature and source of their worries.[19] The child's sense of autonomy is enhanced by responsibility for providing information and sharing thoughts and feelings with the nurse and the physician about the health problem. In turn, the stress for the hospitalized child can be reduced by the warm and sympathetic nurse who supports the school-age child's ability to reason, to generalize, and to understand cause and effect in relation to the illness and treatment. The nurse as partner and child advocate is willing to support the child's autonomy by giving simplified scientific explanations for bodily changes, functions, diagnostic procedures, treatments, and the workings of the various hospital machines. Likewise, the nurse who respects the child gives truthful explanations for illness and treatment appropriate to the child's understanding. Such explanations are significant to children, especially younger children, who believe that their illness is related to their being bad in some way or that it is causing their parents considerable distress. Other misconceptions can be clarified.

The process of nurse-parent-child shared decision making assumes that the child, the nurse, and the parent have the capacity to understand essentials of cause-and-effect disease processes, as well as stages and principles of human growth and development, and that they are oriented toward a Partnership Model.

The nurse who perceives the role of advocate as a meaningful one can then move into shared decision making with the child. The nurse's alliance with the child is supportive of the child's participation in health care decisions. Concretely, the nurse permits as much freedom as possible, and encourages independence. The hospitalized or sick child may be an astute observer, with heightened awareness of bodily changes, and may want to be in control of the self. Enabling children to participate in developing their health care plans, such as making choices about sites of injection, days and times of scheduled visits, or going home to die, is a manifestation of deep respect for children's right to participate in health care decisions when done sensitively and appropriately out of concern for the child's well-being. The nurse can assist parents in helping the child express fears associated with dying, such as pain and abandonment, and in providing the necessary comfort, freedom from pain, and security. The nurse supports the child's participation in his or her own health care until the very end by respecting the child's determination of the need for pain medication, privacy, and peer, sibling, and parental visits. The child is respected throughout illness as a person of worth who is intensely concerned with what is happening to his or her body and life, with the nurse perceiving herself as an ally to the dying young patient. Despite the overwhelmingly tragic outcome to the child, when the nurse and child interact in shared decision making together on a mutually benevolent basis, a morally significant human relationship may occur, an example for other human relationships.

ETHICAL CONSIDERATIONS OF NURSE-CHILD-PARENT RELATIONS

Several Philosophical Moves

There are several ethical considerations by way of an ethical check list for evaluating nurse-parent-child relationships. In addition to the "quorum feature notion" cited in Chapter 9, there is a further philosophical move by two recent philosophers, J. Rachels and W. Ruddick. This move consists in distinguishing biological or zoological life from biographical life. Human beings live anatomically and physiologically biological lives. Human beings who fulfill the majority features of being human also give evidence of being conscious. A person with hopes, projects, a history, joys, frustrations, and expectations of the future with plans and prospects, all of which presuppose consciousness, is said to have a biographical life. That person is not just living a biological life,[20] like Karen Ann Quinlan and others in a similar vegetative state.

A prominent Protestant theologian, Joseph Fletcher, restates the biological/biographical distinction by citing several conditions for being regarded as a person. These include a minimum intelligence of between 20 and 40 I.Q., self-awareness, a sense of past and future time, the ability to have human relationships and to show caring and concern for others, and to exercise some self-control over material and psychological conditions of existence. Fletcher's criteria boil down to the presence of consciousness.[21]

One astute commentator and interpreter of Fletcher's view, Margot Fromer, argues for Fletcher's criteria of personhood. Fromer points out that Fletcher's criteria for personhood are the most commonly used.[22] But she concedes that "many people disagree with them."[23] According to Fromer, for Fletcher "the one characteristic basic to all others is the presence of neocortical functioning, without which biologic life may exist but personhood does not. . . ."[24] To Fromer "health professionals are concerned with the quality as well as the sanctity of life."[25] But she thinks it is unlikely that human beings will ever reach agreement about what is an acceptable quality of life.[26]

Whether one refers to "the quality of life" or to a biographical life, to one's life plan, as does Rawls, or to one's projects, as Sartre does, or to consciousness, one uses these distinctions to refute the contention that the sanctity of life is unconditional, absolute, and undebatable. Although children cannot carry out all the cognitive functions of adults, normal children are expected to develop capacities that will enable them to fulfill more and more of these cognitive functions.

The Concept of Rights Applied to the Nurse-Child-Parent Relationship

A further philosophical move consists in clarifying the concept of rights that apply to children in a health care context. The question of whether children have any rights has one of four responses and accompanying arguments. One view is that children have no rights at all. Parents, nurses, and other adults may have duties, but children have no rights. A second view is that children have claim or subsistence rights to food, clothing, shelter, health care, and education, but no liberty rights to make their own decisions. A third position is that children have limited subsistence rights and liberty rights in relation to their readiness to make responsible decisions. Children, for example, may walk across the street when they show that they are careful. But children do not have the liberty right to stay out all night and imbibe alcohol whenever they wish. A fourth position holds that children have unlimited liberty and subsistence rights shared equally with adults.

Each position has defenders and opponents. In relation to these four views of children's rights, one can, for example, appreciate extreme statements of children's rights, such as that expressed by Holt, which is mentioned earlier in the chapter. The customary philosophical moves consist in arguing on behalf of one of these views. In the process, one may make use of philosophical arguments to clarify the concept of rights applied to children. Several arguments for rights are worth noting. A difficulty with Wiezorek and Natapoff's arguments for the child's right to sexual expression, discussed earlier in this chapter, is that whereas rights imply liberties to rightholders, they also imply corresponding duties imposed on other appropriate persons and groups, such as nurses, schoolteachers, and others.

M. Cranston, a prominent writer, points to three requirements of rights: practicability or feasibility, which means a right can be put into practice; universality, or the equal application of the right to all those to whom it applies without arbitrary exceptions; and "paramount importance," or the singling out of these needs deemed vitally urgent to individuals in society.[27] This third requirement of rights of paramount importance confines rights to the most urgent conditions of social life rather than fads and frills. The paramount requirement or value priority calls for a society to have "fire engines and ambulances," for example. "Fun fairs and holiday camps"[28] are luxuries rather than the rights of persons. If rights have no restraints, then rights become everything, and if they mean everything, as with any other term that has no exclusions, rights become nothing. Applying Cranston's criteria shows that whereas one can speak of a child's right to food, clothing, shelter, health care, and education, the child cannot have a right to be loved in the same way. For every child to be loved may be a desirable ideal, but to refer to a child's right to be loved is, in Cranston's terms, "a utopian aspiration" or ideal, but not a right.

Furthermore, morality may be separated into agent or character morality, act or decision morality, and the critics' or judges' morality. The first concerns classical and contemporary virtues, such as wisdom, courage, compassion, love, generosity, kindness, devotion, and loyalty. The second, act or decision-making morality, is about decisions made or acts or actions agents make. Act morality concerns declarations of rights, duties, justice, equality, and fairness. The third morality, that of the critics or judges, consists in applying critical canons in evaluating both agents and actions as being either courageous or cowardly, wise or unwise, trustworthy or kind, or not, and judging actions as fair or unfair, or as respecting or violating rights.

There can be no right to love, then, because love belongs to agent morality rather than act morality. Rights belong to the class of acts that are either just or fair; violations of rights are their opposite. Around rights, boundaries can be drawn in which this act is fair and that not, but in which love, being also a character trait, is too vague to qualify as a right.

Dependency, Paternalism, and Freedom

One difference between adults and children that needs to be considered in ethical decision making and in ascribing rights to children is that children, while potentially adults, are dependents. As dependents, children are not always able to make effective decisions. There is a three-way child-health professional-parent relationship, in which parents or health professionals, including nurses, have the role of deciding on behalf of a helpless, dependent child what therapeutic intervention is presumably best for the child.

The point is that a child between ages one and six has health care measures, such as injections, vaccinations, and prescribed drugs, and operations, such as tonsillectomy, done for it, often without asking its permission. The doctrine of informed consent does not apply to children in the earliest years of life. This general exemption is connected to the principle that to have rights presupposes consciousness or the capacity for rational behavior. Yet children are expected to become conscious adults who have the capacity to make decisions. The place of children is between other sentient beings governed more by feelings and instincts and those beings who have a rational capacity.[29] This immature state presents a dilemma: How to regard children?

One way out of this difficulty of either denying that children have rights, thus treating them as inferiors with paternalistic intervention, or attributing the same rights to children as to adults, is to carve out a special class of rights for children. These are called "rights-in-trust." These rights-in-trust for children are the rights they will have when sufficiently mature to exercise those rights. Rights-in-trust are held in safekeeping by relevant adults, who in the appropriate time will turn those rights over to the children to whom they properly belong.[30] Appropriate adults, including nurses, have the role of safeguarding children's rights. In that role, appropriate adults are guardians, protectors, trustees, and advocates of the children in their charge.

The question arises, however, as to whose rights nurses and other health professionals protect, the parents' rights or the child's rights. If parents are clearly abusive, the nurse's role is to protect the child's right. But if a parent, such as a Jehovah's Witness, intends no harm but insists on no blood transfusion for a child seriously hurt and in need of blood, nurses may feel they are in the middle of a conflict. One consideration for the nurse is to invoke the prevention-of-harm principle. The harm to the child from an unnecessary death gives the health professionals a strong reason to override the parents' right to decide to withhold a blood transfusion.

On the other hand, if a child of 10 or 11 has a certain form of cancer which only a leg amputation can arrest, and if the child refuses the operation, the parent, invoking the principle of preventing the greater harm, has the moral right to override the child's right to refuse. The parent has the legal right to decide in favor of amputation as well.

There are fairly clear cases of benign versus malignant Paternalism. The abusive parent falls into the malignant Paternalism category. The parent permitting amputation to arrest cancer in the hope of preventing greater harm falls under the benign Paternalism category. Since the term "Paternalism" is and will be used in succeeding pages, a definition of the term may be helpful. Paternalism comes from the Latin word *pater*, meaning father, and refers to the idea that father knows best and has the authority to decide.

There are obviously cases and arguments in which Paternalism is defensible, such as the parent who orders a stomach pump for a three-year-old child who has just swallowed household cleaning fluid. The nurse's role in such a case is solely to aid the parent in saving the child's life, even if the procedure is painful to the child.

There are other cases and arguments in which Paternalism, exercised by parents more powerful than their children, is clearly indefensible. Examples are parents who abuse their children by putting them in scalding hot water, beating them into insensibility, or putting them into a hot oven. In such abuse cases, the nurse's role is to intervene on behalf of the child.

Two sometimes complementary models of patient advocacy may be consulted. One is the model presented by Robin Hood, who fights and overcomes oppressors. There are no conflicts between children and adults on this model. Considerations of justice and fairness determine whose rights the nurse protects. A second nurse-advocate model is presented by the example of Antigone in Sophocles' play of the same name. Antigone directly confronts and defies Creon, king of Thebes, who has decreed that Polynices, her brother, is a traitor and to be left unburied, contrary to custom. Antigone demands the right to bury her brother, even though her power is no match for the king's.[31] We may call this the *direct-confrontation* model of patient advocacy. Some nurses treat their patients in that way, doing what they regard as right, regardless of consequences to themselves. Other nurses use institutional channels to protect children who are victimized by anyone. On a higher, macrolevel, professional organizations are also advocates of children through the organization's sponsorship and support of legislation and social policy affecting children's rights and welfare.

CONCLUSION

Children, the proverbial hope of the future, are developing persons. To become mature persons, children need the nurture parents and health professionals can give to support their growth into adolescence and adulthood. The health and well-being of children places a pleasurable obligation on parents and health professionals to provide maximum resources.

One way to recognize the importance of children is to attribute health care rights to them. An advantage of attributing rights to children in place of imposing duties on parents alone is that rights give extra force to the duties imposed. The duties people feel that are not implied by rights leave those with duties free to ignore one's duty to a beggar. But the kinds and quality of rights children have also leaves us with difficulties. The rights of children cannot include the right to drink alcohol, use drugs, spend their parents' money without restrictions, or absent themselves from school. Children's rights call for constraints.

Most importantly, children have not the capacity to decide what is in their own interests in health matters. So children cannot have such rights as the right to informed consent until they reach an appropriate degree of maturity. To offset these difficulties, the concept of "rights-in-trust" is applicable to children. Such rights, however, presuppose that children are beings who have not only a biological but also a biographical life, one with plans, projects, hopes, expectations, and realizations as well as failures and disappointments. These aspects of one's biographical life give evidence of human consciousness, a necessary condition for being regarded as a person.

The challenge to the nurse working with children is to support the growing independence of the child. One way is by encouraging the child's responsibility for and participation in his or her own health care. The child's growing awareness of his or her bodily processes, recognition of the fragility of a state of wellness, and a relationship of trust with the nurse can all be strong forces in the sick child's return to health. This child can be an articulate participant in planning and implementing his or her health care.

The role of the nurse working with very young or abused and neglected children is largely that of patient advocate. Such children need protection and help. Sometimes, for the sake of the child's very survival, the child needs to be taken out of a home with abusive or incestuous parents. The nurse can effectively advocate for every kind of help available, such as the use of police and referral to child and family welfare agencies.

REFERENCES

1. Wieczorek R.R., Natapoff J.N.: A Conceptual Approach to the Nursing of Children. Philadelphia, Lippincott, 1981, p. 31.
2. Ariès P.: Centuries of Childhood: A Social History of Family Life. New York, Vintage, 1962, p. 128.
3. Holt J.: Why not a bill of rights for children? In Gross B., Gross R. (eds.), The Children's Rights Movement. Garden City, N.Y., Anchor Books, 1977, p. 318–325.
4. United Nations: The Declaration of the Rights of the Child. New York, United Nations, 1959.
5. Ibid.
6. Wieczorek and Natapoff: A Conceptual Approach to the Nursing of Children, p. 33.
7. Holder A.R.: Legal Issues in Pediatrics and Adolescent Medicine. New York, Wiley, 1977, p. 137.
8. Ibid., p. 138
9. Ibid.
10. Ibid., p. 143.
11. Ibid.
12. Ibid., p. 144.
13. Ibid.
14. Brody H.: Ethical Decisions in Medicine, 2nd ed. Boston, Little, Brown, 1981, p. 253.
15. Ibid., p. 233.
16. American Nurses' Association: Code for Nurses with Interpretive Statements. Kansas City, Mo., The Association, 1976, p. 8.
17. Ibid.
18. Ibid.
19. Wieczorek and Natapoff: A Conceptual Approach to the Nursing of Children, p. 810.
20. Ruddick W.: Parents, children and moral decisions. In Bandman E.L., Bandman B. (eds.), Bioethics and Human Rights: A Reader for Health Professionals. Boston, Little, Brown, 1978, p. 165–170.
21. Fletcher J.: Four indicators of humanhood—the enquiry matures. Hastings Center Report 4(6):5, 1974.

22. Fromer M.J.: Ethical Issues in Health Care. St. Louis, Mosby, 1981, p. 12–14, 31–32.
23. Ibid.
24. Ibid.
25. Ibid., p. 32.
26. Ibid.
27. Cranston M.: Health rights, real and supposed. In Raphael D.D. (ed.), Political Theory and the Rights of Man. Bloomington, Ind., Indiana University Press, 1967, p. 50–51.
28. Cranston M.: What Are Human Rights? New York, Taplinger, 1973, p. 67.
29. Houlgate L.: The Child and the State. Baltimore, Johns Hopkins Press, 1980, p. 50.
30. Feinberg J.: A child's right to an open future. In Aiken H., LaFollette H. (eds.), Whose Child? Children's Rights, Parental Authority and State Power. Totowa, N.J., Littlefield, Adams, 1980, p. 125–126.
31. Cranston: What Are Human Rights? p. 9–10.

CHAPTER 11

Ethical Issues in the Nursing Care of Adolescents

Through study of this chapter, the student will be able to:

1. Distinguish the rights of adolescents in relation to physiological, psychological, social, cultural, and legal dimensions of capacity and maturity
2. Define the role of the nurse as patient advocate of the adolescent client seeking health care
3. Develop the role of the nurse in controversies between parental authority and adolescent autonomy
4. Recognize the adolescent's duties and responsibilities to self, family, and society as a dependent, independent, and interdependent person in a Partnership family model

INTRODUCTION

Adolescents differ from other minors with respect to the degree of autonomy claimed and exercised. Middle- and upper-class segments of this society support an adolescent culture of prolonged dependence on parents along with extended liberty and welfare rights to support, education, clothing, and recreational funds. Poor adolescents are forced to earn their own way. Nevertheless, the emphasis is on the differences of this group from all other age groups in matters of dress, communication, music, drug and alcohol consumption, sexual activity, life-styles, and other values. The paradox of adolescent culture is the conflict between claimed independence and actual reliance on parental and other forms of community support by even very young adolescents in the name of rights.

Thus, the whole spectrum of goods and services to each adolescent passenger in the metaphorical lifeboat is borne by the concept of rights. Adolescents tend to claim rights and liberties restricted to adults. These rights include such activities as sexual freedom. This single issue raises many questions regarding parental responsibility for such adolescent problems as pregnancy and care of the ensuing child, abortions for an unwanted pregnancy, compliance with contraceptive measures, and medical care for venereal disease. Thus, a central issue of adolescent health care is the extent of the autonomy of the adolescent in relation to the duties, responsibilities, and rights of parents and other significant adults.

A related issue is the extent of adolescent rights and the duties of society to protect and to provide for those rights. The United Nations' *Declaration of Children's Rights* lists many rights to be provided by society and parents. Despite its good intentions, the *Declaration* may be seen as either a Paternalistic or utopian doctrine, since it places the fundamental responsibility of the child on his or her parents.[1] Moreover, its provisions are in many cases far-fetched—desirable ideals perhaps, but not practical or feasible. There is a false presumption here that adolescents, for example, lack interests that they are able to identify, express, and evaluate independently of the interests and values of their parents, teachers, and others in authority.[2] Arguments can be put forth that adolescents generally are competent to defend their own interests. Other arguments can state that the adolescent is still immature and inexperienced. Therefore, in important matters of health, parental concern for the best interests of the child may be in direct conflict with the values, moral principles, and autonomy of the adolescent. This may place the nurse in the middle of adversarial camps, which he or she may seek to reconcile on behalf of continuing parental-child dialogues concerning rights and other moral principles.

ADOLESCENT CASES ILLUSTRATIVE OF NURSING ETHICS

Selected cases illustrate ethical issues that may be confronted in the nursing care of adolescents.

> Karen, age 16, Catholic, the second of seven siblings, was hospitalized for chronic, active glomerulonephritis in 1968. Her kidneys were removed following two years of intense but unsuccessful treatment. A transplant of her father's kidney was unsuccessful. Hemodialysis before and following surgery caused her to have "chills, nausea, vomiting, severe headaches and weakness."[3] Psychiatric evaluation and treatment was provided for Karen and her parents before and following the transplant. In April 1971, it was obvious that the transplanted kidney was not functioning. "Karen and her parents expressed the desire to

> stop treatment."[4] This decision was unacceptable to the medical staff. Psychiatrist and social worker attempted guidance toward continuation of medical care. The family agreed to home care, which Karen found isolated and restricting. She was fatigued and uncomfortable. She was then hospitalized for high fever and removal of the transplant; the shunt became infected, clotted, and closed. At this point, Karen and her parents again refused dialysis and shunt revision. The staff was angry and frustrated and of the opinion that this was an unsound, immoral, and inappropriate decision for a 16-year-old. Karen discussed the decision with the hospital chaplain. She decided that hell and possibly heaven were nonexistent, but that "nothingness would be far better than the suffering which would continue if she lived."[5]
>
> On consultation, the child psychiatrist found Karen not psychotic and her decision to be a carefully reasoned, rational one. The nephrologist agreed. The staff was then to make her life comfortable "with daily counseling in the event she changed her mind."[6] The alternatives of taking the case to court to force treatment or requiring the parents to take Karen home to die so as to avoid the staff's assistance in what they thought to be a suicidal act were considered. A dialysis nurse visited Karen and insisted on further dialysis. Staff members who had witnessed Karen's prolonged suffering were more supportive.
>
> Karen's spirits and appetite improved following her decision. She thanked the staff, picked a burial place near her home, wished her parents happiness, and supported them in their doubts about the decision. She died on June 2, 1971, suddenly and peacefully, with both parents at her side.

Since there was no consistent parental opposition to Karen's decision, the issues appear to be her autonomy and right to die in conflict with the staff's view of this act as suicidal and immoral. Some staff members, such as the hemodialysis unit nurse, were strongly opposed to Karen's decision and in favor of intervention on a Paternalistic basis.

A case that complements that of Karen is the case of Phillip Becker, aged 12, a mild Down's syndrome person. He needed heart surgery, but his parents refused to consent. Phillip's parents said in court that in their opinion he was better off dead than alive. They regarded him as an "embarrassment."[7]

Less clear-cut are examples of 13- to 18-year old adolescents living dependently under the parental roof who seek abortion without the knowledge and consent of their parents. These minors do not qualify for the status of emancipated minor, since they are neither independent, self-supporting, nor married. One moral stance is that the nurse must protect the privacy and confidentiality of these young patients, after persuasive attempts to inform parents have failed, on grounds of the adolescent's right to her own body. Another issue is that of the parents' rights to be informed of the health concern and to decide for the immature offspring.

Another type of case involves Martin Sieferth, 14, who has a cleft palate and harelip in need of surgery. Martin's father, unlike Phillip Becker's father, shows signs of parental affection. The father believes, however, in "mental healing" and in letting "the natural forces of the universe work on the body."[8] Therefore, he refuses surgery to repair his son's seriously deformed and unattractive jaw. Martin agrees with his father.[9] Martin is consequently disfigured as an adolescent and will need the physical and emotional roadblocks removed. He will need relief if he is to flourish.

The role of the nurse in a case such as the Sieferth case may well be to be health educator and therapist who does the utmost to educate and persuade the father and the son of the benefits of facial surgery, while showing them that their religious values can remain intact. As an "agent of reality," a nurse may also function as an advocate on behalf of the educational reform of the patient.

Adolescents also have health care problems associated with auto accidents, drug and alcohol abuse, suicide, violence, and early and frequent unregulated sexual activity. These cases present acute dilemmas and problems, such as that of "a 16-year-old girl with a five-month-old illegitimate child" who "became pregnant again."[10] The girl's mother "refused to consent to an abortion. The girl sued to have the Colorado statute requiring parental consent declared unconstitutional."[11] The Court found that "she had made an intelligent decision in favor of abortion."[12]

Then there is the type of case, real or hypothetical, involving an adolescent who as a result of drug abuse and careless driving becomes seriously injured and comatose in an auto accident. If the parents no longer want to care for the child, the issue may concern health professionals, who may take different moral positions on whether to save a child or abandon it, or facilitate its death.

MORAL IMPLICATIONS IN THE NURSING CARE OF ADOLESCENTS

Working with the adolescent is particularly challenging. Adolescents tend to shift between determined independence and exercise of autonomy and the delayed recognition that the situation is fraught with problems and possibly peril. This developmental phase is one in which high value is placed on acceptance by peers. Another characteristic of this adolescent phase is behavioral and role experimentation within the peer group. Thus, the adolescent may experiment with drugs and sexual and criminal activity in response to peer pressure. It is extremely difficult for most adolescents to separate from the values of the peer group with which they identify.

Acceptance of peer values, such as positive regard for sexual activity with resulting pregnancy, abortion, or venereal disease, can, for example, be the source of considerable conflict between adolescent and parents. The nurse can be caught between the anger and claimed rights of the parents and the defensiveness and vulnerability of the adolescent. Each believes that his or her choice is the right one. Each expects that the nurse will advocate and actively support his or her position. For example, the 13-year-old seeking an abortion without parental knowledge expects unconditional support from the abortion unit as patient advocate. This adolescent insists on carrying the burden of guilt or regret regarding the abortion decision and of her fear of the procedure without the parental support she might otherwise receive. The nurse tries to help the young person identify and analyze her perceptions of her family in the hope that parents will be viewed in a positive light. The adolescent's negative reasons may be substantive, including abuse and incest. The pregnant adolescent may fear both punishment and rejection from a family that has forbidden premarital sexual activity. The nurse as patient advocate and in accordance with the *Code for Nurses* supports such a patient's self-determination while giving information relevant to making an informed judgment. Such information includes the possible helpfulness of parental support and participation in the decision, the alternatives to abortion of full-term delivery and adoption, the steps and effects of the procedure, and the patient's right to receive or to refuse treatment. Relevant information also includes referrals to family planning for counseling and information regarding contraception. Supportive nursing care includes concern and interest for the tragic choice faced by the young adolescent. Anticipatory guidance is directed toward prevention of future unwanted pregnancies, along with adolescent evaluation of personal values expressed in behavior and in relationships.

The second level of advocacy is for a nurse to refer a sexually active adolescent to a family planning unit or physician for contraceptives or individual counseling. Such agencies aim to counsel, educate, and guide the adolescent toward control of pregnancies and of matters of general health. Care is usually free or low-cost.

A third level of advocacy is appeal to the courts. The Department of Health and Human Resources has regulations requiring that all family planning projects receiving federal funds make "services . . . available without regard for religion, creed, age, sex, parity, or marital status."[13] A 15-year-old whose family was receiving Aid to Families with Dependent Children sued the Planned Parenthood Association of Utah for denying her contraceptives without parental permission. A three-judge federal court in Utah held that the parental-consent requirement was in conflict with federal requirements. To deprive the adolescent of contraceptives from agencies receiving federal assistance was therefore unconstitutional. The court further ruled that the requirement for parental consent was a violation of the minor's right of privacy. Therefore, the federal regulations were to be enforced.[14]

The controversy between parental authority and adolescent autonomy continues. At times, the nurse's role may be much like that of a broker, trying to reconcile the adolescent's insistence on rights to sexual activity, contraception, and abortion with parental authority, parental concern for the adolescent's welfare, and such consequences as unwanted pregnancies. The parent may argue justifiably that the adolescent's rights are limited by her inability to care for a child and her dependence on parental support, or that sexual freedom, contraceptives, and abortion are wrong and therefore undesirable. The nurse may suggest to parents the unrealistic expectations for adolescent sexual abstinence. The nurse may then be in the position of advocating the adolescent's right to contraception as a lesser evil than unwanted pregnancies and abortion.

The dilemma of adolescent sexual activity, contraceptive use, abortion, and childbearing without marriage is a serious and persistent problem. "There were nearly 600,000 infants born to adolescents nineteen years or younger in the United States in 1975."[15] Obviously, the adolescent is asserting her right to sexual freedom. A counterargument is that the exercise of a right requires a correlative duty of someone to provide for that right. According to this argument, it is the duty of a parent to provide decent conditions for fulfilling life for the child produced. Most adolescents cannot do so. The issue for the nurse then becomes one of presenting rational alternatives to adversarial parents and adolescents, if possible. Moral and social consequences of behavior are elicited and analyzed together by parents, adolescent, and nurse. Assumptions of parental support by providing the necessary goods and services to the adolescent regardless of life-style and choices need examination and evaluation by parents and adolescent together.

Adolescents, too, can engage in the process of morally justifying their major decisions. Little recognition is given to adolescent responsibilities for analyzing and evaluating the moral dimensions and consequences of behavior. In the public media, particularly, the adolescent is regarded as glamorous and exciting when experimenting with drugs, alcohol, sexual activity, music, dress, and deviant life-styles. The central issue for the nurse becomes one of supporting those adolescent rights that facilitate a decent, fulfilling life, or, as in the case of Karen, the right to die as a release from meaningless suffering. This is the role of the patient advocate in support of the individual's moral right to self-determination. As problems of very young adolescent sexual activity in the form of pregnancy, abortion, venereal disease, childbearing, child abuse, and substance abuse illustrate, there are morally justifiable limits to adolescent rights. The boundaries to adolescent rights may come from several sources. Compulsory driver education has in many states made a significant statistical difference in the accident rates of adolescents. A close analogy is that moral education regarding family living, relationships, personal rights, duties, and obligations, along with trust, go with the exercise of rights. Thus, the adolescent learns to be both a provider and a recipient of goods and services rather than just a rightholder in a world of rapidly increasing rights and shrinking resources.

ETHICAL CONSIDERATIONS IN THE ADOLESCENT-NURSE-PARENT RELATIONSHIP

Previously the biological-biographical distinction was cited. Missing in this distinction is the fact that one shares social life with others. This process has an important bearing on adolescent development. A socially worthwhile life calls for an adolescent to recognize not only rights but also responsibilities commensurate with the growing physical power to do good or harm to the self and others. The moral education of an adolescent includes the point that social life is shared and people depend on one another. Human relationships call for reciprocal give-and-take, the mutual recognition of rights and responsibilities.

One may consequently argue that the moral-correlativity thesis of rights might well apply to adolescents. This means that for them to have rights, they must demonstrate the capacity to live up to corresponding responsibilities. Driving a car calls for an adolescent's ability to drive effectively. It may well call for the adolescent to earn part or all of the cost of driving. The adolescent may also be expected to refrain from drinking alcohol while driving. Similar constraints govern the use of drugs. These are constraints imposed equally on adult members of society who are expected to fulfill social and economic responsibilities. The new rights adolescents gain, then, such as driving, may be said to be "earned rights," which depend on appropriate assumption of responsibilities. Similar constraints may well govern sexual activities. Adolescents of school and college age who are not yet ready to assume adult responsibilities in bearing and rearing children are not free to engage in sexual activities without appropriate constraints, such as contraceptives.

The governing principle in determining the rights and responsibilities of adolescents is whether such rights and responsibilities are conducive to leading a socially worthwhile life. Even granting the vagueness of such an ideal, nevertheless it rules out socially destructive behavior, such as vandalizing old, helpless women, breaking street lamps, driving at reckless speeds, smoking indiscriminately, and showing no evidence of concern for others. The point is that one does not want adolescents to become veritable savages, like those portrayed in William Golding's *Lord of the Flies.*[16] When shipwrecked on a deserted island, these boys become cannibals. Such behavior is conventionally unacceptable.

The role of the nurse, along with other health professionals, is to be a health educator and therapist in reinforcing positive social values. The nurse supports values that help an individual adolescent become a responsible, upstanding member of society. The nurse helps the adolescent learn both to contribute and allocate, and facilitates individual adolescents' functioning together. In this connection, the concept of wellness, or total physical, social, psychological, and economic well-being becomes a decidedly important nursing model.

A socially worthwhile life also calls for appropriate recognition of and training in standards and skills of sustained intellectual judgment. Such judgment requires a common understanding of the methods and results of cognitive disciplines with appropriate regard and familiarity with rules of evidence in the sciences. The relevance to ethics is that enormous good or evil comes by either considering or ignoring rules of evidence.

The biological/biographical/social/cognitive distinction rules against regarding an adolescent who has been comatose for a long time as a person on the grounds that he or she lacks a biographical life, a life with conscious activities. These distinctions also rule against identifying an adolescent as a full-fledged person if he or she has extreme physical, intellectual, social, or psychological handicaps, such as substance addiction or criminal or antisocial behavior. These biographical and social distinctions also support an adolescent's right to terminate her fifth pregnancy on grounds that she is unlikely to provide a worthwhile human life for yet another child. The biographical/social/cognitive distinction also rules against a biology major's refusal to dissect animals in the course of study. The social/cognitive distinction rationally counts against a nurse's refusal to participate in surgical repair of a boy's cleft palate or in an abortion indicated by social and cognitive considerations. By implication, the cognitive requirement, respect for and familiarity with scientific methods and results, gives a reason against a nurse's recommending Laetrile or faith healing as a rational alternative to scientifically verifiable health care measures.

Some people ask: "Who decides?" or, "Who shall have the justifiable authority to decide whether an adolescent's life is no longer worth sustaining?" One move in philosophy consists in rephrasing the question to ask: "What criteria does a rational person appeal to in deciding nurse-adolescent-parent issues?" or "What counts as a good reason or as evidence?" In some types of cases, such as the faith-healing issue, appeal to scientific evidence is appropriate because it works; and the reason it works is that it has a truth value that appeal to faith healing lacks. The reason for believing in the truth value of cleft-palate surgery over faith healing is that the verifiable evidence favors the results.

In other kinds of cases, such as saving the life of a Jehovah's Witness by giving needed blood, one effective and wise appeal is to conventional or "common morality."[17] While it is true that conventional morality is not the whole of morality, it does address itself to the common moral sentiments and virtues, such as honesty, affection, generosity, wisdom, courage, and happiness, and to the survival and well-being of people.

A distinction made earlier between various models of health care by Szasz and Hollander applies to the issue of restraints versus the freedom of infants, children, and adolescents. Their first model, activity-passivity,[18] holds that a health professional is active and a patient is passive. Their second model, "guidance cooperation," involves the health professional's guiding but not exclusively directing or coercing the patient. Their third model, "mutual participation," makes health professional and patients equal partners in the effort to achieve health.

Applied to the nursing of infants, children, and adolescents, the first, the activity-passivity model, aptly applies to the role nurses have in caring for essentially dependent and helpless infants and children. Children need to be told when to take their medicines, when to go to bed, and what to eat and drink.

As children grow into adolescence, the guidance-cooperation model increasingly applies. Young adolescents will need to learn how to develop increasing degrees of independence and self-sufficiency. The adult, including the nurse, will be analogous to the driver education teacher who sits next to the student and guides the student's driving activities.

The third model, mutual participation, is the goal sought for in a democratic society, a society of equals. This goal guides and orients the adolescent on its way to and through adulthood.

CONCLUSION

The main moral problems in each developmental span—infancy, childhood, and adolescence—are different in some aspects and similar in others. They are similar in concern throughout all phases of growth of human beings, people who are self-respecting persons, who learn to respect others, and who live by sharing social life. As such, young people are brought up not only to be dependents or to be completely independent. The adult, and the nurse as health educator, who brings up a child only to think of itself is overlooking a crucial reality consideration that governs social life. For example, an adolescent who coughs without covering his mouth in a public place is inconsiderate. The role of the nurse as health educator is to teach children and adolescents appropriate public behavior. There are other rules of social life in which the development of a person is not aimed only at independence but at interdependence. These rules admonish a child to eat a wholesome breakfast, to have wholesome and significant physical, intellectual, cultural, and emotional activities continuously, to avoid drug and alcohol abuse, premature and promiscuous sexual abuse, crime, and self-indulgence.

The development of persons with rights and reciprocal responsibilities constitutes goals that apply from birth to death and do not vary from infancy to childhood and adolescence. As Harry Stack Sullivan, the eminent American psychiatrist, said, "Everyone is much more simply human than otherwise."[19]

The moral differences in the three phases of growth are many, but they center on dependence in infancy, development of independence in childhood, and developing interdependence in adolescence. Each phase brings moral problems, some of which have no answers, as in the attempt to decide whether to save an infant, child, or adolescent with few or marginal prospects of living a full human life.

In the nurse's role as health educator, patient advocate, agent of reality, and therapist, the nurse is not alone. Because of the common morality, one that generally aims at the well-being of everyone, the nurse has many allies and resources to call on for help while coping with the admittedly real hindrances and obstacles.

REFERENCES

1. Young R.: In the interests of children and adolescents. In Aiken W., LaFollette H. (eds.), Whose Child? Children's Rights, Parental Authority and State Power. Totowa, N.J., Littlefield, Adams, 1980, p. 179.
2. Ibid., p. 180.
3. Schowalter J.E., et al.: The adolescent patient's decision to die. Pediatrics 51(1):97–103, 1973, p. 97.
4. Ibid., p. 98.
5. Ibid.
6. Bandman E., Bandman B.: The nurse's role in protecting the patient's right to live or die. Advances in Nursing Science 1(3):21–35, 1979.
7. Will G.: Newsweek, April 14, 1980, p. 112.
8. In the matter of Sieferth. In O'Neill O., Ruddick W. (eds.), Having Children. New York, Oxford University Press, 1979, p. 139.
9. Holder A.: Legal Issues in Pediatrics and Adolescent Medicine. New York, Wiley, 1977, p. 284–286.
10. Holder: Legal Issues, p. 283.
11. Ibid.
12. Ibid.
13. Ibid., p. 271.
14. Ibid.
15. Wieczorek R.R., Natapoff J.: A Conceptual Approach to the Nursing of Children. Philadelphia, Lippincott, 1981, p. 260.
16. Golding W.: Lord of the Flies. New York, Putnam, 1954.
17. Donnegan A.: The Theory of Morality. Chicago, University of Chicago Press, 1977, p. 6, 7, 28–31, 102, 172, 210–243.

18. Szasz T.S., Hollander M.H.: The physician-patient relationship. Arch. Intern. Med. 97:585, 1956.
19. Sullivan H.S.: The Interpersonal Theory of Psychiatry. New York, Norton, 1953, p. 32.

CHAPTER 12

Ethical Issues in the Nursing Care of Adults

Through study of this chapter, the student will be able to:

1. Understand adult development in relation to the moral issues significant to this phase of human development
2. Apply ethical principles of the prevention of harm, truth-telling, informed consent, the right to receive and to refuse treatment, and the right to privacy and confidentiality in practice with adult clients
3. Utilize patients' bills of rights in development of the nursing role as patient advocate
4. Facilitate the patient's right to self-determination and well-being through shared decision making in relation to the client's life goals, rational plans, and values

INTRODUCTION

A person's passage from childhood and adolescence to youth or early adulthood is one of the most exciting times of life. Romantic love and attachment to another person marks this period as a peak experience in life. Vigorous health is the norm for youth and young adults. Therefore, serious or chronic illness is devastating to life-styles, educational and social goals, careers, family planning, and realization of hopes. Youth and young adults are especially vulnerable to the consequences of health care decisions that affect every aspect of their lives.

Adult health care development is considered in the context of selected hard cases that call for moral decisions. In this connection, ethical principles are cited and evaluated and applied to nurse-patient relations.

ADULT DEVELOPMENT

Adulthood is the longest and most productive phase of human development. The process is one of continuing change characterized by growth, development, and slow decline. The rate of change differs considerably among individuals. Consequently, all divisions of the adult life span are somewhat arbitrary and apply only generally to a particular individual.

The adult phase is divisible into two parts: early adulthood or youth from ages 20 to 35, and later adulthood, middle age, from ages 35 to 65. The adult in these phases reaches the pinnacle of his or her power physically, socially, economically, and psychologically.

Young Adulthood

Young adulthood is regarded as the years up to age 35. In this period, persons are establishing themselves in occupations and in situations of interpersonal intimacy, including marriage.

Customary developmental tasks of young adults include gradual independence from parents with progressive involvement in the world of education and work. The young adult is concerned with a role in the community and in selected groups. Marriage, childbearing, and child rearing are characteristic of this phase of development.

The young couple are expected to provide for the health, education, and care of their children and for their own welfare and future. Serious illness at this age is unexpected and catastrophic to all members of the family system. Chronic illness in a spouse can be disruptive to the marital relationship and to the security of children. Ethical decisions regarding life-prolonging measures of comatose spouses can be especially difficult at this age, since they involve a healthy spouse and children in need of social, emotional, and financial resources. If however, the young family enjoys good health and good fortune, the couple gradually moves into the developmental tasks of middle age.

Youth. In contrast to this traditional path of development, there are those young adults unable to accept the traditions they were taught without reexamination and anguish. Kenneth Keniston has defined an emerging developmental phase called "youth." He describes it as an "optional stage, not a universal one. . . . Most young Americans who enter this stage of life tend to be between the ages of 18 and 30."[1]

The term describes a new generation born in the nuclear age and usually of college and graduate-school age. They refuse to settle down in traditional ways and "often vehemently challenge the existing social order."[2] They question the principles and practices upon which the major institutions of society rest.

A central concern is the issue of individual autonomy. This is expressed in a variety of ways. One expression is that of living and working arrangements that seek independence from the money economy of the larger society. Mass and local protests against the use of nuclear power and the use and disposal of toxic substances is another expression of autonomy.

This group assumes moral responsibility for the dwindling resources of the planet by conserving resources. Consequently, nutritional patterns are often vegetarian. Another issue is concern for the second-rate status of women, racial and ethnic minorities, and other disadvantaged groups. The attempt is to bring about fundamental change in society's distribution of goods and services on the basis of fairness and need. If such youth were successful in their efforts to create basic change in social institutions, a system free of war-making machines and ideology and of greed and corruption, society would be vastly different in its goals and processes.

The nurse, therefore, who works with patients in this developmental phase recognizes reflective ethical commitments and the relation of turmoil to this developmental phase of youth. Eating a vegetarian diet, for example, may be a means of saving grain for malnourished people and to avoid the slaughter of animals. It may also be for lack of money. Whatever the expressed values and beliefs for elevating the social order, the nurse recognizes that this stage of youth is one more milestone on the developmental path.

In Kohlberg's moral-development terms, less than 40 percent of college-educated individuals and a smaller percentage of the working class have gone beyond conventional levels of reasoning by age 24. Some youth may also be fanatics in the name of the highest ethical principles of "universal good." They may also be charged with arrogance, self-absorption, and alienation from society.[3]

Some youth evaluate society and health care in nonconventional ways. This may mean more support for holistic health approaches and for health care as a right enjoyed equally by everyone. These new ways of youth include home deliveries and natural methods of healing. These young people will question the reasons for care provided. They expect to participate fully in the decisions affecting them and to reserve the privilege of deciding the ethical issues for themselves.

Middle Age

The years of middle age, from age 35 up to age 65, are regarded as the most productive. In these years, individuals consolidate and expand their financial and occupational security. These are years of focus on the rearing, education, and enjoyment of children. There may be additional responsibilities for aged parents. In these years, nursing plays a role in ongoing health education. There is less obstetric care and more care for growing children, in emergencies and in crises. The nurse can be a significant influence in facilitating the processes of moral deliberation in health care that guide the family in its choices of action.

Middle-aged women and men recognize that theirs is the most powerful age group, that it is they who make most decisions and carry forward social norms. Although this society is oriented toward youth, it is under the control of the middle-aged.[4] The middle-aged have most to lose from ill health, incapacitation, and death.

The middle-aged person is the bridge between young and old generations within the family and in the community. Adult women especially see themselves in relation to childbearing and rearing as an integral part of the family cycle of caring for both the generation younger and older than themselves. Thus, middle-aged persons, and particularly women, are responsible for the health status of other significant family members.

Time acquires a new dimension in middle age. Time is felt to be precious and limited. Life is regarded as the time left to live. There is lessened regard for the past. The pursuit of pleasure may increase, along with the awareness of death among peers. Yet this phase of life is the period of maximum competence in self-assessment and çognitive problem-solving abilities. The middle-aged person has developed a wide range of coping strategies. New appreciations come from in-between relationships with younger and older generations. One account summarizes successful middle age in terms of

> . . . the executive processes of personality in middle-age: self-awareness, selectivity, manipulation and control of the environment, mastery, competence, the wide array of cognitive strategies . . . the stocktaking, the heightened introspection, and . . . the structuring and restructuring of experience.[5]

Middle-aged persons find themselves in control and in the driver's seat, in contrast to their youth or to their expectations of old age.

Middle age can also be seen as a period of losses and crisis. Some women see menopause and the departure of grown children as tragic. Other women celebrate the launching of children into adult independence. Members of both sexes may regard the inevitable decline in youthful good looks, strength, energy, and sexual appetites as a cause of bitterness. Other individuals see these as turning points toward serenity and tender expressions of touch and caress.

The occurrence of unexpected events such as sudden serious illness, forced retirement or unemployment, or death of the spouse or of a child out of the natural sequence is highly traumatic for either young or middle-aged individuals and families. Nurses can play a supportive role by helping the family in anticipatory grieving when there is time, or by encouraging appropriate grief after an unanticipated loss. Nurses can be helpful to clients in working through feelings of unrealistic self-blame. It is the unanticipated event that is likely to cause major stresses,

". . . events that upset the sequence and rhythm of the expected life cycle."[6] Consequently, serious illness, impending death of self or actual death of spouse or child, accidents, and loss of job or income are severe stresses to the middle-aged adult especially. The nurse can help alleviate this stress through helping the family identify its strengths and values.

Widespread social change in the form of increasing longevity for both sexes along with the inclusion of nearly half of all women in the work force emphasizes values of personhood and self-actualization for the middle-aged individual. Values of respect for self and others are expressed in demands for accessible health care oriented to the needs and rights of the adult. Women, particularly, are seeking health care that respects their sensitivities and special needs of combining a career, parenthood, marriage, homemaking, and possible further education. Women are not only living longer than men, but are expressing a new sense of freedom in their increased status, reproductive control, economic independence, and the assumption of new career and civic roles.[7]

SELECTED CASES AND PRINCIPLES

Selected cases illustrate the major ethical issues that affect the adult developmental phase. Major issues are the enforcement of patients' rights.

The Principle of Prevention of Harm

Herbert, 28, a depressed suicidal patient, tells Ms. M, the nurse, that he has a right to jump out of the 22nd-story hospital window, that he has a right to die, and that Ms. M has no right to restrain him.[8] The issue here is the patient's autonomy and self-determination versus the principles of "do no harm" and "do good," which the nurse may invoke as guides to action.

One may also consider the case of Phillip, 57, an alcoholic, derelict patient. Phillip claims a right to unlimited medical care, including three dialysis treatments a week, at $160.00 per treatment, $489.00 per week, or $24,960.00 per year. Unlike the person wanting a vasectomy, some people say, Phillip is not a young person making a useful social and economic contribution to society. The issue here is whether or not any person, particularly a noncontributing individual with a self-destructive life-style, has unlimited rights to health care and to the community's limited resources.

Truth-telling and Deception

Robert, a 22-year-old young adult about to be married in a traditional way with plans for children and a home of his own, suffered a serious accident that left him paraplegic. While in intensive care, the patient was repeatedly told that he would recover. He was not told that his paralysis was permanent. On that basis, the patient and his bride-to-be made plans for a large wedding on another date. The nursing staff raised questions regarding the issue of telling the patient and his fiancee of the true nature of his disability. This raises questions of truth-telling and deception. Not to tell, while not a falsehood, is a deception.

In a case adapted from Dan Brock,[9] Edward, a high-anxiety cardiac patient with several previous near-fatal heart attacks, refuses tranquilizers. The head nurse, in consultation with the attending physician, gives Edward tranquilizers, but without Edward's knowledge or permission. The nurse does this for life-saving reasons, thus setting aside the patient's right to know what is being done to his body.[10] The other nurses, Ms. C and Ms. G, are instructed to lie about the real content and effects of the drug given. Ms. C believes the head nurse, the authority figure, knows best. Ms. G thinks the patient has the right to decide what is done to his body. Who is right?

Another example of the patient's right to know the truth about diagnosis, prognosis, proposed treatment, alternatives, risks, and benefits is a case adapted from H. Brody.[11] A 54-year-old mother of four grown children, Ms. Jones, is admitted complaining of severe abdominal pain. She fears cancer. Surgery reveals advanced cervical cancer and distant metastases. The five-year survival rate is less than 20 percent. The chief resident avoids the word "cancer." He believes that a diagnosis of incurable cancer will prompt the patient to jump out the window. The resident later tells the patient that the malignant process has been removed. The patient then confronts the nurse with the statement, "I really have cancer, don't I? And they don't want to tell me the truth." The nurse considers the patient's situation and her need to prepare her children, husband, and herself for dying and death. The nurse considers the possible but unlikely event that the patient will react in a self-destructive fashion to the news, and ponders the assignment of guilt and responsibility for such an act. The nurse then considers his or her own responsibility and loyalty to the chief resident as a member of the team in need of support in a difficult situation, and a nurse's vulnerable status in contradicting a physician's word to a patient. The nurse also considers the use of meaningful silence and verbal reflection of the patient's concern for her diagnosis and prognosis. Finally, the nurse is able to separate the issue of whether to tell the truth or not from the issues of what truth shall be told by whom and in what words and circumstances. The ethical issue has priority. The ways and means are secondary.

The Principle of Informed Consent

Another major issue is the patient's right to informed consent regarding proposed medical, diagnostic, or surgical procedures. Informed consent includes diagnosis, prognosis, and the risks, benefits, and alternatives to the proposed measures in words the patient can understand. Few patients know or are told that a second opinion before consenting to surgery is not only a form of insurance against unnecessary surgery but is paid for by such major health insurance plans as Blue Cross of New York.

Glaring examples of the failure to seek informed consent include the coercive informed consent of parents of mentally retarded children in the Willowbrook hepatitis experiments and the use of 600 United States Army servicemen for an LSD experiment without their knowledge.[12]

The Right to Receive and to Refuse Treatment

Another major ethical issue in the adult development phase is the right to receive and to refuse treatment.

An example is the case of John, age 32, married and with two children. His wife is unable to tolerate oral contraceptives or intrauterine devices. The couple finds condoms unsatisfactory. On the recommendation of the nurse family practitioner, the couple considers a vasectomy among the alternatives. John and his wife conclude that the best method of contraception for them is a vasectomy, since their family is the ideal size. John's request for a vasectomy is refused by the urologist who feels that John is too young and might change his mind or remarry and that the operation is irreversible.[13] The urologist may argue that the right to life includes the right to reproduce. This right is inalienable, which means John may not renounce the right to reproduce through vasectomy. The nurse family practitioner is in a dilemma concerning relationship with the family and the urologist. As patient advocate, the nurse's loyalty is to the family's autonomy and self-determination. In that case, he or she would support John's decision and furnish him with the names of other urologists. The nurse considers the possibility that in the future, after a vasectomy, the patient may remarry and bitterly resent the irreversibility of the procedure and the nurse's advice. The nurse also considers the refusal of the urologist to perform the vasectomy as an infringement on the patient's right to receive treatment. Since this urologist is the only available one in the surrounding community, the patient will have difficulty and incur financial cost in securing the services of a urologist in a distant large city. The nurse's dilemma is that of upholding the patient's right to treatment or agreeing with the urologist's right to refuse treatment on grounds of the patient's best interests.

Despite the best-intentioned and well-planned strategies, psychiatric nurses are still confronted with young, deeply disturbed psychiatric patients who refuse neuroleptic medications. An example is that of Jane, a 22-year-old, unmarried, beautiful girl who does not want to risk repulsive side effects such as tardive dyskinesia, in the form of uncontrollable grimaces, which appears in some patients. Jane, a graduate student, also regards drugs as a form of intrusion and control. She may also refuse drugs on the basis of their effects on mental acuity, the "snowed-under" or "zombie" effect. If Jane is a voluntary patient, the refusal is honored.

Jane may be discharged, however, if she continues to refuse treatment and fails to improve. In extreme cases, the patient's status is converted to involuntary admission and the patient is declared incompetent and forced to take prescribed medication.

The nurse, in possession of all of the facts surrounding the use and misuse of medication and side effects of tardive dyskinesia and dystonias, may be in a genuine dilemma in relation to Jane's refusal. The nurse may deplore the sleepiness and sealing over of acute anxiety that comes from the use of medication. On the other hand, the nurse may, out of loyalty to fellow nurses and workers who prefer quiet patients, feel strongly motivated to influence or coerce Jane to take the major tranquilizers. Another dimension of the nurse's dilemma is that of the community's desire for conformity to social norms and laws. Community pressure on nurses and the mental health establishment to tranquilize troubled or troublesome patients raises questions concerning the nurse's role. The psychiatric nurse is placed in the role of double agent—for the community's good versus the patient's good. In this example, what began as simple truth-telling about the intended effects of drugs to facilitate a patient's compliance with the drug regimen became a genuine dilemma when the psychiatric patient refused medication on reasonable grounds.

This example may be an especially difficult one for the nurse, since the community may frown on the communal life-style, habits, dress, and recreational activities of college youth like Jane, which are largely peaceful and harmless.

Another case is that of Virginia, age 26, a Jehovah's Witness, mother of three, who is wheeled into an emergency room, unconscious and hemorrhaging as a result of a car accident. Her husband refuses blood transfusions on religious grounds. Again, two nurses have the problem of deciding, along with the interns, what is to be done either to save or not save Virginia's life. What is the right thing to do, and how would you reason to a conclusion?

The Right to Privacy and Confidentiality

A patient example that involves the nurse in a dilemma of confidentiality is also adapted from H. Brody. Jim, a young man of 26, is brought into the emergency room following a seizure in a movie theater. Jim is known to the emergency-room nursing staff because he has previously been treated for seizures due to failure to take prescribed anticonvulsive drugs. Meanwhile, Jim drives his fellow workers in a car pool one week out of four and drives twice monthly to a neighboring town to visit his mother. Under the licensing requirements of that state, an individual with uncontrolled seizures is ineligible for a driver's license. The patient begs that the nurses not report him, since he depends on his driver's license and jobs are very scarce.[14] The nurses debate the patient's right to confidentiality and privacy versus the right of others to a safe driver who will not endanger innocent human life.

ETHICAL AND PHILOSOPHICAL CONSIDERATIONS

Reason and Freedom as Marks of Personhood

Several philosophical concepts are helpful in clarifying the cases presented. In the adult years a human being is preeminently a person who has rights and responsibilities. In Joel Feinberg's terms, a person is said to have consciousness, a self-concept, self-awareness, the capacity to experience emotions, to reason and to acquire understanding, to plan ahead, to act on plans, and to feel pleasure and pain.[15] One could add other features of personhood, such as the capacity to form significant human relationships evident in long-term, harmonious marriage and parent-child relationships and friendships. In addition to Feinberg's conditions, H. T. Engelhardt adds a further characteristic of a person, the capacity to develop moral relationships.[16] A person, for Engelhardt and for Kant before him, is also a moral individual. A moral personality is one who lives in freedom in the sense that he or she has an internalized sense of freedom, is a rational being, and is not constrained or coerced into his or her actions, since reason, not compulsion or coercion, governs a rational person's actions. The policeman's or holdup man's pistol is not the motivating force of a free individual. He or she acts by reason.

Openness and Self-Corrective Feedback

To the extent that information is available to health professionals and is communicable and understandable, the principle of *informed consent* applies. Informed consent means that patients and subjects alike are entitled to updated information on which to base their consent or dissent to a proposed health care procedure. The publicness test once proposed by J. Rawls is relevant. According to Rawls, a procedure of justice is fair if, among other conditions, it conforms to the test of publicity.[17] This means that procedures used are openly aired. We may call this the "fishbowl" view of health care, in which procedures and processes such as x-rays are subject to public scrutiny. The growth of health care in doctors' offices may be a trend away from openness and publicity of procedures. The publicness principle or fishbowl metaphor point to the advantages of the teaching hospital, in which mistakes are used as a source of health care learning in the form of self-corrective feedback.

The Right to the Prevention of Harm

One cannot possibly guarantee the right to prevention of harm in a world filled with dangers and vicissitudes. Natural catastrophes, as well as human misjudgments and foibles, do not make the world safe from chance and fatality. Instead, one has the right to live in a society that seeks to practice the prevention, or rather minimization, of harm. The concept of doing no harm figured prominently in Plato's concept of justice. To do justice consisted in not doing harm to anyone. To fail was to countenance injustice, an intolerable obstacle to being civilized. Thus, a standard was set, however woeful or deficient in practice. The prevention of harm in health care also includes the alleviation of suffering. This brings us to the case of Herbert, who believes he has a right to jump out of the 22nd-story hospital window. Ms. M, his nurse, sensing that there is a viable life in Herbert, attempts to restrain him, and succeeds. One may wonder if Ms. M is right or wrong.

A central issue of nurse-patient relationships concerns the role of negative and positive rights. Negative rights are those rights to be left alone, to choose regardless of consequences to oneself. If a person is helpless, too bad for him or her. On this view, no one has a right to be given help.

This view has recently been called the "will" or "choice" view of rights,[18] an unduly stout form of anti-Paternalism. That view seems morally impoverished, for it fails to account for a person's incapacity to express option or autonomy rights if a person is too poor, too sick, too unenlightened, and too powerless to express those autonomy or self-determination rights. There are cases in which a person does not know best and in which he or she needs help to make the wisest decision.[19] This provides a counterexample against a client's right to do whatever the client wants to do at the moment. The example of restraining Herbert shows that to identify one's autonomy right with one's choice of the moment is a faulty moral practice in nursing. Ms. M, the nurse, was justified in interfering.

There are limits to one's self-determination. Identifying one's rights with one's will and desire exclusively is not the only way to determine one's most vital rights. One may also connect one's rights to one's best interests. There are grounds of justified interference with one's liberty both for one's interest and for the good of others. One may be restrained from unknowingly harming oneself, as by taking medically inadvisable forms of treatment. One may also be counseled to take appropriate measures to prolong one's life where the evidence on behalf of the viability of life warrants doing so.

Recently, D. N. MacCormick developed a distinction between a "will"-based view of rights, which emphasizes values associated with freedom, and an interest-based view, which emphasizes benefits conferred equally on all persons, regardless of the capacity to exercise one's will.[20] The *United Nations Declaration of Human Rights* shows that Articles 1-21 are oriented by a will-based view, whereas Articles 22-27, which include the right to a decent standard of living and the right to health care for everyone, are oriented by an interest-based view. These newer positive rights to be free, sometimes called well-being rights, are rights of another kind. Such rights are not recognized by those who believe that rights are only negative rights to be free from interference by others. These newer rights include the right to food, clothing, shelter, education, and health care.

The Right to Truth-Telling and the Avoidance of Deception

To show how well-being rights may have priority over option rights in certain cases, some examples given earlier will be considered. Robert, 22, about to be married, is paralyzed but not told the truth. Edward, a high-anxiety cardiac patient given a tranquilizer, and Ms. Jones, a woman with cervical cancer who the physician fears will jump out of the window, are not told the truth. The right to truth-telling and avoidance of deception is ordinarily an important part of the right to be treated as a rational person. The truth enables a person to decide for himself or herself what course to follow. Ordinarily, a person's will-based negative rights are a vital feature of one's complement of human rights. Paternalism, too often practiced, undermines an essential aspect of one's complement of human rights. Negative rights or autonomy or self-determination rights show respect for a person as a rationally autonomous being. These self-determination rights include the right to be told the truth and not be brainwashed, told falsehoods, or deceived by having information withheld. For health care team members to withhold information from Robert, the intended bridegroom, is a gross violation of his right to know the truth about his body. The withholding of the fact that he will not recover interferes with his future and that of his intended bride.

According to Brock, "medical advisability" does not override a patient's precious autonomy rights by "withholding relevant information from the patient. . . ."[21] Brock appeals to "our right to control what is done to our body" to justify being given "relevant available information."[22] Brock, too, appeals to the metaphor of ownership of one's body as the basis for the right to truthful "relevant available information." The right to truthful information, in turn, serves as a moral standard for criticizing lies, deception, and withholding of information. One cannot be morally free without access to truth about one's body. The case of Ms. Jones, with cervical cancer, who was told, "We got it all," is an example of a lie and a violation of her right to know the truth about her body. In the absence of demonstrable morally compelling reasons for overriding her right, such a lie is reprehensible.

In a pinch, however, showing how well-being rights may have priority over option (autonomy) rights leads one to consider the case of Edward, the high-anxiety cardiac patient. If one believes in the moral priority of the right to prevent harm, even over truth-telling, a case may be made showing that the health team respects the fundamental interest-based rights of the patient by withholding information. The concept of medical advisability, cited in *The Patients' Bill of Rights*, may in some cases give grounds for overriding a patient's autonomy rights. Therefore, Brock rather than *The Patients' Bill of Rights* may be mistaken. The right to live and not be seriously harmed, on an interest-based view of rights, is in a pinch prior to the right to self-determination. The health care team members may know in some selected types of cases, such as the case of Edward, that the only way to save a patient's life is not to tell him that he is being given tranquilizers. If a wise nurse believes that there is still a viable and enjoyable life to be lived in which the patient who is prevented from harm or death could retrospectively say after a time, "Thank you for not listening to me when I wanted to refuse help," then we do not think such a nurse wrongs the patients. Such a patient may become grateful for his life. On the self-determination view, the nurse will be apt to perceive him/herself as the servant and instrument of the patient, willing to assist the patient and to take the client at his or her word. It may be better, however, for the nurse to perceive him/herself as a friend of the client in Aristotle's sense—one who cares with intelligence and wise judgment. One could set aside a patient's will-based rights in such cases by considering a person's more fundamental, deep, interest-based rights that are preemptive and compelling, and that shine over all else. Truth-telling is precious, but in a pinch, prevention of harm overrides truth-telling. This does not mean, however, that truth-telling is canceled, only that truth-telling has a few justifiable classes of exceptions. The Biblical injunction, "The truth shall make you free," is not vacated by a small number of morally certifiable exceptions.

Informed Consent

Truth-telling and the right to informed consent are close cousins that overlap. Nevertheless, there are differences. One difference is that truth-telling, more generic than informed consent, covers accurate information governing all health care states, processes, and procedures. Informed consent enables patients to have the right to decide whether to undergo medical procedures before they occur. Informed consent implies the patient's permission for surgery and stipulates the extent of morally permissible procedures.

Informed consent is an example of a patient's special right to adequate relevant information prior to medically invasive procedures or interventions. The infamous Tuskeegee syphilis experiment and the shameful Nazi Holocaust experiments are examples of violations of the right to informed consent. Similar violations occur when prisoners are offered early parole or other bribes in exchange for their willingness to be subjects of medical experimentation with untested drugs. Such consent may be termed consent by coercion.

But even on the principle of informed consent, there are marginal cases that give rise to legal and moral issues. One such case is the *Canterbury* case. According to one writer, the *Canterbury* case involved a laminectomy "that led to unexpected paralysis, the possibility of which had not been disclosed." Judge S. Robinson reiterated the powerful moral appeal to the right to self-determination in these words:

> The root premise, fundamental in American jurisprudence[, is] that "every human being of adult years and sound mind has a right to determine what shall be done with his own body." True consent is held in this case to be contingent upon the informed exercise of a choice and thus the physician's disclosure must provide the patient an opportunity to assess available options and attendant risks. As to sufficiency of information, the court holds "The patient's right of self-decision shapes the boundaries of the duty to reveal. The right can be effectively exercised only if the patient possesses enough information to enable an intelligent choice."[23]

Thus, the right to informed consent cannot easily be overridden, according to principles of our common morality.

The Right to Receive and to Refuse Treatment

The rights to prevention of harm, truth-telling, and informed consent imply a trilogy of patients' rights: the right to respect, the right to receive treatment, and the right to refuse treatment. The right to respect is manifested in giving kind, considerate, quality care and in honoring every patient's right to receive and to refuse treatment.

In the vasectomy case, the urologist violated the patient's right to decide whether to reproduce or not. The right to decide gives the patient the right to reproduce or not reproduce. It is, again, the patient's body.

In the case of Phillip, the 56-year-old alcoholic who demands too much, the right to receive treatment has to be weighed against the rights of others and so cannot be an absolute, unchallengeable right, for the concept of rights involves the equal rights of all. Since rights are limited by resources, no one individual can have rights to unlimited medical resources.

The case of the beautiful 22-year-old graduate student, Jane, presents a no-win situation, an unsolvable dilemma from the point of view of knowing what is best. Although the behavior-modifying drugs are indicated, some of the side effects are unknown. Since, however, no compelling moral reason, such as prevention of harm, clearly presents itself, and Jane is competent, Jane's right to refuse cannot be overridden. To override her right to refuse is to violate her autonomy rights. Should Jane's symptoms worsen with danger to herself or others, her autonomous rights to refuse might be overriden in favor of her interest-based rights.

On just such grounds as the interest-based rights, one may consider the case of Virginia, the Jehovah's Witness, who is unconscious in the emergency room. Her husband refuses blood transfusions on her behalf. Is he her advocate, however? In a life-and-death situation, she, were she able to speak, might prefer to have a blood transfusion and live rather than die without one.

To respect a patient's right is to know when to honor the patient's right to refuse and when to override it with the patient's right to receive treatment. A precedent for overriding the husband's right in the Jehovah's Witness case is given by the apostle of liberty right, J.S. Mill, who writes:

> If either a public officer or anyone else saw a person attempting to cross a bridge, which had been ascertained to be unsafe and there was no time to warn him of his danger, they might seize him and turn him back without any real infringement on his liberty; for liberty consists in doing what one desires, and he does not desire to fall into the river.[24]

Mill goes on to point out that people may act to prevent a crime before it is committed and if the only function of poison were murder, "it would be right to prohibit [its] manufacture and sale."[25] There is a tacit presumption in society that life is precious. Therefore, the right to seek prevention of harm overrides the right of personal choice. So, by a parity of reasoning, one might similarly safeguard a Jehovah's Witness's real desire to live. If, however, Virginia were conscious and in need of blood transfusions, but on the basis of her religious beliefs refused, the nurse has to consider whether Virginia really prefers no blood and resulting death or prefers to have her life saved at the expense of her religious belief. Virginia's autonomy rights cannot be discounted. They may have to give way in the face of the stronger rights invested in protecting life, endorsed by the common morality. People and subcultures, as Plato long ago observed, are not islands isolated from human relationships with other people. Neither the right to receive nor to refuse treatment is sacrosanct. These are important rights, however, and cannot be ignored or sidestepped. Weighty moral reasons have to be given for overriding either the patient's right to receive or to refuse treatment. Such reasons will involve every person's equal right to respect on behalf of everyone's freedom and well-being.

The Right to Privacy and Confidentiality

Our last case is that of Jim, who drives fellow workers to work in a car pool. Jim gets seizures because he does not take prescribed medications. He begs the emergency-room nurses not to report him to the motor vehicles department. This type of case is in some ways like the *Tarasoff* case, in which a patient reportedly told his therapist that he would murder a young woman who spurned him. The patient did murder the young woman, Ms. Tarasoff, whom the psychiatrist had failed to warn on grounds of patient-therapist confidentiality. The psychiatrist might have prevented this murder.[26] Joseph Fletcher recounts a similar case to that of Jim, that of an English doctor's patient.

> A railway signalman suffers with [such] severe asthmatic attacks that he blacks out altogether. . . . The man works alone in a signal box, regulating fast, express passenger trains. At any time, he may lose consciousness and let a train be wrecked. The doctor would like to warn the company but his patient threatens to sue him for libel.[27]

The rights to confidentiality and privacy, again being crucial autonomy rights, merit high moral consideration. But there are extenuating circumstances in which the paramount right to the prevention of harm overrides even the right of confidentiality and privacy. Therefore, in the *Tarasoff* and Fletcher examples, as with the case of Jim, the right to confidentiality and privacy may be overridden. This does not mean due regard is not given to these important autonomy rights. As with the rights to receive and to refuse treatment, they can in rare classes of justifiable exceptions be overridden, and only by demonstrably compelling reasons in which the equal freedom to live well is a central factor.

THE NURSE'S ROLE

The American Hospital Association's statement of *A Patient's Bill of Rights* may be one response to public criticism of the lack of active meaningful patient participation in hospital care. The various professional codes, such as the American Nurses' Association's *Code for Nurses with Interpretive Statements*, are another answer to the patient's need for an advocate who will defend the patient's autonomy. Malpractice and negligence suits against physicians, hospitals, and sometimes nurses are another patient response to perceived neglect, errors, or omissions of care. Another response is the hiring of a patient advocate by community health boards; this advocate functions independently of administrative control in hospitals. Other hospitals have employed persons, usually nurses, called patient relations coordinators, who respond to patient complaints and problems. The most effective hope for patient advocates, however, is in nurses intelligently involved in patient care. Although participants in hospital technology and bureaucracy, nurses are the main source of personal, intimate, and continuous contact with patients. More than any other health professionals, nurses have frequent opportunities to facilitate and manifest respect for patients' rights. Modern hospital care and medical technology has largely developed into a team effort of highly specialized members. Nurses are that part of the team implementing the delivery of that care to a particular individual.

This provides the nurse with frequent opportunities to inform and to educate the patient, to tell patients the truth about the procedure that the nurse or another professional is about to do in terms the patient can understand. The nurse has many opportunities to inform patients about special diets and the indications for those diets. The nurse who gives medications can inform patients about drugs given, dosages, and expected effects and side effects. The nurse can convey accurate information concerning the patient's body temperature, blood pressure, and laboratory reports.

These nursing practices of health teaching and counseling function to convey truthful information to patients and to facilitate the individual's responsibility for his or her own health.[28] The patient's possession of information regarding health status enhances the patient's independence and self-determination in decisions of health care. Accurate information contributes to the possibility of the patient's choice of the best option among alternatives.

The nurse's respect for persons extends beyond self and patient. It includes others who share in care, such as physicians, social workers, and family. Ideally, therefore, nurses jointly resolve such major issues as telling a young or middle-aged adult the truth about a fatal diagnosis. One goal is to seek consensus among team members concerning how the truth will be communicated to the patient, who will be the bearer of bad news, and what hope can realistically and honestly be given to the patient. In this way, each member of the team is prepared to support the patient's exploration of what it means to receive a diagnosis of a serious, life-threatening, or fatal diagnosis. Since nurses have the most intimate and continuous contact with patients receiving such news, nurses are in the forefront of those who show respect for the patient and for the patient's right to receive and to refuse treatment. Nurses respect the patient's right to information by answering all of the patient's questions, explicit as well as implicit, in a relevant, accurate, sympathetic, and understandable way, as friends of the patient. This means that the patient is not burdened with technical or anatomical details in which he or she has no interest. When, for example, the patient asks how irradiation or chemotherapy will affect him or her, this indicates a knowledge deficit about the side effects, which the nurse fills with relevant facts only.

If the patient inquires about life after a colostomy or similar radical surgery, the nurse again shows respect for patients by sharing relevant information and experiences helpful to educating the patient. The nurse is sensitive to feelings and what are perceived as unstated questions, such as "Can I have sex after a colostomy?" A nurse who lacks up-to-date knowledge has the obligation to tell the patient that he or she doesn't know but will find out or communicate with others who do know. The nurse's duty then is to return to the patient with the latest information or to refer the question to someone more capable of response.

Respect for persons implies patients' rights to know as well as not to know diagnosis, prognosis, treatment alternatives, risks, and benefits. An individual may simply say, "I don't want to know what I have. Just do what you think best. You're the experts." For the right to know implies the right to decide not to know. There are two possible responses the nurse might give to such an individual. One is to offer unconditional support for the patient's right not to know—a statement such as, "It's your right not to know, since this is your body, after all, and you'll decide when you want to know what is happening and being done to your body." This statement supports the patient's right not to know, while clearly indicating that the choice to receive or to refuse treatment is almost always up to the patient. In this way, the nurse indicates the patient's strong right to seek knowledge when, where, and from whom the patient wishes. The nurse's statement defines and supports the patient's autonomy. As time passes, the patient's defense-mechanism processes of denial lessen. The patient then becomes concerned about what is happening in and to his or her body and seeks to regain control on the basis of relevant information.

A different nursing response is that given by Mary Kohnke, who recommends confronting the client with the consequences of not knowing. Kohnke's experience is that the client agrees to know certain things and not others. The nurse then records what the client has and has not been told and why.[29] The patient's family is often the first to know the presence of cancer, for example, from the surgeon, while the patient is still in the intensive care or recovery room. Some families specifically request that the patient not be told of the cancer, or of the extent of its life-threatening properties. There are several objections that nurses in contact with the family can offer to this position. One argument is that not all cancers are fatal. Some cancers may be cured. Other cancers may be treated with good life expectancies for the patient. Only a few cancers are immediately fatal. The second argument is that the patient will naturally want to know the outcome of the surgery and the reason for such treatments as irradiation or chemotherapy. It is the patient's right to know. A third argument is that the nurses' and physicians' primary relationship is with the patient. The relationship is based on trust and honesty. The patient has the right to a truthful answer to the question of "Did you find cancer?"

Educating and informing the patient of his or her diagnosis, prognosis, proposed treatments, risks, benefits, and alternatives tends to raise questions in the patient's mind—such questions as "Do I want to suffer the side effects of chemotherapy for the small and remote possibility of a short remission of my leukemia?"

Another moral issue for the nurse is the question of supporting the patient's right to receive and to refuse treatment. The example of the young father of two whose wife agreed to a vasectomy as the best method of contraception is a case in point of the importance of the nurse's role in supporting patients' rights. Despite the nurse's own misgivings regarding the possibility that the client might change his mind about having more children and the urologist's denial of that right, the *Code for Nurses* supports the client's moral right

> to determine what will be done with his/her person; to be given the information necessary for making informed judgments; to be told the possible effects of care; and to accept, refuse or terminate treatment.[30]

In accordance with the Code, once the nurse is satisfied that the patient has a complete understanding of the procedure, including the fact that it is irreversible, and that the wife concurs, the nurse is obligated to refer the patient to another physician or facility for a vasectomy in as helpful a way as referring a patient for surgery, such as a herniorrhaphy. It is the patient's right to receive treatment of his choice.

The right of psychiatric patients to refuse treatment is more complex because exercise of this right may delay the patient's recovery and return to the community. The use of neuroleptic drugs carry the low probability of undesirable side effects, some of which are irreversible. The possibility that a young woman may develop unsightly muscular movements of her lips, mouth, face, or extremities is an unhappy one. The possibility that the same young woman will languish in a mental institution without treatment and become progressively disturbed over a long period of time is also an unhappy one. The situation becomes one of trade-off—the drugs versus prolonged illness. In these cases, the nurse depends on an accurate store of knowledge of the particular drugs prescribed, the possible side effects, and the effectiveness of the measures used to control side effects. The nurse supports the patient's participation in regulating the dose, the timing of administration, and the possibility of drug holidays in conjunction with the physician and the goals of the treatment plan.

The alternative is for the nurse to support the patient's refusal of drugs, with disclosure of the full range of consequences to the patient and possibly to the nurse. Kohnke recommends that the advocate support the patient's decision without "falling into a defending or rescuing position, in which responsibility for decision making belongs to the advocate and not the client . . . supporting a client's right to make a decision does not mean giving approval for the decision."[31]

One could disagree with Kohnke's position on the grounds that the patient's perception of the nurse's support of refusal of surgery, of neuroleptic drugs, or of electroconvulsive therapy is one of approval. Colleagues may share the same perception. Even some nurses view their role as one of rescuing patients who are victims of the excesses of medical technology in the form of radical surgery and radical drugs. In such examples, patients tend to react globally to the physician as omnipotent and lifesaving or to the nurse as one who really knows the qualifications of the physician and the merits of the case.

The effective nurse tries to avoid the position of broker or intermediary between physician and patient. Instead, the nurse informs and educates the patient regarding measures designed to restore health and prevent illness. The nurse recognizes the physician as a valuable ally in attempting to reach the patient's health goals. The nurse seeks to involve the physician in the process of the patient's deliberations in every possible way.

One way of supporting the patient's right to receive and to refuse treatment is to inform the physician that the patient has questions and doubts bearing upon prescribed treatment. Another way to involve physicians in patients' deliberative processes is to suggest that the patient formulate and write down relevant questions for discussion over the phone or during a visit. The patient's right to a consultation or second opinion is part of what it means to have the right to know.

The nurse who informs patients of the content and therapeutic purpose of nursing actions as their right to know effectively helps demystify medical and hospital infallibility. The nurse is an approachable person who shares expertise and encourages the patient to ask questions of nurses, physicians, and technicians relevant to the patient's illness and recovery.

Unlike the nurse's advocate role in protecting infants and children from harm, the nurse working with adults promotes the autonomy and self-determination of his or her patients. Through nursing activities aimed at case finding, educating, and counseling the patient, the nurse consciously seeks to facilitate the patient's exercise of rights to information concerning diagnosis, prognosis, treatment, risks, benefits, costs, and alternatives as the basis for informed consent and the right to receive and to refuse treatment. In this respect, a nurse functions as a health educator, which is a valuable form for expressing nurse advocacy.

CONCLUSION

Adults are more independent and also more interdependent than other persons, including children and the elderly. Nursing care correspondingly is more verbal and interactive with adults than with younger and older age groups. The adult span is the longest, most significant aspect of personhood and the standard for judging qualities and degrees of personhood. Cases were cited illustrating the centrality of ethical issues. These were discussed under several topics: prevention of harm, truth-telling, informed consent, the right to receive and to refuse treatment, and privacy and confidentiality. These cases dovetailed with key provisions of *A Patient's Bill of Rights* and *The Code for Nurses*.

The ethical issues considered in these topics and cases centered on the values of freedom and autonomy, rationality, well-being, and optimum health care. These ideals are buffeted by world social and economic realities: a growing population with more demands than resources. There are also conflicts within these goals. Prevention of harm, for example, may collide with freedom of expression of a Jehovah's Witness. There are other moral conflicts. New, hard cases sometimes refute entrenched principles.

The relation of principle to practice shows that, to paraphrase Kant, principles without nursing practices are empty; but nursing practices without principles are blind. For moral principles are like the stars or beacons that guide the nursing and health care navigators through the shoals of ethical and clinical challenges. These moral principles are part of the common morality, which function as moral standards and a steady rebuttal that all values are solely relative to time and place. It is frustrating that there is no one principle, but rather a plurality of them, requiring thought and choice without certainty. That, however, is the price one pays for being human and working in the ethics of adult health care without surrendering to dogma.

Nursing implications show how the principles of the common morality are implemented in daily health care practices. These nursing practices, in turn, show how the principles are strengthened or weakened in accord with Kant's principle that he who agrees with the ends also agrees with the means.[32]

REFERENCES

1. Keniston K.: Youth and its ideology. In Arieti S. (ed.), American Handbook of Psychiatry, vol. 1, 2nd ed. New York, Basic Books, 1974, p. 422.
2. Ibid., p. 403.
3. Ibid., p. 423.
4. Neugarten B.L., Datan N.: The middle years. In American Handbook of Psychiatry, p. 596.
5. Ibid., p. 601.
6. Ibid., p. 606.
7. Ibid., p. 593.
8. Bandman E.: The dilemma of life and death: Shall we let them die? Nursing Forum 17(2):118–132, 1978.
9. Brock D.: The nurse-patient relation: Some rights and duties. In Beauchamp T., Walters L. (eds.), Contemporary Issues in Bioethics, 2nd ed. Belmont, Calif., Wadsworth, 1982, p. 144.
10. Bandman B., Bandman E. L.: The nurse's role in an interest-based view of patients' rights. In Spicker S., Gadow S. (eds.), Nursing: Images and Ideals. New York, Springer, 1980, p. 135.

11. Brody H.: Ethical Decisions in Medicine, 2nd ed. Boston, Little, Brown, 1981, p. 46–47.
12. Bandman E. L., Bandman B.: Rights are not automatic. Am J Nurs 77(5):867, 1977.
13. Brody: Ethical Decisions in Medicine, p. 41.
14. Ibid., p. 53.
15. Feinberg J.: The problem of personhood. In Contemporary Issues in Bioethics, p. 108–116.
16. Engelhardt H. T.: Medicine and the concept of person. In Contemporary Issues in Bioethics, p. 95.
17. Rawls J.: A Theory of Justice. Cambridge, Harvard University Press, 1971, p. 133.
18. Hart H.L.A.: Bentham on legal rights. In Simpson A.W.B. (ed.), Jurisprudence. Clarendon, Oxford University Press, 1973, p. 170–201.
19. Bandman, E.: The dilemma of life and death.
20. MacCormick D.N.: Rights in legislation. In Hacker P., Raz J. (eds.), Law, Morality and Society: Essays in Honor of H.L.A. Hart. Clarendon, Oxford University Press, 1977, p. 188–209.
21. Brock D.: The nurse-patient relation, p. 145.
22. Ibid.
23. Beauchamp T.: The disclosure of information. In Contemporary Issues in Bioethics, p. 172.
24. Mill J.S.: Utilitarianism, Liberty and Representative Government. London, Dent, 1948, p. 151.
25. Ibid.
26. California Supreme Court, Tarasoff v. Regents of the University of California, 131 California Reporter. In Contemporary Issues in Bioethics, p. 204–210.
27. Fletcher J.: Morals and Medicine. Boston, Beacon, 1954, p. 58.
28. American Nurses' Association: Nursing: A Social Policy Statement. Kansas City, Mo., The Association, 1980, p. 18.
29. Kohnke M.F.: Advocacy: Risk and Reality. St. Louis, Mosby, 1982, p. 18.
30. American Nurses' Association: Code for Nurses with Interpretive Statements. Kansas City, Mo., The Association, 1976, p. 4.
31. Kohnke: Advocacy: Risk and Reality, p. 5.
32. Kant I.: Fundamental Principles of the Metaphysics of Morals. Indianapolis, Bobbs-Merrill, 1949, p. 34.

CHAPTER 13

Ethical Issues in the Nursing Care of the Aged

Through study of this chapter, the student will be able to:

1. Understand the developmental tasks of the aged in relation to the ethical problems relevant to this phase of development
2. Identify ethical issues of special relevance to the aged, such as the macro and micro level of allocation of scarce resources, rights, competence, and quality of life
3. Formulate the role of the nurse as patient advocate in facilitating the aged person's participation in shared decision making on the basis of goals, values, and rational life plans
4. Utilize Utilitarian and Kantian principles to analyze lifeboat, triage, cost/benefit, and lottery methods of allocating health care

INTRODUCTION

According to one viewpoint, growing old is and ought to be a special time to anyone fortunate enough to have reached old age. It is a time to slow up the pace of work and give up the frenzy of acquiring goods, property, and possessions, to reflect on past achievements and enjoy present satisfactions. Old age is a time for savoring and evaluating life's myriad experiences of people, places, and events shared with intimates and with strangers. One's older years provide an opportunity to reflect on the time left rather than regret the time of life spent. Life goals and processes take on special significance, like the last brilliant colors of autumn.

PROBLEMS AND PROSPECTS FOR THE AGED

Erik Erikson views old age as the ripening period for the fruits of earlier stages. It is, he says, the result of taking care of things and people, of bearing and rearing children, or generating products and ideas, and of adjusting to the inevitable triumphs and disappointments of life. He calls this ripening process "ego integrity. It is the acceptance of one's one and only life cycle as something that had to be and that . . . permitted of no substitutions. . . ."[1] Lidz characterizes Erikson's "integrity" as the phase that "requires the wisdom to realize that there are no 'ifs' in life; that one was born with certain capacities, a set of parents, . . . the past cannot be altered. . . . It is too late to start out on a new life."[2] Integrity means one recognizes one has fewer "ifs," fewer options. It is too late, for example, for a 75-year-old retired machinist to go to medical school. In later life one rounds out one's goals and way of life, but does not start anew. To Erikson, even for the poorest of human beings who understands that birth into a particular culture at a particular time is an historical accident, but who has lived by its precepts with the awareness of integrity, death has no sting. The one and only life cycle is accepted as final, and death is not feared. For those persons living with integrity, old age can be a harvest of contentment and pleasure. Lidz points to the relief from striving and struggle that comes from the lessening of the passions and of unfulfilled ambitions. Leisure can be rewarding, as can be the achievements of grandchildren or the societies and organizations one helped develop. It can be, in Lidz's words, "a time of relaxed closure of life that still contains much to experience and enjoy."[3]

In comparison, Butler views this picture of the tranquility and serenity of old age enjoying the fruits of labor as mythical. It does not square with the values of the general public and its disdain and neglect of the elderly. He sees ageism as a national prejudice based on a systematic stereotyping and discrimination against older people. Older people tend to be classified as ugly, rigid, senile, garrulous, and as less than full human beings. As with any form of prejudice, the aged victims believe this negative definition to be true, place a negative value on themselves, and expect and accept the discriminatory treatment given them.[4] Other negative societal attitudes stem from the high values placed on productivity, with contempt given the nonproducer. Significantly, this society places positive values on youth and negative values on the aged. Prejudice against the old may be a manifestation of the inability to face the inevitabilities of one's own aging process and death.[5]

Both the prejudicial discrimination against the aged and the overoptimistic picture of a serene, tranquil old age enjoying the fruits of labor may be ways of avoiding the personal realities of one's own aging process. Some of these may be psychosocial, others economic, and still others may be reflections or symptoms of the advent of disease. The majority of the aged are women, of whom more than half were widows in 1975. The imbalance between men and women increases with age.[6] Twenty-six percent of the elderly live alone, 36 percent with a spouse,[7] and 95 percent are able to live in the community. Eighty-six percent of the elderly have one or more chronic health problems.[8] It is with this 86 percent of the aging population, plus the 5 percent of the institutionalized aged, that nurses are involved. It is with this 91 percent of the aged, primarily, that moral issues and dilemmas arise.

Siegel notes the social and economic implications for health services related to the aged in this society. An obvious finding is that the elderly are the largest users of health resources.[9] Demand and need rise with age. It follows, therefore, that an increasing amount of health care resources will be utilized for an increasing number of aged persons. This raises ethical issues of the allocation of limited resources. Moreover, as health care and medicine improve their technology, such as drugs, surgery, and home dialysis units, the elderly will increase their utilization. Additionally, the availability of insurance plans, such as Medicaid and Medicare, support more equal and thereby increased utilization of health care resources by all income groups. However, the scarce distribution of health facilities and personnel remains problematic to the elderly in inner cities and in nonurban areas.

Another obvious need is to gear health services toward aged women on the basis of fairness for their much higher proportion among the elderly population. With declining birth rates, the aged person will have fewer siblings or relatives and less of a family support system. This raises ethical issues about letting the aged person with family or friends die if he or she wants to die, versus prolonging the life of that aged person. It also raises issues regarding the obligations and duties of the offspring of aged parents or relatives who may be supporting their own children. The proportion of smaller kinship networks also raises the issues of a greater role of government in providing health and human services to the elderly.[10] This, too, raises problems of the allocation of limited resources. Another aspect of the allocation of limited resources concerns the quality of care given the 5 percent of the elderly who reside in nursing homes and other group-care facilities. These persons may be institutionalized to provide needed care for their incapacities, to save money, or for social convenience. The moral issue is the provision of care that enhances the human dignity and the health status of the aged; this must be of primary concern. Too many elderly in nursing homes have been neglected or exist on substandard food and health care in unsafe environmental conditions. The provision of nursing services with an adequate number of nurses adequately trained and motivated could make a significant difference in the care of the elderly.

The allocation of limited health care resources to this group of persons who are either very old and frail or who are chronically or terminally ill is again relevant to the ethical dilemmas of social justice versus the individual's right to life with dignity or the right to die, if desired.

DEVELOPMENT OF THE AGED

Since the passage of federal Social Security legislation, the age of 65 has become a developmental landmark. It marks the entry point into old age. At this age, the "life expectancy is 13 more years for men and 16 more years for women."[11] Time has, however, different meanings for the aged. Some predominantly grieve the death of a spouse, relations, and friends, and mourn the passing of happier years. Others mainly look forward to the time with optimistic anticipation. All fervently hope for health and independence.

At this time, many face retirement from meaningful work and the financial security that employment provides. For some men and women, retirement is welcomed as a well-earned respite from work and the chance to enjoy leisure, travel, and family and postponed interests and activities. For some aged persons, retirement equals being discarded and rejected as useless; this is dramatically illustrated in the TV play *Patterns*. For the isolated person, the loss of a social network of even superficial relations with fellow workers is detrimental to the enjoyment of retirement. That person may feel condemned to a life of isolation at home.

Whether the person retires happily or grudgingly, that individual is obliged to accept the loss of status that comes with retirement, visible old age, and lessened income and importance. Thus, the ability to enjoy and make use of leisure may be as important a definition of normality as is Freud's definition of normality as "the ability to love and to work."[12] As with love and work, ill health and poverty can be detrimental to the enjoyment of leisure. Some retired persons develop reactive depressions to their lack of meaningful relations and work. Others become fearful and hypochondriacal.

Most persons at the age of 65 are little changed from the middle years, except for differences in their use of time and perhaps money. If they have been fortunate enough to escape disease, they look upon themselves as competent, complete, and capable of independence and self-care. Physical changes such as lessening of the sexual drive occur without diminishing desires for intimacy and affection expressed in touch and caress. As men lose some muscularity and women lose their rounded contours, both sexes look more alike. Likewise, men "become less aggressive and women more assertive as they enter old age and both tend to diminish their activities and become less involved with people."[13] Old friends, relatives, and family become more important, since new friends tend to be less involved. Spouse relationships become more interdependent as the need for help increases. Sexual activity continues into advanced old age in many cases. The wife regards the growing number of widows with alarm and guards her husband's health jealously.

Lidz reports research done by Reichard[14] and her collaborators in 1962 identifying personality types among men who adjusted well or poorly to retirement. Reichard identified the mature type of man who accepted himself realistically and found satisfying activities and relations. The dependent type of man freed of responsibility also found compensation for old age and retirement. Another well-adjusted group protected themselves against their fear of decline and death by keeping active and maintaining strong defenses.

In contrast, men who were angry and bitter about their failures and disappointments in life blamed others and were unable to reconcile themselves to old age. Other poorly adjusted men were self-haters who blamed themselves for failures and disappointments. A great contribution to an understanding of old age would be to study women for their response to retirement, widowhood, solitary living, and the onset of old age. An even greater diversity may exist among women, since many women play more roles than most men. Women who prefer traditional homemaking roles may differ considerably in adjustment to those women who regard their emancipation from conventional women's roles as fulfilling and those women who prefer combinations of homemaking roles, careers, and community service.

Similarly, some men and some women maintain continuing activity and social relationships that contribute to their sense of worth, purposefulness, and social involvement. Others prefer solitary activities or watching television. Loneliness and social isolation may follow, especially if the individual lives alone and has few social skills.

Some elderly people reminisce in the attempt to bring back memories of happier and more meaningful days. Reminiscence serves the dual purpose of bringing closure to life by reviewing people, places, and events that became integrated into patterns of life. Present relationships with children are reviewed and rationalized in the light of past events.

There are several modes of adjustment to old age. Lidz favors the elderly person's acceptance of limitations such as diminished physical capacities, income, and significance to the lives of others. In his view, old age can be a time of growth through sharing the individual's experience, knowledge, and wisdom in ways useful to others. Growth can be achieved by developing new interests and neglected talents. The indispensable element of time is available to "contemplate, observe, and join the many strands together."[15]

Advanced Old Age

Advanced old age is viewed as beginning at the age of 75. Persons of this age hope "to live out their lives with dignity, to remain capable of caring for themselves and their spouses, to continue managing things between themselves."[16] These elderly people hope to be useful, if not significant, to others. They also hope not to become burdens through illness or senility. Many are serene and content, despite the ever present fear of needing a nursing home or mental hospital care. Some elderly people look upon death as a friend whose visit is postponed to a more auspicious time.

Elderly persons who reach 80 generally have the expectation of 10 more years of life.[17] Even though most have multiple ailments such as arthritis, arteriosclerosis, or impaired vision and hearing, some are surprisingly vital. Professional persons who lived full, busy lives dominated by intellectual activities often maintain these pursuits into very advanced old age. Others are grateful to be alive in an era when the elderly have access to television, radio, telephone, cars, Social Security benefits, and community services for senior citizens.

The Frail Elderly

Eventually, the elderly become frail and must depend on others, including nurses. Such dependencies can provoke family conflict and apprehension in the elderly individual in need of help. The aged person may feel rejected by children who are ungrateful. Some children do in fact reject elderly parents and refuse aid. Other aged persons are so insistent on not being a burden that they live alone when it is no longer safe for them to do so. Elderly persons are concerned with losing their independence and consequently their individuality. The nurse caring for elderly patients in the community or in health care facilities can play a significant role in maintaining respect for each person by the time, attention, and quality of nursing care provided. Some communities have well-developed services for the aged. These range from social centers to special housing, delivered meals, visiting nursing services, and homemaking services. Medical technology such as improved cataract operations with implanted contact lenses, electronic hearing aids, and motorized wheelchairs can be of great assistance to the elderly with such needs.

Hospitalization may be a threat that becomes actualized for the elderly fearing separation, mutilation, pain, and incapacitation. The hospital may be seen as a last resort from which the individual is transferred to a nursing home because of the inability to care for himself or herself. Here home care nursing has a role.

The Senile Person

For the senile person living in the community with assistance, the hospital and surgery experience may necessitate transfer to a nursing home. A radical prostatectomy for a man of 80 to 90 years who is confused and forgetful may emphasize his growing dependence on others for what was formerly part of self-care. It may then become obvious to everyone that the critical integrative functions of memory, judgment, and problem solving are seriously impaired. That individual must be given full-time nursing care and supervision. On the other hand, all elderly persons may be completely but temporarily disoriented by the toxic effects of drugs, anesthesia, dehydration, anoxia, diabetes, and urine retention, to name but a few possible causes. As soon as the illness is cleared up, the individual becomes oriented and rational, and is discharged with community nursing supervision. It follows, then, that each elderly person, no matter what the diagnosis, requires respect and attention. A prejudgment of senility may be premature or inaccurate.

The most characteristic feature of senility is memory failure regarding recent events, with only memories of childhood left. Senile persons then both live and act as if in the past, and are unable to care for themselves. Such persons are disoriented as to time and place and need monitoring.[18] There is some loss of control of emotions. Impulses, suspicion, and anger are freely expressed. Loss of inhibitions and judgment may occur, followed by masturbation and sexual advances to children. The onset of senility may be gradual or suddenly precipitated by circulatory deficits, drug toxicity, trauma, death of a spouse, or a move to a new and complex environment. The nurse caring for the elderly individual can help prevent or reduce these events by exercising skilled nursing care.

Happily, not all of the elderly become senile. Some persons of 90 and even 100 remain alert and occupied, even though in need of help from others. The very old may face death cheerfully and distribute their worldly goods while still in control of their faculties. Only 5 percent of the elderly move into nursing homes, but for some who are alone or whose children are unwilling to assume the burden of their care, this remains the only viable option. The quality of health care and human services given in these homes is a direct reflection of the respect for the rights of the aged person to a decent, fulfilling life demanded by a caring or indifferent society. A society that rejects its old and consigns them to brutalized care in virtual warehouses suffers from ethical insensitivity and moral callousness. However, no previous society has been faced with the numbers of aged persons now living and the responsibility for providing for them.

A sad story is told about a prison physician who amputates a prisoner's mutilated finger and, as he throws it into the garbage can, says to the prisoner, "You won't be needing that anymore." Such a remark captures the belief that old people are symbolized by the amputated finger, fit only for waste disposal. Some old people feel acutely that they will not be needed any more, and that they no longer rate having their needs satisfied. The television play *Patterns* presents a biting portrait of a vice-president who is older than other executives and is not wanted any more by the firm's president. A dilemma for society is meeting the needs of the elderly, with all the utilization of health care resources this implies, or limiting this utilization of these resources on grounds of fairness to other age groups.

SELECTED CASES

Eight fairly typical cases that involve moral issues in the health care of the elderly will be presented and considered.

Case 1: Allocation of Scarce Resources. Mr. H, a 23-year-old motorcycle accident victim, is seriously injured and requires a life-support system in the intensive care unit. There are no empty beds. Ms. K, 66, in coma following a major stroke and on a life-support system, is the oldest patient in the intensive care unit. The nurse must recommend which of these two patients will be given the only cardiopulmonary support unit available.

Case 2: Assisting the Patient with Suicide. "Suicide rates for males are higher after age 65 than in younger men. That is because male suicide rates increase from age 15 to 85 in a straight line."[19] There is a substantial increase in suicides of both sexes in the age category of 75 and above.[20]

Ms. A is a mature, experienced staff nurse in a large university-affiliated hospital. She is covering the night shift for an ill member of the regular staff. One of her patients is Dr. D, age 75, a well-known neurosurgeon and a retired member of the medical school faculty. He has recently been admitted for severe, intractable back pain with increasing difficulty in walking. His wife is dead, and his three children are successful professional practitioners in medicine. He has continued to live alone with domestic help in the same large home in the suburbs and to attend medical meetings. Since his radical prostatectomy for a malignancy, his medical practice ceased. There is every reason to believe that examinations performed on this admission will reveal extensive metastatic cancer to the spine. Dr. D may well suspect his true prognosis despite the professionally cheerful and respectful manner staff members accord to him. Ms. A gives him the prescribed injection of narcotics in response to his request. As she turns to leave the room, the patient asks the nurse to open the window wide for ventilation. The room is on the 18th floor, and the window is without a screen. The possibility of suicide crosses the nurse's mind. She wonders if it is not Dr. D's right to determine what shall be done with his disease-ridden, pain-wracked body. She also thinks about the sanctity of every life and the irreversibility of this act. What reasons are there for the nurse either to open or not open the window?

Case 3: A Patient's Right to Decide. Mr. M was an unmarried 82-year-old resident of a nursing home, independent in self-care but needing assistance in dressing, and able to ambulate with a walker. Despite occasional episodes of memory loss and confusion, he continued to care for himself. His loss of hearing interfered with social activities, but he resisted the use of a hearing aid. The development of dysuria led to the diagnosis of benign prostatic hypertrophy and the recommendation of a transurethral prostatectomy operation. When informed of the necessity for surgery, Mr. M readily consented. His nephew and only relative, however, refused to consent to surgery on the grounds that due to the uncle's mental status, his life was without dignity and should not be sustained by extraordinary means. The nephew believed that the uncle had already lived a long life anyway. The nurse appealed for consent for surgery, but to no avail. Without the surgery, Mr. M's condition rapidly declined, and he died unnecessarily of uremic complications within six weeks. What of the patient's right to decide to accept or to refuse treatment?

Case 4: Competence and the Patient's Right to Refuse. George Annas relates the case of a 60-year-old woman, Ms. Yetter, who had been involuntarily committed to a mental hospital with a diagnosis of schizophrenia. A lump in her breast was discovered and a biopsy ordered, to be followed by a mastectomy if the biopsy showed malignant tissue. Ms. Yetter refused permission for the procedure on the grounds that she was afraid of the operation because her aunt had died following a similar procedure. Moreover, she believed the surgery would interfere with her genital system and prevent her from having babies and a career in the movies. The judge decided that although she was delusional, she consistently refused the surgery even in lucid periods. Therefore, the court found Ms. Yetter competent to refuse the biopsy.[21] The nurse wonders what reasons would justify continuing attempts to persuade Ms. Yetter to consent to the surgery or to refrain from doing so on the grounds that she is "competent."

Case 5: A Conflict of Rights. Another related case reported by G. Annas involves

> a 77-year-old woman who suffered from gangrene and who refused to undergo a recommended amputation. Although the court found that the patient was combative, . . . that her train of thought wandered and her conception of time was distorted, it also found that she demonstrated a high degree of awareness and acuity. The patient made clear that she did not wish to have the operation, even though she knew that decision would probably lead shortly to her death. . . .[22]

She made a choice fully aware of the consequences and was therefore "found to be competent."[23] The court said, "The law protects her right to make her own decision to accept or reject treatment, whether this decision is wise or unwise."[24] The moral issue is whether the nurse continues to educate the patient regarding the nature of gangrene and the importance of amputation to the patient's survival or simply supports the patient's decision as final.

Case 6: A Case of Truth-Telling. Ms. G, a 68-year-old active, independent, cheerful grandmother who smokes heavily, is admitted to the hospital for an acute bout of pneumonia requiring intensive care. Her diagnostic tests reveal a widespread metastatic inoperable cancer of the lungs. She is expected to live but a few months. Her devoted children and husband are told the diagnosis while the patient is in intensive care. The family insists that the patient not be told the truth so that the patient's remaining time at home will be as happy as possible. When her nurse comes into the room to prepare her for discharge, Ms. G speaks to the nurse. She says, "I know that I've had a lot of special tests and x-rays of my lungs. I have the feeling that something important is being kept from me. I believe that I have the right to know what's wrong with me." What reasons could the nurse give for telling the patient the truth, and what reasons could the nurse give for not telling the truth?

Case 7: The Nurse as Patient Advocate. This example is adapted from V. Barry.[25] It involves a 78-year-old, independent, nearly deaf convalescent-home patient named Ms. R. The patient had suffered a cerebrovascular accident (stroke), and her prognosis was uncertain. She was a difficult patient to please. Her family was devoted and concerned. Ms. R contracted a case of flu and the family demanded reasons of the nurse as to why Ms. R seemed to be getting worse and why she had not been seen by her physician. On admission, the physician reportedly told the family that with rest and physical therapy, Ms. R would soon be her old self. The nurse knew, however, that when the head nurse called the doctor for medication and treatment, "he instructed her simply to have us make" R "as comfortable as possible because she wasn't going to last very long anyway."[26] The nurse concluded:

> I knew, of course, that professionally I should keep my mouth shut and not make anybody look bad. But I felt sorry for R., and I thought the daughter-in-law was getting the runaround.[27]

Barry then asks what the reader would do if he or she were the nurse. Barry then cites some alternatives, one of which is to tell what the nurse knows. Another alternative for the nurse is to put on the professional hat and "stonewall" the daughter-in-law. Another alternative is to refer the daughter-in-law to one's superiors, again the professionally approved route. There is also the problem of not saying anything derogatory about a doctor, fellow nurse, or hospital. There is also the moral issue of the nurse, as patient advocate, informing the daughter-in-law that the physician has not seen the patient for two months despite being notified of the patient's illness and decline.

Case 8: Allocation of Nursing Resources. Barry reports an essentially true case. A, a law professor, aged 84, was considered to be a "brilliant jurist and legal scholar." He was a giant of a man, and he had an admirable "sense of independence," which even "bordered on conceit."[28] He was married to Kate for over 50 years. They were childless but proud of their independence. At 82, he first suffered from diabetes. By 84 he lost his sight and hearing. He then became isolated even from his wife in an attic. He then suffered a total heart block and needed a pacemaker. His independence vanished by painful degrees. He was diapered and put on a waterbed mattress. Professor A's self-esteem suffered, in addition to the pain of his physical losses.

Adapted somewhat from Barry's account, the scenario continues. The hospital physician concluded that Professor A no longer needed the facilities of an acute care setting. Much against his wife's wishes, he was transferred to a facility giving highly skilled nursing care. His wife visited him every day. She was at his bedside from early morning to early evening. Although she participated in and observed the high level of skilled nursing care he was given, she respectfully but continually interrupted the nurses' work with other patients because of her extreme solicitude for her husband. She held his hand, watched his face, and rang for the nurse every time he moved or made a sound. Some nurses on the unit felt that Professor A was receiving more than his fair share of the available nursing care on that unit and gave reasons for curtailing the time and resources spent on him. These nurses argued for the Utilitarian concept of the greatest happiness of the greatest number. Other nurses on the unit argued that this patient and his wife needed and deserved that care, as should every other patient on that unit. These nurses argued for the Kantian principle of treating every patient as an end and not solely as a means. The problem was to determine what was a fair distribution of limited nursing services.

ETHICAL AND PHILOSOPHICAL CONSIDERATIONS IN THE NURSING CARE OF THE AGED

Macro and Micro Allocation Levels

Moral values have a vital impact on what to do about the aged. The moral problems, dilemmas, and issues associated with aging may be viewed with the help of several different categories. One category or lens is the macro-micro allocation issue. "Macro" refers to whole social systems, whereas "micro" refers to the very small, to the individual patient and the patient's particular, discrete concerns. On the macro level are social policy questions, in which nursing as a profession also has a role. On the macro level are such questions as whether resources are justifiably to be allocated to the aging who are 65 or older. Another question is whether research regarding artificial and organ replacements, such as the heart, kidneys, or liver organs, is justifiable, since the aged might be the greatest users. Other moral questions concern the forms of social, psychological, and economic security society gives to the elderly. Another question concerns the obligation society has to provide an optimum life with socialization opportunities for the elderly. Opportunities include, for example, "Meals on Wheels" programs, regular medical and nursing home visits, ample living allowances, recreation, cultural and educational opportunities, and physical protection.

People who value youth and disvalue aging generally consider moral and intellectual development of the aged to be a waste of resources. Grey is considered an ugly color. Doctors frequently tell older patients, "Considering your age, you're doing fine" or "You're not a spring chicken any more." One message is that the elderly are lucky to be alive, or that the medical and other attention given the elderly is a matter of charity and not a matter of elderly persons' rights. The cases of Mr. M and Ms. R, Cases 3 and 7, illustrate this Aegist attitude of neglect and indifference to the health care needs of the aged.

On a macro allocation level, one issue is how much of the available limited health care resources are justifiably to be distributed to the aged. To avoid isolation and to promote social skills[29] calls for opportunities for meeting other old people of the opposite sex and encouraging the union of old, single people in homes and communities. To give hope and help in these forms to the elderly involves an outlay of economic and social resources. There may be other demands on society, such as allocating resources for infants, children, and adolescents, improved day-care facilities, summer and afterschool programs, and improved schools and colleges.

The macro-micro distinction is helpful toward applying the principle of consistency between macro and micro levels of health care, in which the macro level provides the standard for evaluating the level of health care given at the micro level to the individual in the hospital or in the community. The micro level may also affect the macro level, such as the "Meals on Wheels" program or the independent nurse practitioner movement. The micro level may then serve as a model for other geriatric health care programs to adapt. Although either of these levels may influence the other, generally the macro level provides a standard of consistency for adoption at the individual micro level.

The Utilitarian and Kantian Views of Health Allocations for the Elderly

The issue of macro allocation to the elderly is addressed in ethics by Utilitarianism and by the Kantian view. The Utilitarian emphasis is on providing the greatest happiness for the majority. Since the elderly constitute only 10 percent of the population, one might argue that they do not, on that ground alone, have much of a claim to limited social and economic resources. If one adds another Utilitarian argument to the previous one, that the elderly are less likely to grow to be as productive and creative as children, adolescents, and younger adults are, one may quite easily conclude that the elderly deserve less than younger people.

Readers of Mill's version of Utilitarianism will appreciate Mill's conception of the quality of human life as more than the quantity of pleasure. The quality of human life for Mill means that it is better to be "a human being dissatisfied than a pig satisfied; better to be Socrates dissatisfied than a fool satisfied."[30] A patient who wishes not to be kept alive under all conditions appeals to the "quality-of-life" argument. One can only appeal then to a crude form of Utilitarianism to argue against allocating ample resources to the elderly. For the elderly collectively contribute to the quality of human life through their experience and their wisdom. A more reflective form of Utilitarianism of the kind Mill and contemporary Utilitarians defend does not fall prey to criticisms against the crude form of Utilitarianism. There is nevertheless a view that only those who currently produce deserve resources. A variation of this view holds that society owes the elderly for what they contributed in the past. A refined form of Utilitarianism recognizes the equal right of each individual to happiness regardless of age, sex, race, color, or creed. This view is expressed in Bentham's famous rule, cited by Mill, that "everyone is to count for one, nobody for more than one."[31] The emphasis on equality, on the equal right of everyone to count, implies a restraint on crude Utilitarianism, which either rules by a hypothetical majority that old people do not deserve ample resources or that it is enough to repay old people for what they did. For if everyone counts equally, no persons, young or old, are likely to pursue happiness by voting against their interests.

A similar but not identical principle is expressed by Kant's substantive principle "to treat humanity, whether in thine own person or in that of any other, in every case as an end, never as means only."[32] Kant's principle—to treat people as ends—along with his categorical imperative to act so that one's action is at the same time a universal moral law calls for equal treatment of all people, regardless of their intellectual, cultural, or economic contributions.

Four Methods of Allocating Health Care

There are four alternative methods of distributing health care: the Holmes lifeboat method (Egoist), the triage or some cost/benefit calculation of worth (Utilitarian), the lottery method on the basis of equality; or equal distribution. The Holmes method refers to a shipwreck in 1846 in which the officer in charge of a lifeboat, Mr. Holmes, ordered the unfit thrown overboard. Rescue followed shortly, and the moral question remains to this day whether Holmes should have been charged with murder for which he was found legally guilty. The lifeboat method is the Egoist solution, sometimes called "survival of the fittest." The lifeboat method does not, however, save or serve a maximum number of persons. Nor does it work in the long run by helping a large-scale, complex culture to flourish. Among those thrown overboard, for example, may be some who are physically unfit but intellectually more fit to help the whole group survive. On this ground, the nurse's decision in Case 1 is to allocate the pulmonary life-support system to the younger person and in effect throw Ms. K overboard.

A practical Utilitarianism health care goal calls for a maximum number of persons, but not everyone, to be helped. The "optimum number" and "everyone" may make a telling difference, especially in crunch cases in which the only practical moral solution is to apply triage. Triage serves the maximum number. Triage in health care emergencies means that one sorts people out into three groups: the worst off, who will die anyway; the best off, who will be most likely to recover on their own or with little help; and the median group, those to whom maximum medical and health care attention will be most likely to make the most difference. Since one has limited health care resources, one serves the largest number by distinguishing them into these three groups and singling out the median group on whom to confer benefits. Triage implies the general Utilitarian formula called cost/benefit analysis and cost-efficient analysis. This means: Serve the largest number most effectively. Triage provides more widespread distributive benefits for the cost expended and is also more cost-efficient than any other method of distributing health care under limited conditions.

The lottery method has a serious difficulty. The losers get no care. One can appreciate the general unserviceability of the lottery in deciding, for example, which of 30 emergency patients to care for first or whether to help Mr. H or Ms. K with the pulmonary lifesaving unit. For one of them will be untreated. A key premise in having a life-choosing lottery is that of scarcity. This premise may rest on a fallacious moral assumption that allocating adequate health care for the elderly is not worthwhile in relation to other social values. Like musical chairs, the lottery may begin by allocating too few resources, thus compelling small numbers of winners and large numbers of losers. The method may seem fair, but not if the initial macro-level allocations are unfairly limited. If a member of the best-off or worst-off group picks the lucky straw, health care resources will have been wasted. Yet in some kinds of cases, the lottery method is regarded as the fairest when resources are limited and there is near equality of conditions among candidates.[33] For the lottery treats individuals equally in a micro allocation situation, providing that resources on the macro allocation level are also limited. A practice may be fair, but not wise. In deciding whether to use a lottery or triage in some resource-limited situations, the Utilitarian triage method is the wisest. In other types of cases, such as deciding to save the most intelligent person, a form of Elitism or Egoism may be the best solution. In a battle, one helps the general officer before helping a soldier.

The lottery leaves to chance what may be unwise. Some shortages are genuine. Others are artificial. At any rate, considering the causes of a shortage may help determine whether it was really necessary or avoidable. One alternative to the lottery, lining up on a first-come first-served basis, may eliminate the difficulty of having losers.

The fourth method of distributing limited health care resources is equal distribution. But everyone may get too little to be effective, like dividing a slice of bread into 25 parts. Equality in health care practice means resources are distributed too thinly. There is, however, one way equality works, and that is to combine the equal-distribution principle with the development of merit. What Jesus ostensibly did in multiplying the loaves and fishes, and Edison did by inventing the means to use electricity in every home, is a combination of equality and merit. Appropriately rewarding persons of merit, developing trained intelligence, and supporting medical technology can provide enough pulmonary units so that a young and an old patient do not have to compete. This combination of equality and merit has already been achieved in the production and distribution of antibiotics, making them no longer scarce.

Objections to the Equal-Needs Appeal: Unfair Returns

The equal-needs argument, meaning to distribute roughly equal health care shares to everyone, has as the basis of the right to health care several serious objections. One objection is that those who have not worked as diligently, as long, or as effectively as others would rate equally in having their health needs met. This is the objection expressed by supporters of individual merit, and it cannot be discounted. For example, people who save for sickness in old age and who go without better homes, vacations, and entertainment believe that it is not right that those who spent their earnings receive equal shares. One version of this argument is that if health care resources are distributed equally, the nonsmokers, nondrinkers, and weight watchers may have to pay the bills for the smokers, alcoholics, and the obese. This antiequality argument is sometimes referred to as the "antifreeloader" argument.

A second serious objection to the equal-needs argument is that people's value to society is unequal. The idea that all people are equal, if it is unqualified by some such phrase as "in the eyes of the law," is a myth. In most societies, the oldest people are the least economically valuable. As proponents of the "is-ought" fallacy point out, however, that fact is not a justifiable basis for a moral policy that deprives aged persons of needed health care.

A third difficulty with the equal-needs argument is that all needs cannot be satisfied with available limited resources. Veatch has pointed out that those most in need,

> the incurably ill . . . would end up with all the medical resources. This is . . . inefficient. Furthermore, if they do not benefit from the commitment of resources, it is hard to see why it is just that they get those resources.[34]

To say "X has a need due to old age" does not translate into "X has a right due to old age." Needs, unlike rights, are refusable without contradiction. If one were to say, however, that X has a right due to old age, X's right would not be refusable without a reason. The needs argument, therefore, does not have many teeth in it. All people have many health care needs, but needs are not a sufficient ground for distributing limited health care resources.

Appeals to love, charity, and to one's obligations to others, even appeals to decency, are morally refusable in a way that appeals to the survival of the race or to a well-established right are not. One has to reach for stronger reasons to cancel the application of a right. One can refuse a beggar without being morally blamed for doing so. For however great the beggar's need, being given to is not the begger's right. In contrast, if a patient has a right to health care compensation or if nurses have a right to be paid, to refuse to give the patient compensation or to pay nurses their due is morally and also legally blameworthy. The appeal to the moral sentiment that old people have needs will not by itself carry the day. Their needs are also morally refusable.

Arguments Against Lifeboat Morality and Abandoning the Elderly: The Golden-Rule Argument

The arguments against "need" are minimal compared to those one can mount against the "survival of the fittest," or lifeboat morality. The idea that old people belong on the scrap heap, illustrated in examples of neglect and ignoring the needs of the elderly in Cases 3 and 7, is morally callous. One argument against lifeboat morality is the classic "is-ought" fallacy that what is, such as existing power, does not by itself justify what ought to be. In effect, the is-ought fallacy exposes the invalidity of the claim that "might makes right." There are additional powerful positive moral arguments on behalf of allocating limited health care resources to the elderly. One arguement is the appeal to the Golden Rule, or Rawls's "veil of ignorance" in which one agrees to rules without knowing one's life circumstances. People with moral imagination may appreciate the possibility that if they are lucky, they, too, will become elderly persons, who would like to be treated well.

The weakness of the equal-needs model, namely that needs are morally refusable without necessarily incurring moral blame, points to a strength of Utilitarianism: It emphasizes the Golden Rule of maximizing happiness and minimizing unhappiness. For the Golden Rule provides a basis for reinstituting moral blame for refusing to help those in need. Reproach takes the form: "How would you like it if you were in that old person's shoes?" Only this time, the appeal is not just to the other person's needs, but to one's own actual or potential needs. For the Golden Rule appeals to the reciprocity of everyone's needs, like living under a large-scale insurance plan called the social contract. According to the Golden-Rule argument, one is to treat others as one wants to be treated. This means that one lives by giving and taking on a roughly reciprocal basis. One practical solution then is to have health care insurance plans into which subscribers pay a fair share throughout their lives. This response means that the beneficiaries share the burdens, in accordance with J. Rawls's principle that benefits and burdens be shared equally. On this view, the health care right Professor A has in Case 8 is a limited right. He cannot have unlimited health care resources, such as a private room. And he may have to stand in line like everyone else, not only literally, but also figuratively, as when he must wait his turn for a rare but highly desirable drug or specialist's attention.

Utilitarianism, the Golden Rule, and Cost/Benefit Analysis

Helping all to survive, while ideal, is likely to result in disaster if the available resources are limited in relation to needs. Thus, in Case 1, the nurse or physician cannot save both Ms. K and Mr. H. Some principle for pruning down needs and establishing priorities is called for if morality is to be practically useful. This is the strength of Utilitarian ethics. It provides priorities and procedures for deciding on the distribution of limited health care resources through cost/benefit analysis. Cost/benefit analysis essentially asks and answers: "Who benefits?" and "Who pays?" Cost efficiency calls for accountability. The solution, again referring to Case 1, favors Mr. H, who has more opportunity to be helped than Ms. K. But to discard Ms. K treats her as a means, not as an end, and does an injustice to her. Cost/benefit analysis means (1) that there are no benefits without costs; (2) the benefits are evaluated in relation to the costs; and (3) a judgment is made as to whether the benefit is worth the cost.

In ordinary life contexts, people make decisions as to what to do for a living and how to spend a vacation by using cost/benefit analysis. So, too, in health care and nursing contexts, judging whether dialysis is worthwhile for the terminally ill, comatose elderly patient, for example, is a cost/benefit judgment up to a point. Utilitarian ethics in health care provides a scheme for facilitating ethical decision making, which consists in making value judgments in relation to benefits and costs. For health care has both benefits or beneficiaries and costs. If someone or a group of persons benefits, then someone or a group of persons pays. Health care resources, such as complex medical technology, are expensive.[35] Medical technology is a hard-earned achievement. In health care, as in every other product and service, there can be no free lunches. The cost/benefit analysis frames the problem and tacitly endorses the value of helping those who produce or who have produced. A health care policy without regard to cost is impractical and is therefore ruled out by Utilitarianism.

A difficulty of Utilitarian ethics, however, is that appeal to the majority may overlook minorities, such as the elderly, who also need help. The needs of the elderly may call for taxes for health care, which most nonelderly adults oppose. The majority may benefit from exploiting or abusing a minority, such as elderly, poor women. In geriatric nursing practice, scarcity of personnel, facilities, or resources may rationalize inadequate and negligent treatment of patients who need help. This is illustrated in the case of Ms. R, who suffered from lack of medical attention and negligence. Correspondingly, a strength of Kantian ethics is to remind us of ideals, principles, and rights that ought to govern human conduct. This strength of Kantian ethics is illustrated by the case of the nurse who advocates Mr. M's right to a prostatectomy, despite the nephew's refusal to sign a consent form.

Truth-telling provides a further example of the strength of the Kantian orientation. Truth-telling is a vital obligation nurses ought to show elderly patients, along with other patients, according to this moral point of view. Treating a patient with respect, which is the patient's right, rather than as a mere symptom-bearer to be diagnosed and treated, is another example of applying a Kantian principle to geriatric nursing. To paraphrase Kant, a policy of health care benefits to the elderly without appraisal of costs is empty; a health policy without widespread, decent benefits is blind.

Two Moral Models for Distributing Health Care to the Elderly

There are, then, two main moral models for distributing health care resources: (1) Distribute according to merit; (2) distribute according to need. The difficulty is that while each of these contenders has strengths, each has serious difficulties. The difficulties are so serious as to provide no solution to the issue of who justifiably gets particular health care resources, resulting in a moral stalemate. According to one moral model, Meritocracy, sometimes referred to as Egoism, the elderly are unable to produce. Those get rewards who produce here and now. On this view, Mr. M's nephew did no wrong in withholding prostate surgery from his uncle.

A difficulty with Egoism, however, is that it does not address itself to the quality-of-life argument. Mr. H and Ms. K both need the cardiopulmonary support unit, which only one of these two patients can have. The ideal is to help both patients. To have the Egoist argument in one's "mind set" does not help keep the quality-of-life argument as a consideration. The argument for merit suffers from Elitism and arbitrariness. The question, "Who decides?" is not given a justifiable answer. Thirdly, the appeal to merit, if put into practice, turns society into unequal factions, the rich and the poor. Fourth, the appeal to merit encourages greed. Fifth, it contributes to the "survival-of-the-fittest" mind set. In *Holmes* v. *U.S.* the first mate of a sinking lifeboat ordered 14 "unfit" passengers overboard.[36]

Appeal to either need or merit is inadequate if take alone. Yet each, in pointing to weaknesses in another, reveals moral considerations worth taking seriously. For example, a society cannot function or flourish without merit. But a society that fails to make large-scale provision for legitimate human needs would be heartless and inhumane, and, in a very real sense, immoral. To adapt a statement attributed to Dostoevsky, one can judge a civilization by how it takes care of its prisoners. So one may judge a society by how it takes care of its elderly. The problem remains to reconcile the moral relation between the appeals to needs and merit in a world of limited resources.

Arguments for Reconciling Appeals to Needs and Merit

One argument for reconciling these models is C. Fried's appeal to "a decent minimum."[37] But questions arise, such as whether the minimum is decent. Decency implies more than a floor of health care given grudgingly. Furthermore, the "decent-minimum" proposal suffers from the same arguments against identifying rights with needs. The obligation to provide the decent minimum is morally refusable, and moral blame is not attached for doing so.

A Trilogy of Elderly Patients' Rights

Despite controversies over the meaning of elderly people's rights, three important rights emerge on the basis of the general human rights of all persons. These are the client's (1) right to respect, (2) the right to receive treatment, and (3) right to refuse treatment. Each of these rights has an impact on nurse-client relations and issues in the care of the elderly. The elderly patient's right to respect includes the right to dignity and regard as a rational person, and as an end, not as a means or instrument of someone else's will only. The right to respect of an elderly person implies the right to be treated on the basis of informed consent. The right to informed consent is the client's right to know what treatment is proposed, what its procedures and processes are, and what its expected results are. The right to respect also implies the right to privacy and confidentiality.

The right to receive appropriate treatment implements the right to respect. The right to receive treatment is the right to effective diagnosis and treatment by qualified health care persons, including nurses. A social, political, and economic issue about the right to receive treatment is that of receiving treatment free of individual cost, or on an individually payable basis. Since this issue is controversial, one may refer to the right to receive treatment in either of two senses, as (1) the right to receive treatment on an individually payable basis, and (2) the right to receive nationally paid-for treatment, as yet unavailable.

The third right in the trilogy of health care rights is the client's right to terminate or refuse treatment. There are several views on whether to override an elderly patient's right to refuse. One position is the Libertarian one, which says to respect a patient at face value and comply, as long as risks of failing to act are carefully explained. "It's his or her life, after all." Another view is the Paternalist view, which holds that patients' rights may be overridden in their own best interests or in the best interests of the state. A third position, a Utilitarian view, holds that a patient's right may be overridden on the grounds of cost/benefit analysis, which may include the patient's good or the good of society.

Competence and the Rights of Elderly Patients

A difficulty arises if a patient refuses treatment that will aid him or her to achieve the autonomy a rational patient would prefer. Macklin gives a reason for overriding a psychiatric patient's right to refuse. A compelling reason for the apparent arbitrariness is that a patient's rational powers and autonomy would be increased as a result of treatment when the patient's consenting organ is affected.[38]

According to G. Annas, to be mentally ill, a psychiatric concept, is not necessarily to be incompetent, a legal concept. Annas cites an example of a 60-year-old woman, Ms. Yetter, presented as Case 4, who refused a breast biopsy and was found competent to refuse surgery, since she consistently opposed it in lucid periods.[39] The court was assured that she understood that she might die as a result of having refused.[40]

A moral and philosophical issue raised by the case of Ms. Yetter is to consider under what conditions to override an elderly patient as incompetent. In Plato's *Republic*, Socrates uses the example of whether to deprive a patient of the right to be given back a weapon the patient has lent someone. Socrates points out that if a person lends one a weapon and then goes mad and demands the weapon back, one would be quite justified in not returning the weapon, out of concern for preventing harm.[41] One ground, then, for overriding elderly patients' rights to refuse treatment is to prevent harm, either to themselves or to others. Socrates has quite formidably presented the obvious paradigm for the morally right action in that type of instance and has identified one meaning of "incompetence" as doing harm.

There are, however, other borderline ambiguities that make judgments of competence unclear. In this connection, one may consider several distinctions J. Feinberg has recently proposed that may help clarify the concept of competence.[42] Feinberg cites three scenarios, the first two of which shows that a patient is incompetent, while the third shows the patient to be quite competent. In the first scenario, the patient, a layperson, disagrees with a physician about the properties of drug X, which the physician refuses to prescribe. The patient is *factually* incompetent. In the second scenario, the patient is told that drug X, which the patient wishes the physician to prescribe, will be harmful. The patient says that is exactly what he or she wants. In this scenario, the patient is *normatively* incompetent. In the third scenario, the patient wants drug X, realizing the harm, but says that X will give the patient enough pleasure to make it worthwhile running the risk of physical harm. In this scenario, according to Feinberg, the patient is competent. For the patient shows recognition of risk and, in doing so, reveals an awareness of making value judgments in the real world.

Unnecessary drug use, alcohol dependency, smoking, driving too fast, eating too much, and eating the wrong foods are examples of the third scenario. This scenario shows that one can disagree morally without being incompetent.

One may add two further scenarios to Feinberg's. One is patients' rights to refuse a blood transfusion on religious grounds, although patients realize they may die. In such cases, moral arguments break down, but such patients are competent. A fifth scenario is about a patient's insistence that the patient is the historical Napoleon. This case shows that, as in similar cases of mistaken self-identity, this patient is incompetent. Generalizing, however, a patient could also be delusional about the identity of sects and groups of persons. Sects of "true believers" whose mind-sets are self-sealing, such as the persons in Jonestown, Guyana, who shared a psychotic delusion, being irrational, are similarly incompetent.

The question is to determine which of these five scenarios, if any, appropriately applies to Ms. Yetter's refusal of a biopsy. Ms. Yetter is delusional about a Hollywood career and having children at 60. If there is adequate evidence that her biopsy would lead to effective lifesaving treatment, then one would have a rational consideration for overriding her right to refuse, applying the fifth scenario. If a form of treatment a patient refuses leads to worthy health values the patient wants, such as a lifesaving biopsy, one would have a reason for overriding a patient's right to refuse. The appeal to a patient's own best interests might also be used to override the 77-year-old woman in Case 5 who refused to have her gangrenous foot amputated. The patient's own good might again be cited as a reason for Ms. A's morally justifiable action in saving Dr. D., the would-be suicide in Case 2, from jumping out of the 18th floor window. However, in the case of a woman who requests not to be resuscitated so that her kidneys may be donated to a suitable recipient, the nurse may be justified in supporting the patient's wish. The reasoning is Libertarian. One's liberty rights offer an initial presumption of a person's rights as a person. One's *prima facie* liberty rights are normally honored, unless there is a morally strong reason to override one's liberty rights by other moral considerations, such as prevention of harm to oneself or others. The reasonable moral grounds for honoring this lady's wishes when her life no longer seems viable to her or anyone else seems to place a moral stop sign on all overriding reasons. Even to override an elderly patient's right to refuse treatment does not mean one refuses the patient's right to respect. The reason for overriding, as a nurse might do in a case like that of Ms. Yetter if her chances for living longer would rationally be improved by surgery, shows more rather than less respect. Even if one overrides an elderly patient's right to refuse treatment, this does not overrule the right to respect. If, within the trilogy, the right to respect is accorded priority or is preemptive, an elderly patient's right to treatment or the right to refuse may be overridden. The right to respect means one would do for the patient what the client would, if rational, retrospectively want to have done. The right to respect gives one moral grounds for overriding or preempting Ms. Yetter's right to refuse a breast biopsy, providing a breast biopsy is medically indicated and that she will be helped by it.

Some Common Moral Principles

Geriatric training for nurses implies a common set of moral principles, culled from various ethical views. One principle implicit in geriatric nursing is the prevention of harm. Another principle is truth-telling. Other moral values include respect for equality and fairness, autonomy or self-determination, regard for merit, and recognition of individual rights. These common values have an initial presumption of soundness. On this view, nurses ought, for example, to prevent harm, tell the truth, and respect the elderly patient's autonomy. Nurses ought also to treat patients fairly and equally. Compelling reasons need to be given for overriding these values.

NURSING IMPLICATIONS

Role of Patient Advocate

The nurse plays a pivotal and, in some cases, an indispensable role in providing health care for the aged. The elderly are in the majority on most nursing units of a general hospital. They are in need of daily blocks of nursing time for bathing, dressing, medications, treatment, getting out of bed, and various therapies. The elderly in surgical and intensive care units are a particular source of concern for the nurse. Every aspect of their care over a 24-hour period is provided by nurses.

Nursing care plans and goals are set by nurses. The success or failure of these plans is the outcome both of the wisdom of patients' care plans and goals and the quality and quantity of nursing care given in support of goals. Elderly homebound persons for whom nursing services are the main source of health care are also dependent on the appropriateness, frequency, and effectiveness of that care for survival. The nurse is not only indispensable to the delivery of nursing services, but for coordinating other health and human services on behalf of the patient. Therefore, nurses identify and secure whatever other health services the patient needs. It is the nurse who identifies shortness of breath, irregular pulse, untoward effects of medication, and signs and symptoms of pain and secures medical help both in a home and hospital setting. The nurse identifies deficits in the delivery of effective care. The nurse safeguards the patient from an unsafe environment as well. The nurse then connects with those parts of the system responsible for satisfying patients' particular needs, which have the duty of correcting personnel or environmental hazards.

This view of nursing care as a total responsibility for the elderly patients' health care by coordination of nursing services with medical care and with diagnostic and therapeutic services presumes the role of the nurse as patient advocate. In no other client group except children are patients so vulnerable to outside influences and neglect.

Several definitions of the role of patient advocate may clarify this concept and its application to the nursing care of the aged. Kohnke defines the role of the nurse advocate working with conscious patients able to speak or act as twofold. The advocate's first function is to inform the patient by providing information "in a way that is meaningful to the client."[43] One might ask whether the nurse informs the patient of essential knowledge regarding the client's health and welfare or regarding the patient's rights, or provides answers to the patient's questions. The second function Kohnke views as the nurses' support of whatever decision the client makes. "The role of advocate comprises only two functions: to inform and to support."[44] Robb gives a common example of nurse-patient interaction that provided the nurse with an easy, natural opportunity to be a patient advocate. "Mrs. K had asked the nurse, 'If I don't want to have surgery, can anyone make me be operated on?'"[45] Robb reports that the nurse's fear of the patient's response may have "prompted the nurse to tell the 78-year-old Mrs. K that she would have to discuss with her physician the matter of refusing surgery for possible lung cancer."[46]

The patient advocate's function here, according to Kohnke, would be to inform. Since this patient requested information, she deserved an honest, direct answer informing Mrs. K that she had both a moral and legal right to refuse surgery. If Mrs. K then refused surgery, the nurse as patient advocate is bound to support that decision, in Kohnke's definition of the role. Evidently, Mrs. K's nurse assumed that others, such as the physician, would not want Mrs. K to be informed regarding her right to refuse treatment. However, since many states, hospitals, and nursing homes have adopted variations of the American Hospital Association's *Patient's Bill of Rights*, first proposed in 1973, the nurse may have been incorrect in that assumption. Nurses may well be supported by institutions in informing patients of their right to refuse treatment. Some nurses are unduly intimidated by the presumed authority of physicians over nursing practice. As a consequence, such nurses misperceive the situation as one in which their continued employment is threatened when the facts are otherwise.

Kohnke recommends that the nurse learn how to support the client's decision without either defending the decision or rescuing the patient. Her reasoning is that clients are responsible for their decisions, which the nurse supports without necessarily approving. Nor, in Kohnke's view, is the advocate obligated "to fight their battles for them."[47] Such behavior may be regarded as disloyal to colleagues and family members, who also claim to give priority to the patient's best interests.

The nurse who seeks to be effective as patient advocate therefore needs to know all aspects of the health care system, including the stated and the correct policies and goals of the institution, the supervisory and administrative practices of the staff, and the provisions of the law. This kind of knowledge enables nursing staff members to develop and test strategies for developing the role of patient advocate and for coping with the risks that may come with implementation. Some groups of nurses have become enormously creative in advocating for patients' rights by pointing out the legal pitfalls of less-than-informed patient consent or unsafe conditions of patient care. Utilizing the provisions and protection of a nursing contract with the facility in which the patient-nurse ratio is specified, or specifying the American Nurses' Association code of ethics as a guideline to practice, may be most useful to the nursing staff striving to develop the role of patient advocate. The ethical orientation examined in this book may serve as the basis for principles stated in the plan of nursing governance and the body of ethical principle in support of that governance. If, for example, support of patients' rights is considered to be an essential feature of nursing care, then the role of patient advocate follows naturally. If the principle of preserving all life at all costs is the rule, support of Mrs. K's rejection of lung surgery becomes problematic. Hopefully, it results in dialogue and resolution without coercing the patient to consent to unwanted surgery.

The American Nurses' Association develops the concept of the patient advocate as that of guardian of patients' care and safety. In this role, the nurse is expected to "take appropriate action regarding any instances of incompetent, unethical or illegal practice(s) by any member of the health care team or the health care system itself, or any action on the part of others that is prejudicial to the client's best interests."[48]

On some occasions, patient advocacy may be an insupportable burden for an individual, and one more appropriate perhaps to an outside system fulfilling just this function. In one state, New York, there is specific legislation and a department that functions solely to investigate reports of patient abuse and neglect in extended-care facilities, such as nursing homes. The report must be submitted in writing, with confidentiality provided for the individual submitting the complaint. Most states now have separate agencies to investigate charges of malpractice and to receive complaints directly.

If the health care facility administrator refuses to correct incompetent, illegal, or unethical practices, the individual nurse may wish to institute documented allegations to the appropriate licensing authorities. For a nurse to do so may be a large responsibility involving some risk. One way to reduce risk is to report nurse or physician malpractice through groups of nurses. Employment contract provisions provide for such grievances. Assistance of the professional nursing organization and legal counsel may be helpful.

Nurses giving direct care to patients can keep the family informed of the patient's condition through informal contacts during visiting hours. When concerned family members raise questions as to why one treatment was given instead of another or none, the knowledgeable nurse can provide technical and ethical reasons for using current treatment. The nurse can also point out that the physician in charge may have additional reasons for favoring one treatment over another. In any case, the family is informed of its right to pursue questions, issues, and problems of patient care with any and all responsible persons inside the facility, as well as outside the system.

Respect for Persons

The health care of the aged too often reflects the bias of society toward the mental acuity of the elderly. A person has the ability to ponder, to judge, to conceptualize, and finally to decide. Such capacities may be slower and more laborious in the aged. Nevertheless, nurses' respect and support of this process has moral implications for the care of the aged. Like any other human being, the aged person "is an original center of being and action. His (or her) actions are his (or her) own. . . . Each of us is an autonomous source of our own deeds, at least in principle, each is also responsible for those deeds. We are responsible in so far as we know what we are doing and in so far as we are free to do it."[49] Aged persons are wise and generally know, far better than younger persons, what they are doing and what is good for them. The aged are necessarily sensitive to the limits of their support system. On this view, it is the person, not the family or physician, who decides whether to be hospitalized or to remain at home with the illness, to have surgery, or to be resuscitated. On this basis, the nurse can support the concept of patient advocacy and of personhood as central to working with the aged.

The Right to Care

There are said to have been 23 million persons over 65 in 1976, and that number will increase to 32 million in the year 2000 and to 45 million, or double, in the year 2020.[50] This age group will be 17 percent of the population and could go higher if there are significant improvements in health care.[51] If current trends continue, the majority of these will be women, who will face about 11 years of widowhood.[52] The older woman has major problems of aging. Lifelong poverty or the act of outliving one's money is real. So is women's vulnerability to crime, desocialization, and isolation as mobility and support systems decrease. Diseases such as osteoporosis and Alzheimer's disease, or senile dementia, affect many and contribute to the large number of nursing home admissions.[53] There are now 1.2 million people in nursing homes, the majority over 65. Elderly persons are known to be warehoused in state institutions for the mentally ill, occupying single rooms in dilapidated and dangerous hotels, or living on the street in boxes or in subways and railroad stations. As hospital nurses have experienced, outside of pediatrics and obstetrics, the majority of patients consist of the aged.

Yet the fact that so many people are living so long is a triumph. Nearly everyone wants to live longer. Unhappily, society was and still is unprepared for this "demographic revolution," and the home health services, the welfare services, the advocacy services, the nursing homes, the social resources, and the hospitals are still insufficient and unprepared.[54] The aged are still undervalued and underserved. They deserve respect as persons who have contributed and who can still contribute in different ways. Every old person is in principle a center of being and action, an autonomous human being in charge of his or her own destiny.

Yet, since nearly everyone wants to live as long as possible, and as well as possible, and increasing numbers of the aged are living long at great cost to society, the issue of the right to health care is highly controversial. Questions arise as to whether there are limited or unlimited rights to medical, surgical, nursing, social, rehabilitative, and home care for everyone. There are also questions as to whether taxpayers ought to give an ever-increasing share of earnings to support the nonproductive aged, and whether the quality of life of elderly persons makes a difference in deciding what rights they have.[55] One answer given is in the form of the Medicaid and Medicare systems, which give some rights to some persons for some kinds of health care. The care given is often fragmented, however, and lacking in the comprehensiveness of services needed by the aged. For example, a national nursing and health care program is needed to enable the elderly to stay at home as long as possible, under the direction and supervision of gerontological and geriatric nurses. This is preferable to the expense and discomforts of a nursing home or hospital. Such a comprehensive program enhances the personhood of the aged, and maintains the integrity of the family as well as the aged couple.

The issue of unlimited rights to health care is difficult and controversial. The example of dialysis emphasizes the problem of rising costs. Although the price of dialysis varies from one center to another, one New York City dialysis center was recently compensated $180.00 per treatment per patient. Elderly patients, some over 80, some comatose, some senile, some ridden with terminal cancer, are taken from nursing homes in ambulances to a dialysis center two or three times a week for treatment of which they are unaware or which they resist. The cost of maintaining a rising number of elderly senile and comatose patients on dialysis, added to the growing numbers of nonelderly dialysis patients, is now in the billions of dollars and rising geometrically rather than arithmetically. England attempted to solve the problem by withholding dialysis from anyone over age 65; public clamor forced the regulation to be rescinded. The English then relied on the cost-effective method of home peritoneal dialysis. This option requires a family that is able and willing to do this, along with a community nursing service having the resources to supervise many such client systems. Such a practice is clearly unjust to the elderly couple or to the single individual who lacks the necessary help to perform the procedure. Writers, such as Fried, object to health care as a subsistence or well-being right that must be supported by others who pay and who then have less money for the other goods of life, such as education, nutrition, or police and fire protection.[56]

Informed Consent

The American Hospital Association developed a *Patient's Bill of Rights* in 1973. It speaks to the human rights of patients to know their "diagnosis, treatment, and prognosis in terms the patient can be reasonably expected to understand."[57] The statement designates the physician as the source of that information. However, some nurses have at times faced the dilemma of the patient and family's questions regarding the patient's diagnosis, treatment, and prognosis. Patients and families reveal a knowledge deficit due to lack of information or lack of understanding. Large medical centers used for training and research present more barriers perhaps to the patient and family in need of information than smaller facilities, where the primary practitioner is more available. Even so, studies have shown that physicians speak in technical terms to patients at times when patients are highly anxious. Therefore, patients understand little, and the family is not present to persist in asking pertinent questions. Patients and families are overwhelmed and immobilized by the situation.

The patients' problems become the nurses' problems, as patients turn to nurses as the persons most involved in their care and closest to them in socioeconomic status and the level of language used. As patient advocate, the autonomous nurse has the duty to remedy the patient's knowledge gap, preferably before the surgery or treatment so that there is time for discussion. The nurse notifies the physician and surgeon of the patient's questions so that the information gap will be closed in ways most useful to patients and families. This may prevent lawsuits.

A further ethical problem for nurses is to respect the patient's right to decide in giving nursing care that involves drug studies, electroconvulsive therapy, or surgery for elderly and possibly brain-damaged patients. One example of this problem was that of Mr. M in Case 2. He needed surgery, but his nephew refused to consent. His life could have been saved. Yet this and similar decisions to operate or not to operate, or to resuscitate, are made for the patient by the family and physician. The rationalization is that the family, not the patient, will sue if dissatisfied with care provided, so that it is their wishes that are honored, not the patient's rights. Advocacy groups for the elderly are formed to prevent just such abuses. The American Nurses' Association clearly states that "each client has the moral right to determine what will be done with his or her person."[58]

The issue of whose consent is to be respected and whose passed over is a major problem that requires vigilance by nurses individually and collectively, so that prompt action may be taken through the appropriate nursing, medical, and legal channels of the health care facility. One example of the failure of vigilance was in the case of elderly residents of a nursing home in Brooklyn, New York. They were asked for permission to participate in research, to which they agreed. These elderly patients were then injected with live cancer virus. At the time of the injection, the effects of these live viruses were unknown. Clearly, informed consent means more than the act of a nurse witnessing the patient's signature, which is the extent of the nurse's legal commitment. As advocate, informed consent means the nurse's moral commitment to the patient's clear understanding of the procedure, surgery, medication, or research being proposed. This can be done best by the nurse's presence and participation in the physician's explanation to the patient. The nurse can then ask in the presence of the physician, as in Case 5, "Do you understand what the word 'amputation' means?" If no response is forthcoming, the nurse may say, "Dr. Smith is talking about cutting off your leg to save your life. Your leg is not healing because there's no circulation. The gangrene will spread and threaten your life. But you can learn to walk again using an artificial leg. We'll all help you." Thus, the nurse actively facilitates dialogue between the patient, the nurse, and the physician. In this way, the nurse can be a patient's advocate and health educator who willingly witnesses the signature of the patient in the secure knowledge that the patient understands what procedure will be done, with what consequences, and consents on that basis. Then the nurse is free to do all of the patient teaching helpful to that situation. If the nurse works in the community, a phone call or a visit to the physician's office might facilitate a clear understanding of the procedure and the need for patient education. The easily remediable problem is that not all elderly patients are given the necessary respect, time, and effort needed to give them an understanding of the proposed treatment. Aged persons easily accept and expect the lack of interest shown in their welfare as a necessary part of being old; they view themselves as victims. The caring nurse expects that her aged clients will be given sufficient information, help, and time to consider consequences and alternatives as the basis of informed consent.

The Sanctity of Life Versus the Quality of Life

One of the most difficult dilemmas for the ethical reflective nurse to face is between advocating courses of action that favor as primary considerations the sanctity of life and those that favor as primary considerations the quality of life of the elderly person. Nurses working in intensive care units must sometimes rank patients in terms of prognosis, so that a new admission may be given a bed, as in Case 1 involving Mr. H, aged 23, and Ms. K, aged 66. Age and prognosis are factors to be considered. The dilemma is in assigning weights to the variables as the basis of decisions that are fair. This poses ethical problems for the nursing staff of the intensive care unit having to decide or to recommend a transfer of someone out of the unit who is aged so as to give a young person a chance. The question is whether it is fair, if the young person was injured as a result of drunken driving, to condemn the old person to certain death. If, however, the aged person's time is short anyway, the question is whether her life is less precious than the younger man's. There is no easy answer to these questions. They call for careful consideration of ethical principles.

The dilemma of the sanctity of life versus the quality of life arises also in deciding whether to resuscitate. Some aged patients with pain and a fatal prognosis specifically request that they not be resuscitated. If that patient's family wants "everything done for the patient," as might be the case with Professor A, and the hospital has no policy, the question is to determine the moral basis on which the nurse makes the decision. A patient advocate would press for respect and consideration of the patient's wishes. Before the particular event, it is easier to work with colleagues for a clear and unequivocal policy on resuscitation, which calls for written "no code" orders. It is morally indefensible to accept tacit and sly orders such as "Make haste slowly" in cardiac arrest or pencil-written orders not to resuscitate, to be erased on the patient's death for the purpose of defense against malpractice suits. The opposite situation, which also presents a dilemma, prevails on some intensive care units in which a patient is repeatedly resuscitated by an exhausted, frustrated, and perplexed staff. Annas cites one example of a 70-year-old woman who was resuscitated over 70 times within a few days.[59]

Truth-telling

The question "Am I going to die?" raises an important issue of truth-telling. Aged persons long in touch with their body functions and feeling states are sometimes knowledgeable about their terminal conditions. Such individuals gain great comfort in discussing the disposition of their property, their funeral arrangements, and the living arrangements for a surviving spouse. Visits from family members and friends are cherished and eye contact maintained even when the patient is unable to speak. The nurse's confirmation of the patient's knowledge of impending death may be simple assent to the patient's question. Some patients, however, steadfastly deny the obvious decline of their bodies and neither ask nor wish to hear information regarding their condition. Perhaps all patients, even the most curious and determined individuals, need time and preparation, assuming one can prepare for death, before hearing the most profound truth, "You will soon die." Therefore, even the nurse advocate who supports truth-telling may, out of consideration, surround this final truth regarding dying with sufficient focus on the "here and now" of reality to enable individuals to reach their own conclusions. Harsh, naked truth can be destructive to the aged person's capacity to face this last test of ego mastery and control in the face of the "unthinkable" loss of one's only life. The decision to tell the truth needs the seasoning of compassion and wisdom.

CONCLUSION

To grow old is also to grow in "integrity," in Erikson's term. Older age sharpens one's awareness of where one has been and who one is, even though one becomes vague and unsteady around the edges. Old age is a time of irony. One is both sharper and aware and yet more forgetful and slower. There are reasons to value and also to disvalue old age. Wisdom, long associated with old age, goes side by side with infantile regression.

Attitudes toward the elderly are also paradoxical. The old are castigated, reviled, and regarded with contempt by some. Yet others see and appreciate successful old people as exemplars and models for others to follow. Great old women and men are cited and looked up to with admiration. These opposing attitudes are reflected in allocating health care to the elderly, and in dealing with the tough problems of deciding who gets what and how much. Like a seesaw, striking a balance between what a society can provide for its elderly and how much to allocate to the young, to adults, and for other human goals, such as vacations, recreation, and education, leaves deep questions and moral uncertainty. The purpose of this chapter has been to clarify some of the ethical considerations that arise in deciding on the amount and quality of nursing care for the elderly.

REFERENCES

1. Erikson E.H.: Childhood and Society, 2nd ed. New York, Norton, 1963, p. 268.
2. Lidz T.: The Person, rev. ed. New York, Basic Books, 1976, p. 512.
3. Ibid., p. 514.
4. Butler R.N., Lewis M.I.: Aging and Mental Health, 2nd ed. St. Louis, Mosby, 1977, p. ix.
5. Ibid.
6. Robb S.S.: The elderly in the United States. In Yurick A. G. et al. (eds.), The Aged Person and the Nursing Process. New York, Appleton-Century-Crofts, 1980, p. 35.
7. Butler and Lewis: Aging and Mental Health, p. 24.
8. Ibid., p. 21.
9. Siegel J.S.: Recent and prospective demographic trends for the elderly population and some implications for health care. In U.S. Department of Health and Human Services: Second Conference on the Epidemiology of Aging. Washington, D.C., The Department, 1980, p. 309.
10. Siegel: Recent and prospective demographic trends, p. 310.
11. Lidz: The Person, p. 511.
12. Ibid., p. 513.
13. Ibid., p. 517.
14. Reichard S., Livson F., Peterson P.: Aging and Personality. New York, Wiley, 1962.
15. Lidz: The Person, p. 518.
16. Ibid., p. 521.
17. Ibid.
18. Ibid., p. 525.
19. Atchley R.C.: Aging and suicide: Reflection on the quality of life? In Second Conference on the Epidemiology of Aging, p. 141.
20. Ibid., p. 143.
21. Annas G. et al.: The Rights of Doctors, Nurses and Allied Health Professionals. New York, Avon Books, 1981, p. 80.
22. Ibid., p. 81.
23. Ibid.
24. Ibid.
25. Barry V.: Moral Aspects of Health Care. Belmont, Calif., Wadsworth, 1982, p. 3.
26. Ibid.
27. Ibid.
28. Ibid., p. 266–267.
29. Bennett R.: Aging, Isolation and Resocialization. New York, Van Nostrand, 1982.

30. Mill J.S.: Utilitarianism. Indianapolis, The Liberal Arts Press, 1957, p. 14.
31. Ibid., p. 76.
32. Kant I.: Fundamental Principles of the Metaphysics of Morals. Indianapolis, The Liberal Arts Press, 1949, p. 46.
33. Childress J.: Who shall live when all cannot live? Soundings 53, 1970, p. 339–355.
34. Veatch R.: What is a "just" health care delivery? In Veatch R., Branson R. (eds.), Ethics and Health Policy. Cambridge, Mass.: Ballinger, 1976, p. 134.
35. Beauchamp T.: Morality and the social control of biomedical technology. In Bondeson W., Engelhardt H.T., Spicker S., White J. (eds.), New Knowledge in the Biomedical Sciences. Dordrecht, Holland, Reidel, 1982, p. 55–76.
36. *U.S.* v. *Holmes*. In Davis P. (ed.), Moral Duty and Moral Responsibility. New York, Appleton-Century-Crofts, 1966, p. 102–118.
37. Fried C.: Equality and rights in medical care. In Beauchamp T., Walters L. (eds.), Contemporary Issues in Bioethics, 2nd ed. Belmont, Calif., Wadsworth, 1982, p. 385–401.
38. Macklin R.: Man, Mind, and Morality: The Ethics of Behavior Control. Englewood Cliffs, N.J., Prentice-Hall, 1982, p. 90, 91–95.
39. Annas et al.: The Rights of Doctors, Nurses and Allied Health Professionals, p. 80–81.
40. Ibid.
41. Plato's Republic, Grube translation. Indianapolis, Hackett, 1974, p. 5–6.
42. Feinberg J.: Social Philosophy. Englewood Cliffs, N.J., Prentice-Hall, 1973, p. 50–51.
43. Kohnke M.: Advocacy: Risk and Reality. St. Louis, Mosby, 1982, p. 5.
44. Ibid., p. 2.
45. Robb S.S.: Attitudes and behavior in the environment of the aged. In Yurick A.G. et al. (eds.), The Aged Person and the Nursing Process. New York, Appleton-Century-Crofts, 1980, p. 93.
46. Ibid.
47. Kohnke: Advocacy: Risk and Reality, p. 5.
48. American Nurses' Association: Code for Nurses with Interpretive Statements. Kansas City, Mo., The Association, 1976, p. 8.
49. Van Melson A.G.M.: Person. In Reich W. (ed.), Encyclopedia of Bioethics. New York, Free Press, 1958, vol. 3, p. 1207.
50. Siegel: Recent and prospective demographic trends, p. 290.
51. Butler R.N.: Introduction. In Proceedings of the Second Conference on the Epidemiology of Aging, p. 1.
52. Ibid., p. 3.
53. Ibid., p. 4.
54. Ibid.
55. Bandman E.L., Bandman B.: Introduction: Rights in and to health care. In Bandman E.L., Bandman B. (eds.), Bioethics and Human Rights: A Reader for Health Professionals. Boston, Little, Brown, 1978, p. 255.
56. Ibid., p. 259–260.
57. American Hospital Association: A Patient's Bill of Rights. Chicago, The Association, 1973.
58. American Nurses' Association: Code for Nurses, p. 4.
59. Annas G.: Remarks on the law-medicine relation: A philosophical critique.

In Trans-Disciplinary Symposium on Philosophy and Medicine. Unpublished paper given at the University of Connecticut Health Center, Farmington, Conn., November 11, 1978.

CHAPTER 14

Ethical Issues in the Nursing Care of the Dying

Through study of this chapter, the student will be able to:

1. Identify the ethical issues related to the care of dying persons throughout the life span

2. Apply ethical principles of respect for the dignity and worth of the dying person and for the individual's right to accept, refuse, or terminate treatment

3. Evaluate ethical principles for the relief of suffering versus the principle of double effect, ordinary versus extraordinary treatment, the active vs. passive distinction, voluntary vs. involuntary euthanasia, and suicide

4. Counsel clients in the provisions of the Living Will and organ donation

5. Distinguish between definitions of circulatory and respiratory death

6. Respect the religious values and practices of the patient and family

7. Implement supportive physical and psychological care to the dying patient, with consideration of stages of dying and hospice concepts

INTRODUCTION

Everyone dies. Although nurses are intimately involved with the care of the dying, to be a nurse in every important sense of that term is to be on the side of life. The profession and the activities of nursing support the most fundamental value beliefs of human beings. These values are twofold:

1. We want to live as persons.
2. We want nurses and physicians to help us live a long, healthy life.

This simple means-ends belief was a reasonable goal throughout nursing and medical history. Until recent times, intense and continuous skilled nursing care was the only hope of saving lives. There were no miracle drugs, radical surgery, or life-sustaining machines. Beyond using heat, cold, food, fluid, rest, and a sanitary environment, nurses and physicians relied on the natural healing powers of the body. If the body failed to be healed and the patient died despite the efforts of nurses and physicians, the conditions of the professional means-ends value statement had been met. Nurses and physicians fulfilled their moral obligations on the side of life. Their power was simply not equal to the strength of the disease. And their sense of moral obligation was reinforced by the nature of the struggle against death.

Nursing care consisted almost wholly of the direct laying on of hands. Nurses witnessed the cardiac patient's gasps for breath, the cyanosis, the diaphoresis, and the swollen abdomens as challenges to the skill and ingenuity of their nursing care. Death was the enemy that came too soon and too often. In the early 20th century, "influenza and pneumonia were the leading causes of death followed by tuberculosis and 'gastrities.'"[1] The causes of death were then mainly due to communicable diseases. The victims were often young.

The then prevailing patterns of communicable diseases, early deaths, and home care have changed dramatically. By 1976, the leading causes of death were heart diseases (34 percent), malignancies (22 percent), and cerebrovascular disease (7 percent).[2] These diseases are progressive and occur in later life. The individual concerned is usually receiving health care and medical interventions. With the advent of miracle drugs, radical surgery, and life-sustaining technologies available in hospitals, persons with heretofore life-threatening prognoses are now seeking restoration of health and function. Moreover, the capacity to prolong life and to ease the plight of dying patients has improved to the extent that almost all acutely ill and seriously ill persons are also hospitalized. As a consequence, most deaths now occur in institutions.

> By 1949, institutions were the sites of 50 percent of all deaths; by 1958, the figure was 61 percent; and by 1977, over 70 percent. Perhaps 80 percent of the deaths in the United States now occur in hospitals and long-term institutions, such as nursing homes.[3]

Increasingly, death comes quietly within the blinking lights and low hum of the monitors, the pumps, the drips, and the suctions of critical care units. Death is impersonal under such conditions. Death can seem to be a separation of body from tubes and machines. Death is due to someone's decision rather than the failure of the heart to pump blood. There is only a deteriorating organ system present. In some cases, the person of the patient has long been absent. The family has exhausted its grief during the prolonged period when the patient was neither responsive nor dying, seemingly neither dead nor alive. The family aches for resolution of an ambiguous situation in which neither grief nor hope is appropriate. The family longs to resume normal feelings, responses, and living.

Nurses are central characters in these dramas who are intimately and continuously involved with the dying patient and significant others. This care involves the coordination of nursing with health care services of other disciplines, medicine particularly, on behalf of the patient. Care of the dying may require prolonged close contact with the dying person's family and friends. Those who are concerned may look to the nurse for guidance or information helpful to reaching decisions of life-and-death proportions. Thus, one function of the nurse is to facilitate communication and the dissemination of information among all the participants involved in the care of the dying person. Another function of the nurse is to be an advocate for dying patients, who quite often are unable to talk or to fend for themselves.

SELECTED CASES INVOLVING NURSING JUDGMENTS AND ACTIONS

We cite cases to illustrate moral issues in the care of dying persons.

Case 1: The Johns Hopkins Case of Active/Passive Euthanasia. A baby with Down's syndrome "was born with an intestinal obstruction at Johns Hopkins Hospital. The parents . . . refused to give consent to surgical repair of the duodenal obstruction. The infant could not be fed and died within 15 days."[4]

Two issues arise in this case: (1) If Nurse A believes in the infant's right to life, and Nurse B believes that the parents have a right to decide, what argument is there for either side? (2) Is passive euthanasia morally equivalent to active euthanasia?

Case 2: Sandy, 5: A Case of Active Euthanasia. Sandy, aged 5, had a malignant brain tumor. There were three major operations. The scars on her head looked like zippers. "She got worse and worse and slipped into a coma." Her mother, distraught, attempted suicide. "One night, Sandy stopped breathing . . . and some nut jumped on her chest and her heart started beating again." She was put on a respirator. When she got infected, the doctors gave her antibiotics. Nurse A said the child's arm looked "like a pincushion. She was black and blue. Nothing worked. She smelled like decaying flesh. She had been such a pretty little girl. . . . I went into her room to bathe her. This time, I closed the door, took her off the respirator, bathed her and powdered her. I hooked her up again, but her heart had stopped. I felt relief."[5]

In this case, Nurse A committed active euthanasia. If you were Nurse B and learned about Nurse A, what would your response be?

Case 3: Jack, 14: Should the Plug Be Pulled? Jack, 14, was injured in a football accident and comatose for two months. Jack's mother asks the nurse to "just unplug the respirator. . . . The physician who has not discussed this case with the parents . . . has adopted a 'wait and see' attitude because he knows of a similar case where a patient on a respirator is now back in school."[6]

This case illustrates a conflict between the mother and the physician. Nurse A believes her role is to inform the mother that she has a right to know the patient's diagnosis, prognosis, treatment, risks, and alternatives as the basis for accepting, terminating, or refusing care. The physician is the best source for this information. Nurse B believes that she should not comply with the mother's wishes.

Case 4: Carolyn, 21: Leukemia: A Patient's Right to Know the Truth. Carolyn, 21, is dying of leukemia. She wants to know what is happening to her. However, her devoted mother believes in shielding Carolyn from this prognosis. Nurse A believes her client, who repeatedly asks about her worsening signs and symptoms, has a right to know the truth. Carolyn's mother, a wealthy, influential woman, threatens to sue the hospital if her daughter finds out that she's dying. Nurse A wishes to support the patient's right to know the truth. Nurse B wishes to acquiesce to the mother's wishes.

Case 5: Tom, 26: The Right to Suicide. Tom, 26, is a brilliant and handsome young man who has contracted Acquired Immune Deficiency Syndrome (AIDS). His family, friends, and lover have abandoned him because of fear of contagion. Tom is still ambulatory. One day he walks to an open window on the 17th floor and starts climbing onto the ledge in a suicidal move. Should the nurse stop him?

This case illustrates a conflict for both the patient and the nurse. If Nurse A believes in the self-determination rights of patients, she may perceive her role as letting the patient jump and die. If, however, Nurse B sees herself as protecting the best interests of the patient, then she may see her role as restraining Tom. What should the nurse nearest the window do?

Case 6: Mr. C, 40: An Adult's Right to Die. Mr. C, blind, a severe diabetic on renal dialysis, wants to die. When P.C. has a cardiac arrest, he is resuscitated, in accordance with hospital policy. Despite his protests, Mr. C is resuscitated several more times. The hospital authorities contend that life must be preserved and these are their policies. Mr. C's family then sues the hospital on behalf of his right to die. By this time, Mr. C has become comatose. The hospital is finally required by the court to comply with Mr. C's wishes.[7]

Three nurses discuss Mr. C's right to die versus the hospital's moral and legal duty to preserve life. Nurse A takes the position that Mr. C's right to die is his right and must be honored. Nurse B maintains that hospital staff members have no right to commit murder. Nurse C says that the physician ought to decide. Which nurse is right in this case, and on what moral grounds?

Case 7: Mrs. W., 50: Who Decides Not to Resuscitate? Mrs. W, a 50-year-old, is 50 percent burned. She has been alert, cheerful, happy, and positive. When Nurse A returned to her room after an hour, Mrs. W was not breathing. "I decided not to call a code. . . . I remembered the doctor saying 'Her spirits are good, but I still don't think she'll make it, but . . .' There would have been so much pain, and there was practically no chance that she would have survived the burns."[8] Nurse A told Dr. C and he decided not to resuscitate, because he did not know how much time had elapsed since Mrs. W. had stopped breathing.

Unlike Mr. C in the last case, Mrs. W had not expressed a wish to die. Would an additional lifesaving effort have been morally justified in this case? Nurse B believes so, but not Nurse A, who knew Mrs. W better and who found her not breathing. Who is right, and why?

Case 8: Ms. M, 52: Honoring the Patient's Wishes for a "Do Not Resuscitate" Directive. Ms. M is a 52-year-old woman who faces surgery for a possible malignancy of the brain. She asked not to be resuscitated. The order was written on her chart. When she suffered a cardiac arrest following surgery in which an inoperable cancer was found, the nurse resuscitated her. The result was that after three days, the kidneys she wished to donate were unusable.[9]

This case, unlike the case of Mr. C, could have resulted in a kidney transplant, which might have aided some other person. Was the nurse wrong to resuscitate the patient? On what grounds do you base your decision?

Case 9: Mr. W, 75: Paternalism vs. Libertarianism. Mr. W, aged 75, was admitted to a community hospital with pneumonia, advanced pulmonary edema, urinary tract infection, and anemia. He did not respond well to treatment, but his wife asked that everything be done for him. On the 14th day, he stopped breathing. Nurse A, on finding him, reported that "vital signs were absent." She summoned Dr. B, who immediately gave a "Do Not Resuscitate" order. The cause of death was recorded as ventricular fibrillation. Mr. W had not been sent to the intensive care unit "due to a shortage of beds." Dr. B said afterwards, "I saw no sense calling Code Blue with a 75-year-old who has no future to look forward to. That's doing him a disservice with increasing hospital costs."[10] Nurse B disagrees with Nurse A and Dr. B.

In this case, should Nurse A have called Code Blue instead of calling Dr. B? Was Dr. B playing God or responding to medical reality? But then why did Dr. B make a gratuitous observation about Mr. W having no future? And why wasn't Mr. W put in intensive care, where he might have had a better chance to be resuscitated? What role is there for a nurse advocate in aiding Mr. W's best interests?

RELATED ETHICAL ISSUES

Trilogy of a Dying Patient's Rights

To respect a person consists in recognizing the dignity and inherent worth of that individual as being uncompromisable. Respect for persons is in some religiously oriented traditions defined as reverence for persons. Mother Theresa expresses this tradition when she says that her mission is to convert the lepers, the homeless, the poor and abandoned children, and the dying persons of Indian cities into angels. An example of respect is to treat patients in the order in which they arrive, on the principle of "first come, first served." This replaces preferential treatment or unfavorable treatment on the basis of prestige or social or economic standing. A patient's right to respect means that the patient is treated as an "end," not as a means only, in Kant's sense. In that sense, the patient's right to respect includes the right to know the truth and to be told the truth insofar as it is known. A conscious patient's right to respect implies importantly the right to informed consent prior to treatment or nontreatment. On the basis of a patient's right to respect, Carolyn in Case 4 has a right to know the truth about her diagnosis of leukemia and her imminent death. In another example, P.C. in Case 6 has a right to have his wish to die respected, as does Ms. M in Case 8, who does not wish to be resuscitated.

A second right, the right to receive treatment, means that a patient has the right to be given the best available treatment. The right to treatment flows out of the right to respect and is a special health care right. The patient's right to treatment means that the patient is not ignored or given custodial or palliative care if more aggressive measures are needed. For example, Mr. W's right to treatment includes the right to the intensive care unit, where he would in all likelihood have been resuscitated.

The patient's right to refuse and even to terminate all treatment is an especially important right of competent patients. Such a right assumes that hospital personnel are willing to take on the legal and moral responsibility associated with the death of patients who wish to discontinue treatment. This decision implies that health professionals will accept corresponding duties, such as providing competent, compassionate care while the patient is dying. The patient's right to terminate treatment also applies to Mr. C, the blind diabetic in Case 6. He too has the right to have his wishes honored. So does Ms. M, the woman with a brain tumor who refused resuscitation because she wanted to donate her kidneys. Finally, the trilogy of a dying patient's rights means a dying patient is treated with care and comfort and not left alone. For to show respect for a dying person is to provide maximum well-being for that person.

Quality vs. Length of Life

Some of these cases illustrate the moral issue between the principle of saving all life versus the principle of preserving only a life of quality. Those who say all of life is a gift aim to protect all life, regardless of its quality. Others defend the idea that control of one's life and body are fundamental rights. These individuals are apt to evaluate the quality of life and would discontinue the respirator for the brain-dead in particular.

On the other hand, deciding who shall live or die can present a serious moral dilemma. The physician in the case of Mr. W arbitrarily decided that the patient's quality of life did not warrant his admission to an intensive care unit. Those who invoke a quality-of-life argument are, in effect, playing God. A safeguard, then, to a quality-of-life argument is to obtain freely given first-person consents for health professionals' interventions.

Relief of Individual Suffering vs. the Principle of Double Effect

Another issue that concerns a dying patient is whether to relieve suffering in the presence of competing goals, expressed through the doctrine of *double effect*. This doctrine recommends doing the least of several evils when evil cannot be avoided. One example of double effect is that of giving a suffering terminal patient increasing doses of morphine, which relieves pain but which also inhibits respiration. Pope Pius XII addressed this topic specifically in 1957. He said, "If . . . the actual administration of drugs brings about two distinct effects, one the relief of pain and the other the shortening of life, the action is lawful."[11] According to the President's Commission for the Study of Ethical Problems, "health care professionals may provide treatment to relieve the symptoms of dying patients even when that treatment entails substantial risks of causing an earlier death."[12]

Ordinary vs. Extraordinary

Treatment which at one time is extraordinary, scarce, and expensive later becomes ordinary. Antibiotics, dialysis, open-heart surgery, organ transplants, and cardiopulmonary resuscitation are examples of extraordinary treatments and procedures that have become ordinary. In an important papal statement of 1957, Pope Pius XII said, "One is held to use only ordinary means—according to circumstances of persons, places, times and culture—means that do not involve any grave burden for oneself or another."[13] The Pope's statement seems to say that deciding who lives and dies, especially among elderly patients, is relative to the degree of available technology in one's time and place.

In any event, the words "ordinary" and "extraordinary" are fraught with vagueness and ambiguity. The President's Commission identifies several, often confused and conflicting meanings of terms, such as "usualness," "complexity," "invasiveness," "artificiality," "expense," or "availability."[14] The Commission prefers "useful" and "burdensome to an individual patient" as having an important advantage over other distinctions, such as "common/usual."[15] A difficulty with the useful/burdensome distinction is that despite the reference "to an individual patient," this distinction overlooks other problems. What about the burden to the physician, nurses, family members, other hospital personnel, the patient, society in general? A further question is: Who decides whether a treatment or procedure is useful or burdensome to the patient if the patient cannot speak for himself or herself?

In one standard sense of the "ordinary" and "extraordinary" distinction, the extraordinary is associated with doing for a patient something exceptional, extra, heroic, supererogatory, or special. On this view, "ordinary" means applying conventional procedures and treatments, which are routine. However, to associate "ordinary" medicine with "useful" medicine and "extraordinary" with "burdensome to an individual" may do a disservice to the advancement of health care. The efforts made for Barney Clark, the recipient of the first artificial heart, shows that advances in health care depend occasionally on extraordinary rather than ordinary efforts. Unknown patients who selected burdensome, extraordinary means for themselves made it possible for caregivers to accumulate the experience that rendered those means ordinary. To give up the extraordinary flies in the face of the human spirit of struggling to improve the human condition. Moreover, a word like "useful" offers no great gain in clarification over "ordinary." For the minimum done for a patient might well be useless and call for the maximum to be done. For example, doing what was useful in the case of Mr. W might have involved putting him in intensive care, which would have been extraordinary.

Since "useful" overlaps with "extraordinary," some of the same problems are apt to arise, namely, what to do for a given patient when all cannot be helped?

The ethically sensitive and intellectually critical nurse will in any event not be satisfied with any distinction that is not both effective and justifiable in considering what to do or refrain from doing for a given patient. One proposed usage is to drop the distinction altogether and do one's best in every situation. With reference to cardiopulmonary resuscitation, in particular, one tries to make it commonplace, as has occurred with so much in health care. This principle implies that Mr. W be transferred to an intensive care unit, where more resources for resuscitation are available. If he still has a life of quality, his hopes and expectations are unjustifiably ended by a physician who settles for the ordinary.

In the cases of Sandy, of Mr. C, or of Ms. M, these patients had no hope of recovery and treatment was refused. The appropriate thing to do is for nurses to help these people achieve a good death through compassionate, skilled nursing care. But in the case of the Johns Hopkins infant or with Mr. W, where something more could have been done to improve life chances, doing more would be the good thing to do. Also, some extraordinary efforts, like those of the "nut" who resuscitated Sandy or the nurse who resuscitated Ms. M, are not good. Moreover, countless ordinary, standard efforts are useful in helping patients.

Despite the difficulties, there are still advantages in using the ordinary/extraordinary distinction on occasion. Use of these terms sharpens one's awareness that the principle of what to do is decided on the basis of doing good and not harm.

The Active/Passive Distinction

A moral issue that persists is the question whether letting die is morally equivalent to killing, or omission is equivalent to commission. The American Medical Association House of Delegates in 1973 adopted the following position on the distinction between active and passive euthanasia:

> The intentional termination of the life of one human being by another—mercy killing—is contrary to that for which the medical profession stands.... The cessation of... extraordinary means to prolong the life of the body when there is irrefutable evidence that biological death is imminent is the decision of the patient and/or his immediate family.[16]

Killing is wrong, but letting die in the sense of not exercising extraordinary efforts or discontinuing extraordinary efforts is morally permissible, according to the AMA.

Rachels has recently argued that the distinction between active and passive euthanasia is a distinction without a morally justifiable difference. Whether one drowns someone directly or does nothing to prevent a person from drowning, both the act and the omission are morally equivalent if the intent and result are the same. Rachels cites the example of the case of the Johns Hopkins Down's syndrome infant whose parents refused to give consent for surgical repair of a duodenal atresia.[17] The pediatrician mother defended her refusal to consent on the ground that omitting to help is not morally wrong, unlike outright killing. Rachels objects to this appeal to the distinction for sliding out of the charge of murder. If killing a Down's infant is murder, so is letting it die by refusing to perform a minor piece of lifesaving surgery. One may present the counterargument that a patient died by himself or herself without assistance, and that the nurse or physician did not actively kill the patient. Rachels' active/passive equivalence may apply to those cases in which the active/passive distinction is used as a pretext for failure to save a life. But there are other types of cases in which there is a morally important difference between killing and letting die.

The case of Sandy, in irreversible and terminal coma, is an example of the nurse's deliberate shutting off the respirator to end the child's life. Had she not done so, the child's life would have continued for an indefinite time. Although, in this case, the prognosis was hopeless and irreversible, the saying, "Where there is life, there is hope," has its truth value. In some cases, killing is worse than letting die. To let die in contrast to active euthanasia implies the possibility that a patient might recover, go into a remission, or survive long enough for a new and effective treatment to be discovered. Insulin, for example, saved the lives of diabetics. To let die instead of practicing active euthanasia may "buy time" for a patient. That time may be spent in pointless suffering, or it may be a meaningful, enriching experience.

The flaw in Rachel's argument is that the intent and the consequences in either passive or active euthanasia are not always the same. In those cases, like the Johns Hopkins' infant with Down's syndrome, in which refusal to consent is used as a pretext for killing, killing and letting die are identical. Although many patients in cardiopulmonary intensive care units will probably die, such patients are better off being allowed to die rather than be killed outright. For to let die instead of killing may effectively result in letting live. Without the killing/letting die distinction, one could argue that a dying patient might as well be killed, since letting die and killing are equivalent. With the case of Jack, the comatose football player, for example, if the nurse refuses to pull the plug, Jack might be back in school in another six months.

The case of Sandy presents a morally defensible case for preferring killing to letting die. But whether the nurse had the right to decide to remove Sandy from the respirator is an issue for further careful reflection. Without consulting the family and allied health professionals, such an act may be one of individual arrogance and arbitrariness. Decisions based on reflective dialogue are preferable to decisions made by individuals without consultation. In situations involving unbearable and futile prognosis, killing may be morally preferable to prolonging dying patients to shorten an unbearably painful dying process. Such a case was that of Charles Wertenberger.

> Mr. Wertenberger, upon learning that he was terminally ill, decided to bear the test of pain and live as full a life as possible as long as it was a meaningful one. In the end, he takes his own life in the company of, and assisted by his wife. . . .[18]

Nursing activities are aimed at effective intervention for improving both the quality and the length of life. The processes and goals show that letting die is, on the whole, morally preferable to killing.

Finally, making omissions morally equivalent to commissions places too heavy a burden on health professionals, which they cannot possibly fulfill. Not doing may have many reasons, such as avoiding the pain or expense of a useless procedure. The murderer, after all, is the cause of death and not the hopeless spectator.

Voluntary and Involuntary Euthanasia

A related issue to that of an active versus passive euthanasia or between killing and letting die is between voluntary and involuntary euthanasia. We all die, but when and under what circumstances is not always known. Some people die suddenly;[19] others die with time to prepare for their death within a finite time frame, ranging from a few days to a few years. In the case of Karen, a 16-year-old adolescent who refused further dialysis, her death involved her decision, consent, and wish. Tragic and terrible as death is for a 16-year-old, respect for her rationality and letting her decide shows that she died with informed consent, and thus illustrates voluntary euthanasia. One cannot apply voluntary euthanasia to a neonate or to a comatose person. One can, however, consider how they would like to be treated. For this purpose nearest of kin are given the power of proxy consent or what is called "substitute judgment." Nurses who do not secure a patient's consent are well advised to consider proxy consent.

In practicing active euthanasia on Sandy, the five-year-old in irreversible coma, the nurse did not consult the family but acted on her own. The principle of voluntary euthanasia may be stated as follows: Whenever possible, consult the patient's wishes concerning the manner and procedures leading to that patient's death, including the withdrawal or withholding of life-sustaining treatment. Mr. C's wish to terminate treatment and die was ignored, thus violating the principle of voluntary euthanasia. The case of Jack leaves us with a dilemma. For the parent in this case wants a course of action taken that may not express the patient's preferences, and would thus violate the principle of voluntary euthanasia.

An advantage of applying the principle of voluntary euthanasia is that one treats a dying person as a rational being to be honored and respected as a person. Such treatment of a person exerts a moral barrier against other persons, such as family members, health professionals, or officials who would decide who lives and dies and under what circumstances. In this connection, voluntary euthanasia is said to constitute a necessary condition of a good death.

In those cases in which patients have no opportunity to exercise voluntary euthanasia, one tries to do the next best thing, which is to consider what the patient in a rational frame of mind would want done.

The California Death Statute and the Living Will

One safeguard of a dying patient's rights is the "Living Will," which has been implemented as the California Death Statute. The Living Will is a legal instrument (in some states) in which a person in a presumably rational and sound frame of mind declares what shall be done regarding life-sustaining measures in the event of incapacity.

> A natural death statute establishes a way for patients while competent to direct that treatment at the end of their lives, if they are not then able to make decisions, shall not include artificial interventions that prolong dying.[20]

The Living Will can function as a safeguard of a dying or incompetent patient's rights. But a Living Will can be used by those who may wish to hasten the death of unwanted individuals if the wording does not clearly express the well-informed consent of a dying patient's wishes, or if, as with any wills, such declarations are not carried out in good faith. But if such Living Wills are carefully, clearly, and thoughtfully worded and appropriately carried out, they can serve to strengthen rather than weaken a dying patient's final interests.

Organ Transplants

A person's willingness to donate usable organs, as with the woman with the brain tumor who wished to donate her kidneys, shows how people can help one another. Views, however, differ on the moral permissibility of organ transplants or of the transfer of any bodily tissue. Jehovah's Witnesses, for example, object to the transfer of any bodily tissue, including blood transfusion, and consider such a transfer as a moral impurity.[21] Some religious and metaphysical views of the organism have held that all the organs naturally belong to a given organism, not to any other.[22] Others compare a person's body with machinery and find nothing wrong with replacing defective parts of bodies. Still others, out of respect for donors, impose restrictions on transplants. The patient's right to respect requires free and fully informed consent from the donor or nearest of kin, as with any other intrusion into the body.

A morally favorable attitude toward organ transplants may be found by appealing to Utilitarianism, which looks to the "greatest happiness of the greatest number." A positive attitude toward organ transplants also consists in appealing to the Christian love-based ethics as well as a metaphysical organicist's view, which holds that we are all part of the cosmic process and that nothing is impure. With appropriate safeguards of donors' and recipients' rights, more good than harm is served by favoring organ donations and transplants.

The nurse plays an important role in the altruistic donation of an organ of a brain-dead patient by communicating with appropriate authorities before the organs deteriorate. Moreover, the nurse can be supportive of the family by emphasizing the generosity of this contribution to others.

Suicide

Suicide is of particular concern to health professionals, who may be in a position to prevent it. Some cultures and individuals oppose suicide under all conditions. "Life is a gift," which no one has a right to take, is a summary of that position. In the cases before us, Tom, 26, in Case 5, is morally wrong to attempt suicide, because it is unnatural or contrary to the moral law or to the law of a religion. Suicide, they say, is evil. One practical argument against suicide is that if everyone who felt like committing suicide acted on such a feeling, there would be no human beings left.[23]

Some other cultures, such as the Japanese, and some individuals favor suicide over other negative values, such as dishonor. When Shakespeare's Brutus becomes aware that he will be marched through the streets of Rome in disgrace as a vanquished general, he prefers suicide. Cho-Cho-San in Puccini's *Madame Butterfly* prefers suicide to dishonor as a rejected and abandoned woman in 19th-century Japanese culture.

The topic of suicide holds out a fascination, partly morbid and partly concern with fundamental questions of being. Hamlet's "to be or not to be" affects everyone in this curiously morbid way. Hamlet, who at one time thinks he cannot right the wrong of his father's killing by his uncle, seriously considers suicide. Albert Camus, who thinks all of life is absurd without hope of a future, does not seem to object to suicide. Other thinkers, like William James, regard life as worthwhile. Prematurely "cashing in one's chips" is a "failure of nerve," a departure from the robust. Still other thinkers, like David Hume, Schopenhauer, and Mill, regard suicide as each person's private business, and immune from moral and legal censure. To Schopenhauer, to say suicide is wrong is "mere twaddle," for "no one has a greater right over anything in the world than over his own person and life."[24] Schopenhauer additionally thought it ridiculous to pass laws against suicide, since those who make a successful attempt can never be punished.

Some defenders of the right to commit suicide, however, seem to confuse suicide with self-sacrifice. The fireman who saves someone's life at the cost of his own does not thereby commit suicide. Yet R.B. Brandt says that

> suppose an army pilot's plane goes out of control over a heavily populated area; he has the choice of staying in the plane and bringing it down where it will do little damage but at the cost of certain death for himself, and of bailing out and letting the plane fall where it will very possibly kill many civilians.[25]

So we need a concept of suicide that does not confuse it with self-sacrifice.

Is suicide right or wrong? In some types of cases it is wrong. In other types of cases, in which it is regarded as the only alternative to prolonged futile suffering, as in Karen's case, it does not seem to be wrong. The case of Tom, the 26-year-old with AIDS, presents a dilemma, with good arguments on both sides of the suicide issue but with no conclusively right or wrong answer.

Suicide *per se* may not be wrong or right; it may be that other conditions accompanying suicide help us judge whether a given suicide is right or wrong. In this process, it helps to clarify the point that suicide is a self-regarding, self-inflicted death, which occasionally depends on assistance from others.

There are two analogies for a reflective nurse to consider in questions of suicidal patients. One analogy is that human beings are compared to property owners who may dispose of their bodies as they wish. On this view, suicide is morally permissible. More precisely, whether one commits suicide is neither moral nor immoral, but is amoral, being up to each person to decide. A second analogy is one in which human bodies are compared to property, only this time belonging to someone else. If life is either a gift or on loan in this sense, one may not do with one's body as one wishes. Instead, one depends on a higher benefactor to decide the time of death. Neither view seems free of difficulties. Surely, one cannot do just anything one pleases, even with one's life and body. Airplane hijackers who threaten to blow themselves up along with their hostages provide an example against the individual property view. Secondly, life for some people, like Karen, is no longer a gift, but rather a burden, which they do not wish to keep. Suicide, then, has not been shown to be morally right or wrong. It is an issue about which reasonable health professionals and patients may disagree.

Definitions of Death

Deciding what death is depends on one of two definitions: either irreversible cessation of respiration and circulation or "irreversible cessation of all functions of the brain."[26] A brain-death definition is appealed to for deciding vegetative cases, in which "cerebral silence" is a basis for donating organs for transplant. As Barney Clark's case illustrated, the heart can be kept beating indefinitely while other organ systems deteriorate and fail.

The concept of "death" masks an ambiguity between the heart and brain definitions. The brain-death definition affords more latitude for bodily experimentation and transplant uses than the heart-death definition. If one is brain-dead but the heart is still beating, health professionals can make use of various bodily parts in "harvesting the dead" to aid the living. But at what price to the dignity of rights of the brain-dead? Does the use of such people's bodies have their consent? If not, the practice of using the brain-dead to aid the living may come close to grave robbing or, worse, to cannibalism. The loosening of boundaries between life and death and also loosening of boundaries around the concept of an individual person can result in the decline of individual rights in favor of community goods. The nurse who resuscitated Ms. M, the woman with the brain tumor who wanted to donate her kidneys, may have erred in trying to save the dying woman's life; but in doing so, the nurse showed a certain regard for the life of that individual. The nurse may have meant well, but in disregarding the patient's wishes, the nurse violated the woman's rights, and prevented good from being done.

Since "there is no possibility that a person fitting" the brain-death criteria "will return to useful life,"[27] by identifying such beings as dead, one is then morally free to treat the remains as one treats other objects. If such a moral policy is generally adopted, it provides a ringing tribute to a 17th-century philosopher, René Descartes (1596-1650) who said that for a human being to exist is to think, and that for a human being not to think is not to exist.

A practical difficulty is that by ruling that if one organ is dead, the organism is dead, one is free to use the "dead" as means for other ends, on the assumption that cerebral activity defines the person. The question is: Can one be a nonthinking person? If the answer is: "No," then the brain-death definition is morally acceptable, with all of its social and economic consequences, including Elitism. If, however, the answer is "Yes," then the world will soon be overpopulated with mindless or brainless beings who may morally not be tampered with because they are not yet regarded as dead. However, they must be cared for by others and receive the benefit of resources.

The growing appeal of the brain-death definition is not only a tribute to Descartes. It is also a way of showing the role of the mind-body problem in relation to health care ethics. Although people now speak of the brain in place of the mind, the two are equivalent, at least on the identity theory, which holds that the mind is nothing more than a brain state. Secondly, the mind-body problem of showing how the body and the brain or mind are related is also a basic presupposition of teaching right from wrong and of doing health care ethics. For if our brains and bodies were different, our ethics would be also. If we had the brains of bats, we might have no ethics. We could expect either more or less responsibility from one another if we had either greater or fewer mental capacities. We are defined by our minds.

Personhood

To be a person, as distinct from being human, derives from the Latin *persona*, meaning a mask from which an actor spoke.[28] In subsequent Roman law, a person was identified as a bearer of rights and responsibilities. A person is a human being who is in a position to perform social roles, like being a nurse, physician, engineer, teacher, waiter, husband, wife, mother, or child. Human characteristics, such as laughing, crying, eating, drinking, eliminating, being hungry, thirsty, and afraid, are biological features. These answer the question: What is a human being? To have social roles and acquire recognition as a member of a community means one can write and read, work, take a vacation, vote, treat patients, reconcile conflicts, develop friendships, and show sympathy for others, for example. To be able to do so is to live not only as a human being, but as a person. As humanhood is biological, personhood is biographical. Personhood calls for respect and recognition of individual rights. Such rights provide individuals with freedoms, powers, entitlements, responsibilities, and boundaries which others may not trespass without a rightholder's permission.

Pivotal to a person as a rightholder is the right to informed consent, a point well made by Paul Ramsey. According to Ramsey, "a human being or person is more than a patient or experimental subject, he is a personal subject. . . ."[29] Consent establishes and sustains a relation of fidelity between persons, according to Ramsey. One writer endorses the *Oxford English Dictionary* definition of a person as "a self-conscious or rational being."[30] Although J. Fletcher refers to humans, the criteria he uses aptly identify persons. Fletcher's criteria of personhood include neocortical activity, an effective I.Q. (operationally at least 20-40), exemplified in a sense of the past and future, self-awareness, consciousness of others, the capacity to communicate with others, and the ability to form and sustain significant human relationships with others.[31] One who has hopes, plans, projects, a past, the sense of the present, joys, frustration, the capacity to regret, and a sense of a future with expectations and prospects, all of which presuppose consciousness—such a being is said to have a life[32] as a person. If one can plan a vacation, drive a car, play a musical instrument, or have some similar project, then one is living a biographical life and is said to be a person. To live as a person is more than just breathing and eliminating.

A reason for distinguishing a human from a person is that additional restrictions can be agreed upon and imposed on who qualifies as worthy of receiving scarce health care resources. This distinction facilitates ethical decision making in regard to those who have priority for being helped to live and those who are valued as being less important.

A related reason is that one invests scarce health care resources and medical attention on persons, treating them as ends, never as means only, in accordance with Kant's substantive ethical principle. One form this principle takes is the right to informed consent and respect for a person as a rightholder, one who has some control of what happens in and to his or her life and body. This is sometimes referred to as the right to self-determination. As a rightholder, a person has a veto power, a moral barrier over what others may morally do to him or her.

A further reason for distinguishing a human from a person is to restrict the attribute of being a person to beings who meet the personhood criteria. Becoming human happens over time. Potentiality is a term that applies to biological processes rather than social roles. One does not attribute potentiality to persons. To speak of a potential or unborn person or child is a contradiction. Personhood is a conferred role depending on social role achievements.

A disadvantage in distinguishing humans from persons is that one is apt to decide quite arbitrarily who counts as a person and consequently rule out those one dislikes or deems unworthy. The application of flat deductive rules, like deciding who lives or dies on the grounds of personhood, without reference to a case-by-case approach, commits an ethnocentric fallacy of simply preferring one's own kind. This practice leaves the resolution of who lives or dies to those with the most power. Making "person" synonymous with being a member of an elite club is an obvious misuse of language.

There are nevertheless advantages in distinguishing humans from persons, as long as such a distinction is not excessively restrictive. For one needs some criteria for deciding who lives or dies. Those with severe mental, social, or emotional incompetence may not qualify as persons. When there is only so much room at the table, hard choices have to be made. The softest of these is a reasonably restrictive set of criteria for personhood, such as a minumum I.Q. and the capacity to form and sustain interpersonal relationships.

Applying Personhood to "Do Not Resuscitate" Orders: Tracing and Examining Arguments for Appropriate Metaphors and Models

A philosophical move, which may be helpful in deciding what nurses are to do about DNR orders, is to consider a viewpoint and trace it to some acknowledged metaphor, analogy, or comparison on which defense of that viewpoint depends. One may compare a comatose person either to a "vegetable" or to a spiritual object, such as an angel. One may compare a bedridden man of 75 to a piece of useless "deadwood" or to a wise ruler. Thirdly, one examines the metaphor to determine how it applies or breaks down in practice and in practical discourse. So if one is a "vegetable," he or she cannot be a person. A comatose individual who after being "on a respirator for eight months is now back in school,"[33] to cite a case against "pulling the plug," shows that such an individual is not necessarily or always a vegetable. Such a case refutes the metaphor of a given person being a vegetable, and provides a counterexample to the advisability of "pulling the plug," as Jack's mother wanted the nurse to do in Case 3. Thus, one tests an analogy to see if it applies in practical discourse. Questions of truth or falsity arise here. One may consider, fourthly, whether supplementary or alternative metaphors or analogies aid in defense of a given viewpoint.

In regard to a comatose or dying patient, one may ask the question, "Does patient X own his or her body?" If X owns her or his body, then X has the right to control what happens in and to her or his body, including, importantly, the right to refuse all treatment, including the right to forgo resuscitation. To own property is to be the boss over what one owns. If individuals do not own their bodies and lives, and if life is to be saved at all cost and taken only by the "one who gives life," then health professionals have no choice but to resuscitate everyone, regardless of whether what is called "brain death" has occurred.

The point is that each metaphor may be examined for its illumination and practical applicability as well as for its implied difficulties. Life, for example, is not always a gift, as the cases of Sandy or Mr. C amply show. Yet, life was regarded as a gift by Mr. W's wife, who spoke on his behalf; and life is regarded for most of us most of the times as a gift, which reveals Aquinas's insight. However, one can also see how Aquinas's metaphor of life as a gift breaks down when it comes up against some hard cases, such as some of those cited here.

On the other hand, human life is not quite like someone's property or factory, on which one can do anything one wishes. A person with a contagious disease can be quarantined, for example. One can see dangers in both extremes. Trying to save everyone has counterproductive consequences. Too many malfunctioning or nonfunctioning beings cannot support the growing demands of sustaining life now or in the future. On the other hand, playing God by deciding who has the required quality of life and who therefore lives or dies also reveals a serious moral pitfall of arbitrarily abridging the equal rights of individuals to decide whether to live or die. Persons' rights to informed consent are crucial to their "rational life plans," whatever else they may want, to cite J. Rawls.

Let's take a closer look, however, at Ms. M, the patient in Case 8. The patient asks the nurse not to resuscitate her under certain circumstances. To comply with this patient's right to die requires the nurse—on one view, that all life is a gift—to commit murder. But is it murder? It is not, if that life is no longer a gift to that person.[34] In hopelessly terminal cases, if we consult the patients' most fundamental interests as friends, in

Aristotle's sense, we might then recognize that since their life prospects are hopeless, were we in our friends' place, we would not consider life a gift. To be a friend in that type of hopeless case is to help, even if it means ending our friend's life, as Freud's physician was willing to do. If a nurse does not resuscitate a terminal patient who has asked not to be resuscitated, we would not think it wrong.[35] The appeal of such rights is not to the older view of option rights, which says, "Don't interfere," but the newer view of rights, which says, "Help me, assist me." A view of rights that addresses a patient's or nurse's vital, rational interests seems the more adequate at certain key moments in one's life. These deeper rights to live well are associated with a good life and provide the conditions for effectively exercising one's freedom. But if it is not already evident, a defense of such rights comes down on the side of a life of quality, but not without the constraints one finds with well-considered rights, such as the test of other people's retrospective judgments.

To have rights is to have a form of moral standing. With rights, like one's right to a paycheck, one knows where one stands. In health care, a resulting trilogy of patients' rights includes the right to be treated with respect, to receive treatment, and to refuse treatment. These rights are vitally important to one's moral standing as a person, regardless of whether one is a dying patient refusing resuscitation, a nurse, or a physician. Beyond that, rights break down, in the recognition that tragedy and stalemate, too, are aspects of the ethical life of persons, which no formalization or objectivity can overcome.

RELIGIOUS ASPECTS OF THE NURSING CARE OF THE DYING

Religious beliefs are ultimate values that guide and are thought to justify the believer's moral conduct in important matters of living and dying. Firmly held religious beliefs influence perceptions of human relationships, religious duties and obligations, and notions of immortality following death. For those patients and families it is essential that all prescribed religious practices are fulfilled. In contrast, some patients have been inactive in religious matters, but when death is imminent, they confront and reevaluate religious beliefs learned as children. As a consequence, some will request the comfort of appropriate religious ritual. The nurse respects these values regardless of the nurse's own beliefs of deism, agnosticism, or atheism. The nurse offers to contact the appropriate clergy or religious representative and follows through until the patient's religious desires are fulfilled.

Since religions and individuals who identify themselves with a particular sect vary widely in their beliefs and practices, each patient's desires regarding religious rites and rituals need to be considered. On admission, the patient is usually asked to state a religious preference. As part of the assessment process the nurse has the opportunity to elicit the patient's wishes for religious involvement. If the answer is affirmative, then a hospital chaplain of that faith is reached. If the patient's response is negative toward religious involvement, the nurse respects that point of view as well. This view provides the nurse with the singular opportunity to offer expressions of concern and caring as the last human contact while alive. The dying person's need for human presence emphasizes the concept of personhood until the last breath is drawn.

Some of the major religions have particular rituals and rites for the dying, which should be observed. Other religions do not have specific rites for the dying. Instead, these nonritualistic religions emphasize human attachments, care, and concern throughout life up to the moment of death. These groups have leaders, visitors, or simply members who visit the dying and provide support. Whatever the patient's or nurse's constellation of religious beliefs or nonbeliefs, the nurse has the opportunity to coordinate human support, care, and concern for the dying person in the effort to soften the impersonal, technical, and sometimes disrespectful means of prolonging dying. The nurse accepts the reality of a patient's belief system, whether religion is or is not an important value, as deeply rooted in that person's personality and way of life. The values of an individual facing death are an expression of personal choice and an extension of the person's right to freedom of thought and of speech.

Health Care, Society, Literature, Nursing, and Religion

The role of religious beliefs is to give dying patients reassurance that the lives they led were good rather than useless or evil. Religion, thus conceived, is designed to help overcome the sense of alienation of the individual dying patient in the face of modern societal demands for youth, productivity, and comfort. Religion increasingly finds a pastoral and therapeutic role, with a message of love, communion, and emotional support. Religions help strengthen family and community life, keep families from falling apart, counsel suicidal persons, alcoholics, the jobless, the undervalued, and the diseased, and offer them reassurance of their essential worth. Religion means a bringing together. In the fragmented state of society, religion has the role of uniting people through love and wisdom in human relationships. It aims to give individuals reassurance that their lives are meaningful.

It is no accident that Robert Veatch's three models of patient-health professional relationships include the "priestly model" along with the engineering and collegial models. People seek trust, love, compassion, character, goodness, and individual security, and they find it by appealing to priestly relationships with health professionals.

The force of religion is also expressed through literary works, like Tolstoy's *The Death of Ivan Ilich*. In this novel, the dying man who is rejected by his family is accepted to the end by his servant, who his cancer wounds and cares for him with religious love. Al religions differ in the form of their expression, they seek to unite the true, the good, the faithful, and the beautiful.

A therapeutic perception may be that even though most religions believe in or seek God, what they also believe in and seek is some idea of the good in human relations and experience. God for the nonbeliever may be spelled with two o's as another way of interpreting religious experience.[36] Finally, a religious belief or "blik," as R.M. Hare has put it, orients and guides one's moral beliefs. We may reason out what is good or bad for the dying patient, but religion helps us to put our hearts into it.

THE ROLE OF THE NURSE IN THE CARE OF THE DYING PATIENT

Helping an indidvidual to die well is to support that person's sense of self-respect, dignity, and choice until the last moment of life. Achievement of this goal requires skilled and compassionate nursing care to minimize suffering and maximize comfort. The nurse provides calm, sensitive, individualized care to each person so that this final human experience is as free from pain and anxiety as possible.[37]

Patients differ enormously in their attitudes toward death. The term "attitude" has affective, cognitive, and behavioral dimensions. These attitudes, along with ethical and religious or humanistic principles, are integral parts of how individuals think and feel about death, and ultimately how they behave when faced with death.[38] Some patients want to know all of the truth as their condition deteriorates. Other patients steadfastly find benign reasons for their symptoms of failing health. The individual's personality, maturity, cultural and ethnic orientations, education, religious belief or its absence, age, role, social status, and family relationships are but some of the variables that influence the patient's response to imminent death.

One widely recognized work on the attitudes of the dying stresses stage approaches. Elisabeth Kübler-Ross describes five stages through which dying persons move. The first stage is one of denial and isolation, in which the evidence of impending death is rejected and ignored or regarded as false. "No, not me," "It's not true," or "It's just arthritis (not cancer)," are typical denials. In the second stage, outrage, and bitter anger and resentment are expressed toward death as unjust and unfair. "Why me?" is a typical response to this stage. The third stage is characterized as a bargaining phase in which the individual promises to reform or to make amends to postpone death until the marriage or birth of a grandchild, for example. "Yes, but after . . ." is a remark typical of this stage. In view of the advancement of the disease process, however the dying person recognizes the bargaining to be futile and becomes depressed. The fourth stage, depression, is a reaction to the anticipated loss of life and of loved ones. "Yes, I am slipping" is acknowledgment of impending death. The fifth stage is one in which the inevitability of death is accepted. "I have done my best" is one expression of acceptance and resignation.[39]

Kübler-Ross views these stages as normal and adaptive for the individual's progression toward acceptance of death. She views the stage of acceptance of death as the culmination of the necessary work of grieving to be done by the patient. Kübler-Ross sees the role of the health care provider or counselor to facilitate the dying patient's movement through these stages with "minimal regression . . . to denial or anger" after a more advanced stage has been reached.[40] Yet she concedes that patients move back and forth between stages and may hold two stages simultaneously.

Kastenbaum speaks for the concerns of some in stating that

> the rapid acceptance of the stage theory of dying has quite outdistanced any attempt to examine the theory empirically or logically . . . and no effort has been made to test out the theory as it continues to become more widely disseminated and applied.[41]

Kalish points to the possibility that the stages are so familiar that there is danger of their "becoming a self-fulfilling prophecy. . . . It is difficult to ascertain whether the stages are universal, modal, culture-bound, or even adaptive, since no consistent research findings have been reported, and medical clinicians themselves are in disagreement."[42] Kalish identifies the ethical issue as one that questions the practice of intervening with dying persons to help them pass through the five stages, given the lack of research.[43]

Other investigations with different questions and different methods have produced other insights. One study by Hinton, who conducted interviews with the dying, demonstrated that dying persons want to understand their prognosis and are aware, especially those with children and with discomfort, of their condition, even without being given an official medical diagnosis.[44] Another investigation conducted with the dying adds another category to their awareness of their condition. Weisman calls this "middle knowledge," which lies between open acknowledgment of death and its denial. He warns against trying to set firm categories, since patients appear to know and want to know their conditions, yet talk as if they did not want to be reminded of information received.[45] The nursing implication is, "Wait until the patient is ready to discuss his or her condition and to focus the discussion on those questions and issues with which the patient is presently able to cope."

In several studies reported by Kalish, the coping ability of dying patients is enhanced by "good marital relationships, having good interpersonal relationships in general, expressing greater life satisfaction, and maintaining open communication about dying."[46] Competent and sensitive nursing also supports the coping abilities of dying patients as they struggle to maintain control and equanimity in the face of declining powers.

Another investigation shows that patients who live longer than predicted are likely to have good human relations and maintain intimacy until death. They have the capacity to ask for and receive support in relation to medical care and emotional relationships. They accept the fact of a serious illness, but not the inevitability of death. They are able to express resentment about their illness and treatment, but are seldom deeply depressed.[47]

Thus, another function of the nurse is to regard the anger and resentment of a dying patient as the natural expression of powerlessness without personal animosity. The anger serves the purpose of ventilating negative emotions.

Nursing Interventions

A useful assumption is that fear of death is natural and present in everyone and that attempts at control, attaining power, and relating to the transcendent are ways of reducing that fear. Thus, an important goal of nursing practice is to enhance the patient's right to self-determination as a manifestation of power over self and limits on the interventions of care providers. One way of accomplishing this goal is through involving the individual in the planning and implementation of care as the prime decision maker.[48] If, for example, the dying patient decides that a visit with loved ones is more important than a dressing change or treating a bowel obstruction, that is a priority to be respected. This is a way of lessening the fear of abandonment by significant others and to bolster the sense of control by "making available those experiences that the patient values."[49]

Symptom control is important to the self-esteem of persons in fear of losing control and to those who find pain frightening and burdensome. The prospect of uncontrolled pain is a specter that haunts most patients. Mental dysfunctions, nausea, constipation, diarrhea, infections, bedsores, and respiratory problems may be equally distressing. Most can be controlled through well-known measures and the remainder through aggressive therapies. Each patient's situation is best considered individually as an effort to control present and anticipated symptoms. Staff and resource shortages, as in the case of Mr. W, who was not put in intensive care, can result in loss of control of symptoms with resulting death.

Pain can almost always be easily controlled. Causes of pain are expected to be identified and followed by specific interventions, such as prophylactic nailing of pathological fractures and radiation or chemotherapy for relieving symptoms.[50] The choice of drugs and combinations of drugs to relieve pain, apprehension, and depression are increasing and improving constantly. The recommended administration of narcotics, such as morphine, in small, frequent doses is recommended for the rapid control of pain for patients not previously taking narcotics.[51] Effective control of pain can be maintained, along with alertness, through continual experimentation with changes over time. For some patients who are close to death, the patient or family may agree to sedation in order to avoid pain. The President's Commission recommends that the administration of narcotics be regularly scheduled so that each new dose takes effect as the last one wanes. Sometimes increased frequency is more effective than increased dosage. Orders written as PRN enable the nurse caring for the patient to adjust the dose to prevent pain without excessive sedation. However, respiratory depression and oversedation can be reversed by use of naloxone (Narcan) in prescribed amounts and intervals.[52] The concerns of nurses and other caregivers regarding the "dying patients becoming addicted to narcotics are both mistaken and, in any case, irrelevant. Few patients develop problems because of physical dependence. . . . Furthermore, physical and psychological addiction, when it occurs, is not particularly troubling to a patient who is dying, nor should be to caregivers."[53] This statement is a direct application of Kantian ethics, which treats humans as ends rather than as means only. This statement applies the principle to every dying patient for control of pain and of symptoms that otherwise dehumanize the dying patient.

The nurse can effectively utilize nursing observations of the patient's responses to medications as the basis for recommending changes in drugs, in dosage, or in frequency. From systematic nursing assessments of patients' responses to the illness and to the therapeutic regimens, the nurse is best able to evaluate the effectiveness of current therapies and raise the issue of change when indicated. Competent nursing care is essential to control of pain and other symptoms, enabling the patient to live as fully as possible for as long as possible. A nurse who promises control of a patient's pain and who demonstrates the truth of that statement eases the patient's fear of and attention to pain. The patient is more able to trust the staff on other matters and is usually more cooperative as a consequence.

The trust that a dying patient is able to invest in skilled and compassionate nursing staff may contribute directly to reducing the patient's fears of abandonment and of losing control of the situation. The family's trust in the competence and concern of the nurse may reduce the family's fears that the patient will be neglected in their absence. Trust among patient, family, and care providers is significant when mental dysfunctions appear as a consequence of the disease or of treatment. Anxiety and depression are expected expressions of behavior in dying patients. Consistently given sympathy and support by the nurse along with pain and symptom control, comfort measures, mild psychotropic drugs, and attention to the environment can give relief.

Whatever the symptoms of the dying patient—and some, such as dyspnea, can be quite agonizing—there are relieving measures that can be used. These measures cover a wide range of specific nursing techniques such as bathing, positioning, suctioning, skin care, care of bedsores, bowel and urinary control, providing an esthetic environment free from noxious smells, and administering analgesics on time and without unnecessary discomfort. The nurse's opportunities to implement the Kantian principle of treating persons as ends are varied and plentiful. The nurse caring for the dying has multiple chances and ways to help make this experience deep and meaningful for patient, family, and self.

The central principle is that the nurse as advocate of the dying person seeks to protect the basic human values of dignity, respect, and self-determination while providing the highest standards of care possible. The nurse's competence and compassion will largely determine how well this last human experience comes to an end. The nurse's concern can be extended to the family through kindnesses and courtesies, which show respect for them as well as to the dying person. Family members can be guided in offering nourishment, in wiping the brow, or in holding the patient's hand and lending their presence. In this last phase of relationship, unfinished projects and unresolved tensions can be put aside as family members and significant others, with the help and support of nurses, conduct this last human experience with the sensitivity and consideration that the finality of death warrants.

The Hospice Concept

The hospice movement provides compassionate, skilled care for the dying adult and child that is consistent with the Kantian imperative of treating humans as ends. The term *hospice* is defined as a "lodging for travelers, young persons, or the underprivileged."[54] The term "hospitable," which follows the word "hospice" in the dictionary, is defined as "given to generous and cordial reception of guests."[55] The concept of hospice incorporates the idea of lodging for those in need of shelter and the notion of cordiality and generous treatment of guests. These terms were translated into care of the dying by the founder of the modern hospice movement, Dr. Cicely Saunders, a physician and former nurse, now director of St. Christopher's Hospital in London. Saunders' conception of the hospice is to provide the dying with a comfortable, cheerful environment with the amenities of a home in which family members, friends, children, and pets are welcomed and given hospitality. Pain and other symptoms are controlled so that the dying process will be a meaningful, enriched, final separation from life and one's loved ones. The patient is cared for skillfully and compassionately until the last breath. Patients feel secure in the skill and concern of their nurses and care providers. Thus, there is less suffering and less anxiety about the control of pain and symptoms and more serenity about imminent death. The topic of dying and death is openly discussed. Emotional support is consistently given by everyone, including patients to one another, since the concept of a sharing, caring community pervades the hospital. At St. Christopher's and elsewhere in England, "Brompton's cocktail," which contains heroin as one of its ingredients, is given orally as often as necessary to keep the patient free from pain and from the anticipation of pain. The patient need never suffer while waiting for the next dose of medication to come due. Addiction does not necessarily happen, but if it does, priority is given to freedom from pain and to helping the patient achieve a "good" death.

In the United States, the hospice concept has undergone variations. Some hospice programs, such as that in New Haven, Connecticut, began as a home care program with community health nurses and progressed to include full-time hospice care. At St. Luke's Hospital in New York City, the hospice team, which includes nurses, assumes responsibility for the supervision of the care of dying patients in units throughout the hospital. The team gives care, advocates for the patient's best interests and wishes to the unit staff, counsels the family and staff concerning their feelings about death, and works toward providing a caring environment for the dying patient. Another hospice program in Summit, New Jersey, involves the family, community, and hospital staff in providing care at home and in the hospital if needed. Hospice staff are on call 24 hours of every day so that no one need feel abandoned.

These and many other programs in the United States not discussed are consistent with the hospice concept. The dying patient is identified and supported as a self-determining human being worthy of respect, care, and affection until the very last moment of life. The traditional isolation of the dying is transformed into inclusion of the individual as a member of the community of the living, fully participating in all of life's joys. The physical suffering of the dying is controlled. The patient need not fear pain. The patient need not fear abandonment. Death is treated as an inevitable and acceptable part of life that comes to everyone.

CONCLUSION

Death is a tragedy to each individual who has no choice. Death to each person is, as L. Wittgenstein remarked, "not an event . . . lived through."[56] Some physicists say that in billions of years, the universe will be a "black hole," which means that nothing will be left. That is how some people believe it is for the individual who dies. To those who continue to live. the griefs and satisfactions of life continue. For them, the death of others is an event lived through.

The nurse at a dying patient's bedside can give succor and support to that patient, helping the patient through the stages of dying, sharing the patient's grief with compassion, support, and understanding. The nurse with ethical sensitivity, oriented by a love-based ethics at a dying patient's last hours, gives as one person to another in the recognition that they have this life and this fate in common. The nurse who can share as a person is aware that she or he, too, will die, and that how one ends life, whether well or badly, depends partly on the wisdom and love or lack of it shown by relevant others at this time.

REFERENCES

1. President's Commission for the Study of Ethical Problems in Medicine and Biomedical and Behavioral Research: Deciding to Forego Life-Sustaining Treatment. Washington, D.C., U.S. Government Printing Office, 1983, p. 16.
2. Department of Health, Education, and Welfare: Facts of Life and Death. Washington, D.C., U.S. Government Printing Office, 1978, p. 31–33.
3. President's Commission: Deciding to Forego Life-Sustaining Treatment, p. 17–18.
4. Heifetz M.D., with Mangel C.: The Right to Die. New York, Berkley, 1975, p. 59–60.
5. Muyskens J.: Moral Problems in Nursing. Totowa, N.J., Littlefield, Adams, 1983, p. 92–93.
6. Davis A.J., Aroskar M.A.: Ethical Dilemmas and Nursing Practice, 2nd ed. Norwalk, Conn., Appleton-Century-Crofts, 1983, p. 223.
7. Cross J.: Whose life is it anyway? Empire State Report, March 1983, p. 25.
8. Muyskens: Moral Problems in Nursing, p. 92.
9. Levine M.: Nursing ethics and the ethical nurse. J Nursing 77(5):843, 1977.
10. Carson R., Siegler M.: Does "doing everything" include CPR? Hasting Center Report 12(5):27, 1982.
11. Pope Pius XII: Symposium on Anesthesiology. In Hayes E.J., Hayes P.J., Kelly D.E., Moral Principles of Nursing. New York, Macmillan, 1964, p. 131.
12. President's Commission: Deciding to Forego Life-Sustaining Treatment, p. 90.
13. Ibid., p. 85.
14. Ibid., p. 62.
15. Ibid., p. 85.
16. Rachels J.: Active and passive euthanasia. N Engl J Med 292(2):78, 1975.
17. Ibid.
18. Kohl M.: Karen Quinlan: Human rights and wrongful killing. In Bandman E.L., Bandman B. (eds.), Bioethics and Human Rights: A Reader for Health Professionals. Boston, Little, Brown, 1978, p. 125.
19. President's Commission: Deciding to Forego Life-Sustaining Treatment, p. 16.
20. The Society for the Right to Die: Handbook of Enacted Laws. New York, The Society, 1981.
21. Machlin R.: Consent, coercion and conflicts of rights. In Arras J., Hunt

R. (eds.), Ethical Issues in Modern Medicine, 2nd ed. Palo Alto, Calif., Mayfield, 1983, p. 231-238.

22. McCormick R.: Organ transplants: Ethical principles. In Reich W. (ed.), Encyclopedia of Bioethics. New York, The Free Press, 1978, p. 1169-1172.
23. Kant I.: Fundamental Principles of the Metaphysics of Morals. Indianapolis, Bobbs-Merrill, 1949, p. 39.
24. Schopenhauer A.: On Suicide. In Beck R., Orr J. (eds.), Ethical Choice. New York, Free Press, 1970, p. 78.
25. Brandt R.B.: The morality and rationality of suicide. In Beauchamp T., Perlin S. (eds.), Ethical Issues in Death and Dying. Englewood Cliffs, N.J., Prentice-Hall, 1978, p. 125.
26. Guidelines for the Determination of Death. In Legal and Ethical Aspects of Treatment for Critically and Terminally Ill Patients. New York, American Society for Law and Medicine and Concern for Dying, 1981, p. 54-63.
27. Black P.: Definitions of brain death. In Ethical Issues in Death and Dying, p. 9.
28. Downie R.S.: Roles and Values. London, Methuen, 1971, p. 131.
29. Ramsey P.: The Patient as Person. New Haven, Yale University Press, 1970, p. 5.
30. Singer P.: Value of life. In Encyclopedia of Bioethics. vol. 2, p. 823.
31. Fletcher J.: Four indicators of humanhood: The enquiry matures. Hastings Center Report 4(6):51, 1974.
32. Ruddick W.: Parents, children and medical decisions. In Bioethics and Human Rights: A Reader for Health Professionals, p. 165-170.
33. Davis and Aroskar: Ethical Dilemmas and Nursing Practice, p. 223.
34. Bandman B., Bandman E.: The nurse's role in an interest-based view of patient's rights. In Spicker S., Gadow S. (eds.), Nursing Image and Ideals. New York, Springer, 1980, p. 135-136.
35. Ibid.
36. Hare R.M.: Religion and Morals. In Mitchell B. (ed.), Faith and Logic. London, Allen & Unwin, 1957, p. 192.
37. American Nurses' Association: Code for Nurses, p. 6.
38. Kalish R.A.: Death, attitudes toward. In Encyclopedia of Bioethics, vol. 1, p. 286.
39. Kübler-Ross E.: On Death and Dying. New York, Macmillian, 1969.
40. Kalish: Death, attitudes toward, p. 287.
41. Kastenbaum R.: Is death a life crisis?: On the confrontation with death in theory and practice. In Daton E., Ginsberg L.H. (eds.), Life-Span Developmental Psychology: Normative Life Crises. New York, Academic Press, 1975, p. 42.
42. Kalish: Death, attitudes toward, p. 287.
43. Ibid.
44. Ibid.
45. Ibid.
46. Ibid., p. 288.
47. Ibid.
48. American Nurses' Association: Code for Nurses, p. 4.
49. President's Commission: Deciding to Forego Life-Sustaining Treatment, p. 276.

50. Ibid., p. 278.
51. Ibid., p. 279.
52. Ibid., p. 283.
53. Ibid., p. 284.
54. Webster's New Collegiate Dictionary. Springfield, Mass., Merriam, 1974, p. 553.
55. Ibid.
56. Wittgenstein L.: Tractatus Logicus Philosophicus. New York, Humanities Press, 1951, p. 185.

Appendix

American Nurses' Association Code for Nurses

Preamble

The *Code for Nurses* is based on belief about the nature of individuals, nursing, health, and society. Recipients and providers of nursing services are viewed as individuals and groups who possess basic rights and responsibilities, and whose values and circumstances command respect at all times. Nursing encompasses the promotion and restoration of health, the prevention of illness, and the alleviation of suffering. The statements of the *Code* and their interpretation provide guidance for conduct and relationships in carrying out nursing responsibilities consistent with the ethical obligations of the profession and quality in nursing care.

Code for Nurses

1. The nurse provides services with respect for human dignity and the uniqueness of the client unrestricted by considerations of social or economic status, personal attributes, or the nature of health problems.
2. The nurse safeguards the client's right to privacy by judiciously protecting information of a confidential nature.
3. The nurse acts to safeguard the client and the public when health care and safety are affected by the incompetent, unethical, or illegal practice of any person.
4. The nurse assumes responsibility and accountability for individual nursing judgments and actions.
5. The nurse maintains competence in nursing.
6. The nurse exercises informed judgment and uses individual competence and qualifications as criteria in seeking consultation, accepting responsibilities, and delegating nursing activities to others.
7. The nurse participates in activities that contribute to the ongoing development of the profession's body of knowledge.

[Adopted by the American Nurses' Association in 1976 and reprinted by permission.]

8. The nurse participates in the profession's efforts to implement and improve standards of nursing.
9. The nurse participates in the profession's effort to establish and maintain conditions of employment conducive to high quality nursing care.
10. The nurse participates in the profession's effort to protect the public from misinformation and misrepresentation and to maintain the integrity of nursing.
11. The nurse collaborates with members of the health professions and other citizens in promoting community and national efforts to meet the health needs of the public.

International Council of Nurses
Code for Nurses: Ethical Concepts Applied to Nursing

- The fundamental responsibility of the nurse is fourfold: to promote health, to prevent illness, to restore health and alleviate suffering.
- The need for nursing is universal. Inherent in nursing is respect for life, dignity and rights of man. It is unrestricted by considerations of nationality, race, creed, color, age, sex, politics or social status.
- Nurses render health services to the individual, the family and the community and coordinate their services with those of related groups.

Nurses and People

- The nurse's primary responsibility is to those people who require nursing care.
- The nurse, in providing care, promotes an environment in which the values, customs, and spiritual beliefs of the individual are respected.
- The nurse holds in confidence personal information and uses judgment in sharing this information.

Nurses and Practice

- The nurse carries personal responsibility for nursing practice and for maintaining competence by continual learning.

[Adopted by the International Council of Nurses, May 1973 and reprinted by permission.]

- The nurse maintains the highest standards of nursing care possible within the reality of a specific situation.
- The nurse uses judgment in relation to individual competence when accepting and delegating responsibilities.
- The nurse when acting in a professional capacity should at all times maintain standards of personal conduct which reflect credit upon the profession.

Nurses and Society

- The nurse shares with other citizens the responsibility for initiating and supporting action to meet the health and social needs of the public.

Nurses and Co-Workers

- The nurse sustains a cooperative relationship with co-workers in nursing and other fields.
- The nurse takes appropriate action to safeguard the individual when his care is endangered by a co-worker or any other person.

Nurses and the Profession

- The nurse plays the major role in determining and implementing desirable standards of nursing practice and nursing education.
- The nurse is active in developing a core of professional knowledge.
- The nurse, acting through the professional organization, participates in establishing and maintaining equitable social and economic working conditions in nursing.

The World Medical Association Declaration of Geneva

Physician's Oath

At the time of being admitted as a member of the medical profession: I solemnly pledge myself to consecrate my life to the service of humanity; I will give to my teachers the respect and gratitude which is their due; I will practice my profession with conscience and dignity; the health of my

[Adopted by the General Assembly of the World Medical Association, Geneva, Switzerland, September 1948 and amended by the 22nd World Medical Assembly, Sydney, Australia, August 1968. Reprinted by permission.]

patient will be my first consideration; I will maintain by all the means in my power, the honor and the noble traditions of the medical profession; my colleagues will be my brothers; I will not permit considerations of religion, nationality, race, party politics or social standing to intervene between my duty and my patient; I will maintain the utmost respect of human life from the time of conception, even under threat, I will not use my medical knowledge contrary to the laws of humanity; I make these promises solemnly, freely, and upon my honor.

American Medical Association Principles of Medical Ethics

Preamble

The medical profession has long subscribed to a body of ethical statements developed primarily for the benefit of the patient. As a member of this profession, a physician must recognize responsibilty not only to patients, but also to society, to other health professionals, and to self. The following Principles adopted by the American Medical Association are not laws, but standards of conduct which define the essentials of honorable behavior for the physician.

1. A physician shall be dedicated to providing competent medical service with compassion and respect for human dignity.
2. A physician shall deal honestly with patients and colleagues, and strive to expose those physicians deficient in character or competence, or who engage in fraud or deception.
3. A physician shall respect the law and also recognize a responsibility to seek changes in those requirements which are contrary to the best interests of the patient.
4. A physician shall respect the rights of patients, of colleagues, and of other health professionals, and shall safeguard patient confidences within the constraints of the law.
5. A physician shall continue to study, apply and advance scientific knowledge, make relevant information available to patients, colleagues, and the public, obtain consultation, and use the talents of other health professionals when indicated.

[Adopted by the American Medical Association in 1980 and reprinted with permission.]

6. A physician shall, in the provision of appropriate patient care, except in emergencies, be free to choose whom to serve, with whom to associate, and the environment in which to provide medical services.
7. A physician shall recognize a responsibility to participate in activities contributing to an improved community.

American Hospital Association A Patient's Bill of Rights

The American Hospital Association presents a Patient's Bill of Rights with the expectation that observance of these rights will contribute to more effective patient care and greater satisfaction for the patient, the physician, and the hospital organization. Further, the Association presents these rights in the expectation that they will be supported by the hospital on behalf of its patients, as an integral part of the healing process. It is recognized that a personal relationship between the physician and the patient is essential for the provision of proper medical care. The traditional physician-patient relationship takes on a new dimension when care is rendered within an organizational structure. Legal precedent has established that the institution itself also has a responsibility to the patient. It is in recognition of these factors that these rights are affirmed.

1. The patient has the right to considerate and respectful care.
2. The patient has the right to obtain from his physician complete current information concerning his diagnosis, treatment, and prognosis in terms the patient can be reasonably expected to understand. When it is not medically advisable to give such information to the patient, the information should be made available to an appropriate person in his behalf. He has the right to know, by name, the physician responsible for coordinating his care.
3. The patient has the right to receive from his physician information necessary to give informed consent prior to the start of any procedure and/or treatment. Except in emergencies, such information for informed consent should include but not neces-

[Approved by the American Hospital Association House of Delegates, February 6, 1973, and reprinted by permission of the American Hospital Association, © 1975.]

sarily be limited to the specific procedure and/or treatment, the medically significant risks involved, and the probable duration of incapacitation. Where medically significant alternatives for care or treatment exist, or when the patient requests information concerning medical alternatives, the patient has the right to such information. The patient also has the right to know the name of the person responsible for the procedures and/or treatment.

4. The patient has the right to refuse treatment to the extent permitted by law and to be informed of the medical consequences of his action.
5. The patient has the right to every consideration of his privacy concerning his own medical care program. Case discussion, consultation, examination, and treatment are confidential and should be conducted discreetly. Those not directly involved in his care must have the permission of the patient to be present.
6. The patient has the right to expect that all communications and records pertaining to his care should be treated as confidential.
7. The patient has the right to expect that within its capacity a hospital must make reasonable response to the request of a patient for services. The hospital must provide evaluation, service, and/or referral as indicated by the urgency of the case. When medically permissible, the patient may be transferred to another facility only after he has received complete information and explanation concerning the needs for and alternatives for such a transfer. The institution to which the patient is to be transferred must first have accepted the patient for transfer.
8. The patient has the right to obtain information as to any relationship of his hospital to other health care and educational institutions insofar as his care is concerned. The patient has the right to obtain information as to the existence of any professional relationships among individuals, by name, who are treating him.
9. The patient has the right to be advised if the hospital proposes to engage in or perform human experimentation affecting his care or treatment. The patient has the right to refuse to participate in such research projects.
10. The patient has the right to expect reasonable continuity of care. He has the right to know in advance what appointment times and physicians are available and where. The patient has the right to expect that the hospital will provide a mechanism whereby he is informed by his physician or a delegate of the physician of the patient's continuing health care requirements following discharge.

11. The patient has the right to examine and receive an explanation of his bill regardless of source of payment.
12. The patient has the right to know what hospital rules and regulations apply to his conduct as a patient.

No catalog of rights can guarantee for the patient the kind of treatment he has a right to expect. A hospital has many functions to perform, including the prevention and treatment of disease, the education of both health professionals and patient, and the conduct of clinical research. All these activities must be conducted with an overriding concern for the patient, and, above all, the recognition of his dignity as a human being. Success in achieving this recognition assures success in the defense of the rights of the patient.

The Nuremberg Code

The great weight of the evidence before us is to the effect that certain types of medical experiments on human beings, when kept within reasonably well-defined bounds, conform to the ethics of the medical profession generally. The protagonists of the practice of human experimentation justify their views on the basis that such experiments yield results for the good of society that are unprocurable by other methods or means of study. All agree, however, that certain basic principles must be observed in order to satisfy moral, ethical, and legal concepts:

1. The voluntary consent of the human subject is absolutely essential. This means that the person involved should have legal capacity to give consent; should be so situated as to be able to exercise free power of choice, without the intervention of any element of force, fraud, deceit, duress, overreaching, or other ulterior form of constraint or coercion; and should have sufficient knowledge and comprehension of the elements of the subject matter involved as to enable him to make an understanding and enlightened decision. This latter element requires that before the acceptance of an affirmative decision by the experimental subject there should be made known to him the nature, duration, and purpose of the experiment; the method and means by which it is to be conducted; all inconveniences

[Reprinted from *Trials of War Criminals before the Nuernberg Military Tribunals under Control Council Law No. 10*, vol. 2 (Washington, D.C.: U.S. Government Printing Office, 1949), pp. 181-82.]

and hazards reasonably to be expected; and the effects upon his health or person which may possibly come from his participation in the experiment.

The duty and responsibility for ascertaining the quality of the consent rests upon each individual who initiates, directs or engages in the experiment. It is a personal duty and responsibility which may not be delegated to another with impunity.

2. The experiment should be such as to yield fruitful results for the good of society, unprocurable by other methods or means of study, and not random and unnecessary in nature.
3. The experiment should be so designed and based on the results of animal experimentation and a knowledge of the natural history of the disease or other problem under study that the anticipated results will justify the performance of the experiment.
4. The experiment should be so conducted as to avoid all unnecessary physical and mental suffering and injury.
5. No experiment should be conducted where there is an *a priori* reason to believe that death or disabling injury will occur; except, perhaps, in those experiments where the experimental physicians also serve as subjects.
6. The degree of risk to be taken should never exceed that determined by the humanitarian importance of the problem to be solved by the experiment.
7. Proper preparations should be made and adequate facilities provided to protect the experimental subject against even remote possibilities of injury, disability, or death.
8. The experiment should be conducted only by scientifically qualified persons. The highest degree of skill and care should be required through all stages of the experiment of those who conduct or engage in the experiment.
9. During the course of the experiment the human subject should be at liberty to bring the experiment to an end if he has reached the physical or mental state where continuation of the experiment seems to him to be impossible.
10. During the course of the experiment the scientist in charge must be prepared to terminate the experiment at any stage, if he has probable cause to believe, in the exercise of the good faith, superior skill and careful judgment required of him that a continuation of the experiment is likely to result in injury, disability, or death to the experimental subject.

A Living Will

To My Family, My Physician, My Lawyer and All Others Whom It May Concern

Death is as much a reality as birth, growth, maturity and old age—it is the one certainty of life. If the time comes when I can no longer take part in decisions for my own future, let this statement stand as an expression of my wishes and directions, while I am still of sound mind.

If at such a time the situation should arise in which there is no reasonable expectation of my recovery from extreme physical or mental disability, I direct that I be allowed to die and not be kept alive by medications, artificial means or "heroic measures". I do, however, ask that medication be mercifully administered to me to alleviate suffering even though this may shorten my remaining life.

This statement is made after careful consideration and is in accordance with my strong convictions and beliefs. I want the wishes and directions here expressed carried out to the extent permitted by law. Insofar as they are not legally enforceable, I hope that those to whom this Will is addressed will regard themselves as morally bound by these provisions.

Signed______________________________

Date ______________________________

Witness______________________________

Witness______________________________

Copies of this request have been given to ______________________________

____

____

____

Reprinted by permission of Concern For Dying, 250 W. 57 St., New York, N.Y., 10019.

IMPORTANT

Declarants may wish to add specific statements to the Living Will to be inserted in the space provided for that purpose above the signature. Possible additional provisions are suggested below:

1. a) I appoint ______________________________ to make binding decisions concerning my medical treatment.

   OR

   b) I have discussed my views as to life-sustaining measures with the following who understand my wishes

   ____

   ____

   ____

2. Measures of artificial life support in the face of impending death that are especially abhorrent to me are:

   a) Electrical or mechanical resuscitation of my heart when it has stopped beating.

   b) Nasogastric tube feedings when I am paralyzed and no longer able to swallow.

   c) Mechanical respiration by machine when my brain can no longer sustain my own breathing.

   d) ______________________________

3. If it does not jeopardize the chance of my recovery to a meaningful and sentient life or impose an undue burden on my family, I would like to live out my last days at home rather than in a hospital.
4. If any of my tissues are sound and would be of value as transplants to help other people, I freely give my permission for such donation.

To make best use of your Living Will

1. Sign and date before two witnesses. (This is to insure that you signed of your own free will and not under any pressure.)
2. If you have a doctor, give him a copy for your medical file and discuss it with him to make sure he is in agreement.

   Give copies to those most likely to be concerned "if the time comes when you can no longer take part in decisions for your own future." Enter their names on bottom line of the Living Will. Keep the original nearby, easily and readily available.
3. Above all discuss your intentions with those closest to you, NOW.

4. It is a good idea to look over your Living Will once a year and redate it and initial the new date to make it clear that your wishes are unchanged.

35th printing
Revised May, 1978

Index